W9-CIL-984

Business Decision Theory

Paul Jedamus
Professor of Business Statistics
University of Colorado

Robert Frame
Associate Professor of Quantitative Analysis
Southern Methodist University

McGraw-Hill Book Company
New York St. Louis San Francisco London
Sydney Toronto Mexico Panama

Business Decision Theory

Library of Congress Catalog Card Number 69-13609

32307

1234567890 MAMM 7654321069

Preface

The purpose of this book is to provide a self-contained treatment of statistical inference and decision theory at an elementary level. It aims at an integration of classical statistics and decision theory with "modern" Bayesian concepts. The approach used is based on the authors' conviction that the reader will benefit most from exposure to this subject matter as a unified whole instead of as a smattering of seemingly disjointed topics. Thus such diverse topics as mathematical programming, computers, forecasting, and the like—important though they are to the study of business and economics—are not included here. The focus is squarely and solely on the process of decision making in the face of uncertainty, with emphasis on the combined use of information in the form of historical data, business judgments, and sample results.

The text substitutes intuitive explanations of important principles for mathematical proofs. Indeed, the mathematical sophistication required of the reader is merely at the level of elementary algebra. The particular focus on the decision-making process has grown out of our own experience in teaching a first course in "business statistics." Too often, students come to this course regarding it as an ordeal to be endured or as a hurdle that is difficult to cross but meaningless in relation to their other studies. We have found that the early introduction of concrete business decision situations in their economic framework stimulates interest and facilitates the understanding of statistical inference.

Chapters 1 through 7 provide complete coverage of the fundamental concepts of both classical and Bayesian statistics by utilizing only discrete probability distributions. Essentially parallel development of continuous (normal) probability methods and some treatment of descriptive statistics occupy the remainder of the book (Chapters 8 through 12). Although the material is designed for a one-semester course, the book may prove too long (or the semester too short) to allow adequate coverage. In such a case the last two chapters may be omitted conveniently. Chapters 1 through 10 should provide the student with sufficient background to go on to more advanced courses in statistics or other quantitative areas. The nearly 200 problems included are of varying difficulty and can be selected so as to make the book suitable for a basic course at the graduate level.

The authors have chosen to use this material in the first semester of a two-semester quantitative analysis sequence (both undergraduate and graduate). In this sequence, topics in operations research, computer programming, and econometrics are deferred to the second semester. The book could also be used in a second course that is designed to follow a "traditional" business statistics course (emphasizing such topics as descriptive statistics, time series, correlation, and index numbers) or as a supplementary text for such a course.

We cannot begin to identify the source of all the ideas in this book. However, our debt to the path-breaking work in decision theory by Robert Schlaifer, "Probability and Statistics for Business Decisions," McGraw-Hill Book Company, New York, 1959, is obvious. We are also indebted to the Literary Executor of the late Sir Ronald A. Fisher, F.R.S., and to Oliver & Boyd, Ltd., Edinburgh, for their permission to reprint Table IV from their book "Statistical Methods for Research Workers." We wish to acknowledge the contributions of our friend R. A. Postweiler, whose thinking influenced our general approach and several chapters, and of our other colleagues and students whose constructive criticisms helped the final product. The errors, omissions, and inconsistencies are ours.

Paul Jedamus
Robert Frame

Contents

chapter 8 DESCRIPTIVE STATISTICS 123

chapter 9 THE NORMAL DISTRIBUTION AND PROBLEMS OF ESTIMATION FOR CONTINUOUS DISTRIBUTIONS 150

chapter 10 STATISTICAL DECISION RULES AND TESTS OF HYPOTHESES FOR CONTINUOUS DISTRIBUTIONS 179

Business Decision Theory

1
Introduction to Business Decision Theory

DECISIONS, DECISIONS

Decisions play an important role in our everyday lives. Whether or not to study for a quiz, what to order for lunch, or what color tie (or dress) to wear—these are the sorts of decisions we must make daily. Of course not all decisions are trivial. Many involve millions of dollars or even life and death. Indeed decision making may constitute one of the highest forms of human activity. Psychologists tell us of a universal desire to avoid making decisions whenever possible, and there is abundant evidence that those who are willing to perform this activity and perform it well are among the best-paid members of society. Corporate executives who work in air-conditioned offices may receive many times the wages of employees whose duties involve constant exposure to heat, cold, noise, physical danger, and other unpleasant working conditions. Do the decision makers earn their salary? Who could argue seriously that the President of the United States or other heads of state, faced as they are with some of the gravest decisions of all, are overpaid?

Why is such a premium placed on the willingness and ability to make decisions? Perhaps it is because the decision maker always runs the risk of being wrong. By its very nature, making a decision involves choosing between a number of possible courses of action that could be taken. After the decision has been made and action taken, time and hindsight may show that a better choice among the alternatives could have been made. We are rarely sure, at the time we make it, what all the ramifications of a particular decision may be. There is always the chance that a well thought out decision may produce unfortunate, even disastrous results. Even a truly superior decision maker lives with the knowledge that some of his decisions will, in retrospect, prove costly.

But can we really characterize a particular decision as "good" or "bad" depending solely on how things finally work out? The decision to repair the motor of an old car may seem perfectly sound to us in the light of an anticipated trip and the car's generally sound condition, at least at the time the decision is made. If the car is totally wrecked in an accident a week after the repair is made, we may lose all the money invested in the repair, but can we fault ourselves with a "bad" decision? If we make an investment that appears highly speculative with very little chance of working out well, can we credit ourselves with a "good" decision if it brings returns beyond our expectations? In one sense we may answer these questions "yes," in another, "no."

The ambiguity here may be resolved by recognizing that there is a difference between the merit of the alternative chosen (viewed from an after-the-fact perspective) and the merit of the method or procedure used to select that alternative. While we can never be sure that a particular decision will turn out well, we owe it to ourselves to be sure that the *method* used to make the decision was the best available.

Thus it is that this book is concerned with the methodology of business decision making. It offers the reader an introduction to some powerful tools, the use of which can lead to more rational (and more profitable) decisions. Perhaps more important, the reader should gain an insight into the decision process in business, enabling him to extend the analytical framework for decision making developed here to a broader and more complex class of problems. Certainly the methods discussed in subsequent chapters, despite their broader implications, are elementary in nature and apply specifically to a relatively restricted class of decision problems. The remainder of this introductory chapter will identify the focus of this book.

DECISIONS UNDER CERTAINTY

As indicated earlier, every decision problem involves at least some element of uncertainty. However, in some classes of business problems the effects of uncertainty are so small that they can be ignored for purposes of analysis. These problems involve what is known as *decision making under certainty*.

It might seem that if all the facts relevant to a particular decision were known, making the decision would be easy. This is not necessarily the case, as the following example will illustrate. Suppose you were given the assignment of visiting each of the 50 state capitals in the United States. Your problem is to decide on a routing or travel schedule which minimizes the total transportation cost of making the 50 visits. Starting from where you are now, there is clearly a very large variety of possible routes by which you could proceed. Some of these are obviously better than others. For example, you would hardly suggest visiting Hawaii first, New Hampshire second, and Arizona third. That schedule might provide for interesting changes of scenery, but it would run up your travel bill in a hurry.

Notice that the facts needed to solve this problem are all known or easily obtainable. Certainly you can find out the air fare, for example, between Sacramento and Phoenix. While there is some possibility that the figure you obtain might change (due to a rate change) by the time you purchased your ticket, you could, for practical purposes, ignore this minor element of uncertainty. Yet, even under these certainty conditions, solving this problem is not going to be easy. Although your intuition might lead you to a "good" transportation schedule, be forwarned that proving that it is the *best* possible schedule is a formidable task.

Many business problems involve a relatively secure knowledge of all the relevant facts. Selection of an optimal method for routing work through a job shop production system is one example. Another is the decision problem an oil company might face in allocating crude oil from hundreds of oil fields around the world to a dozen refineries. These problems are conceptually straightforward in that a sufficient amount of computation should always lead one to arrive at the best decision. But because the number of possible courses of action may be in the millions, some systematic methods for locating the best alternative seem desirable, if not essential.

A number of mathematical methods have been developed to aid decision makers with these certainty-type decision problems. The most notable come under the term *mathematical programming*, of which *linear programming* is an important subclassification. Although a knowledge of these methods is of great value to the business student, they are beyond the scope of this book. Instead we shall deal here with the conceptually more difficult class of decision problems in which uncertainty plays a major role.

DECISIONS UNDER UNCERTAINTY

In most cases the business decision maker does not have a sufficient knowledge of the facts relevant to his problem to analyze it as a "certain" situation. He must instead deal with *uncertainty* as a key element in the structure of the problem facing him. A mining-company executive must decide whether to invest money in an ore field without knowing with certainty either the exact size of the deposit or the price of ore in future years. A baker must decide how many loaves of bread to bake without certain knowledge of the number consumers will wish to buy. Such uncertainty must be squarely faced and decisions made if the business is to proceed.

The argument is sometimes raised that analytical methods lose their usefulness in situations where too little data are available and where the uncertainties are too great. "You can't use those fancy methods if you haven't got the numbers to put in" is the way this argument usually goes. We disagree. The greater the uncertainties faced by the decision maker, in the authors' view, the *more* the need for an analytical structure to assist him in problem solving.

In this text no distinction is made between risk and uncertainty. Some practitioners define *decision making under risk* as occurring when different odds can be assigned to the various possible outcomes in a decision situation. They reserve the term *decision making under uncertainty* for the case where even these odds are unknown and no reasonable estimates can be made. We shall not make this distinction and shall characterize the situations studied as decision making under uncertainty regardless of the degree of prior knowledge.

BUSINESS DECISION THEORY

As you should now know, this is a book about *business* decision making. However, the elements of a decision problem are often the same whether the problem is in a business context or some other. Indeed, some of the examples in this text involve such things as the rolling of dice or the dealing of cards, which hardly play a role—at least a legitimate role—in most business operations. Such examples, apart from their possible practical use to the reader, will prove an aid to understanding those techniques of analysis that are useful in business decision making under uncertainty, called *business decision theory*.

More broadly defined, decision theory is a term used to apply to those methods for solving decision problems in which uncertainty plays a crucial role. Some of these methods were developed centuries ago, but many were developed quite recently. All rest on the two principal foundations of decision theory: *probability* and *statistical inference.*

Probability, as used in this book, has a meaning not very different from its meaning in everyday language. Although we shall develop some formal ideas about probabilities (the mathematics of probability if you prefer, but that sounds more imposing than it should) in a later chapter, no further discussion is necessary here. And although most of this book is concerned, in one way or another, with statistics and statistical inference, they are the subject of so many misconceptions that we elaborate on these terms here.

STATISTICS AND BUSINESS DECISIONS

"Statistics" above all else, is a word that strikes fear into the hearts of most students of business. Some can't spell it; some can't pronounce it; most misinterpret it in the context of current business practice.

Statistics (plural) are numerical data that serve as a record of the past. Statistics (singular) is the collection, analysis, and interpretation of numerical data. Statistics (singular) is a process for making informed business decisions. Let us examine each of these definitions in more detail.

Statistics as numerical data can be dry bits of irrelevant trivia or interesting clues to future performance, depending upon their nature and their meaning to the person using them. Casualty lists of Civil War battles, for example, are grim reminders of the magnitude of human suffering and the folly of war but are of interest mainly to the antiquary since they provide few clues that relate to the future. Similarly, the record of bank failures in the depression of the 1930s may provide a measure of the weakness of a past economic system but little useful information to guide current economic policy. Both the latest report of stock market transactions and the profit and loss statement of General Motors may be boring statistics to the average English professor but interesting or even exciting to an investor. The difference, of course, is how knowledgeable the reader is about the statistics and how meaningful they may be with respect to future decisions of the reader.

A considerable body of knowledge has been accumulated dealing with the collection, analysis, and interpretation of numerical data for business use. This process—the study of statistics—is demanding and requires considerable training and experience. It involves the use of a scientific process to decide what data need to be collected, how they are to be obtained and analyzed, and how the outcome of the analysis bears upon the problem that initiated the effort. This process is problem oriented and forward-looking. Its foundation is mathematics, particularly probability theory; its methodology is scientific; and its focus is on problem solving.

In recent years, particularly since World War II, tremendous strides have been made in developing more powerful statistical techniques for the analysis of business problems. These new techniques, incorporated with the accumulated knowledge of the past, constitute a large part of the framework of business decision theory, to which this text is an introduction. You will find that studying statistics will be demanding, but more important, it should be interesting and perhaps even exciting because its focus will be on developing your capacity to make better-informed business decisions—and this is the stuff that turns management trainees into corporate executives.

EXPERIMENTS, SAMPLING, AND STATISTICAL INFERENCE

When confronted with uncertainty, the scientist usually resorts to experimentation. He formulates some basic notion, which he calls a *hypothesis*, about the behavior of the phenomenon under consideration and designs an experiment whose results he hopes will either confirm or refute the hypothesis. (It may, of course, prove to be inconclusive.) Usually his experiment cannot encompass every possible case involving the subject being investigated, so he must resort to sampling. The same situation holds in business. Does a manufactured product meet specifications? Will customers accept a new product? Is brand A really better? Will a new inventory policy reduce total inventory costs? To answer these questions, an investigator must design an experiment that involves basing a conclusion about the characteristic being studied upon evidence obtained from a sample.

This is no simple matter because even the most carefully selected samples will not have exactly the same characteristics as the larger set of items from which the samples were obtained, and no two samples will be likely to be exactly the same. Therefore one must use rather sophisticated statistical techniques to measure sampling error and to guard against arriving at a false conclusion about the hypothesis in question.

Until the 1950s these problems were approached from the standpoint of a methodology known as *classical statistical inference*. This method attacks the problem by explicitly measuring the risks of sampling errors using probability and statistical theory and by incorporating these risks into the formulation of appropriate decision rules.

In 1959 Robert Schlaifer extended this methodology by enabling the decision maker to bring to bear on the problem not only the evidence obtained from sampling but also his accumulated past experience.[1] Further, the costs as well as the probabilities of possible errors in interpreting the sample were systematically incorporated into the process of formulating decision rules. This extension of classical analysis is called *Bayesian analysis*.

This text views Bayesian analysis as a logical and fruitful extension of classical analysis and attempts to integrate these concepts into a unified and consistent theory for making business decisions under uncertainty.

MATHEMATICS OR MANAGEMENT?

In the chapters that follow you will find neither a treatise on mathematical statistics nor a cookbook compendium of formulas for all occasions. To be an intelligent user of the statistical method and to form a base from which he may become a proficient practitioner, the student needs to obtain a firm grasp of the logic behind the process he is learning to apply. In a sense, then, the text becomes an exercise in applied logic more than in applied mathematics. While formulas and techniques are important, they should be understood for what they are—a means of transition between a nonmathematical process of applied logic and solutions to practical problems in applied decision making.

The world of business is extremely complex. To make a mathematical model that exactly described all the variables and interrelationships in even a small part of such a system would match in complexity the mathematics involved, say, in putting a man on the moon. Therefore it is obvious that the models of the business world that you will be using in an introduction to business decision theory will be very much simplified versions of the real thing. Nevertheless, all the models of business situations used will bear a resemblance to the real world. Some will be general enough so that solutions derived from them will represent a significant improvement over solutions that are now commonly applied every day in business practice.

ORGANIZATION OF THE TEXT

One approach often used in books of this nature is to devote the early chapters to equipping the student with a number of the tools that he will need to cope with problems encountered later. This approach is logical enough but is rather dull and sometimes leads to an illusion that the text lacks reality.

[1] Robert Schlaifer, "Probability and Statistics for Business Decisions," McGraw-Hill Book Company, New York, 1959.

Although some preparation in the form of basic tools and methods is inevitable, our approach will be to confront the student immediately with a very real type of problem and then to develop both techniques needed to solve the problem and the complexity of the model in succeeding chapters.

In order to emphasize the flow of the reasoning process as the basic model is extended, we shall go through the entire development of a decision model—from the selection of the best decision without sampling to the determination of the expected value of sample information—for the simpler case of *discrete distributions* before introducing continuous distributions. (Discrete distributions are those for which only a limited number of possible outcomes are possible.) Thus the essential methodology is developed in the first seven chapters. The remaining chapters extend this same methodology to *continuous distributions* (which do not restrict the possible outcomes), enabling the student to apply the tools he has learned earlier to the solution of a wide variety of commonly confronted business problems.

PROBLEMS

1.1 Important decisions that do not work out well usually attract a good deal of attention. Consider, for example, Ford's decision to build the Edsel. Can you think of other now infamous decisions in business or politics that hindsight has shown to be "bloopers"? Are these necessarily "bad" decisions? Explain.

1.2 What factors do you consider in deciding whether to take along a raincoat or an umbrella? Have you ever been drenched from a failure to take either? Or have you lugged both along on what turned out to be a hot, sunny day? Should the blame be placed with the decision-making process you used, or did a sound decision simply go awry?

1.3 Give some examples of some situations you have faced involving decision making under uncertainty. Identify the source of the uncertainty in each situation.

1.4 (*a*) Give two examples of business decisions that would be made under conditions of certainty as described in Chap. 1.

(*b*) Give two examples of business decisions that would be made under uncertainty.

1.5 (*a*) Suppose you have to visit the state capital buildings in Sacramento (California), Austin (Texas), and Albany (New York), returning to your present location. How would you plan your visits to minimize transportation expense?

(*b*) Assuming that you solved (*a*) easily, how is it any different from the travel problem posed in the text? Does your answer suggest any generalization concerning decision making under certainty?

1.6 Find a list of statistics (from a newspaper, periodical, or book) that might be of interest to a businessman and describe a situation in which such statistics might be useful in making a business decision.

1.7 State a hypothesis that a businessman might make relative to the operation of his business. Outline in general terms a possible method he might use to test the hypothesis.

1.8 A supermarket chain is considering building a store in a new suburb. Make a list of factors that the decision makers would be likely to consider in deciding whether or not to build. For each factor identify pertinent statistics they might want to obtain, and state whether or not uncertainty would be involved in obtaining them.

1.9 The corner newsboy may appear to have an environment free of the stresses of executive decision making. The economics of his business are indeed simple. Suppose he buys papers for 7 cents each and sells them for 10 cents. However, if he has only one opportunity at the start of his day to purchase his inventory of newspapers, he *does* have to decide how many to try to sell.

(*a*) Is this decision making under uncertainty?

(*b*) What factors should be considered in making this decision?

(*c*) What (if anything) complicates this seemingly simple decision situation?

2
Decision Making under Uncertainty without Sampling

When confronted with the problem of decision making under uncertainty, the unsophisticated person usually reacts in a remarkably sophisticated way. A statistician might say that the decision maker should consider alternative courses of action and choose the act that maximizes his expected utility. The decision maker himself would have a simpler explanation. He would say that he considers the possibilities and chooses the one that is the "best bet." In the rest of this chapter we shall attempt to show that the decision maker's "best bet" and the statistician's "maximization of expected utility" are in fact very similar, the main difference being that the statistician's method is more systematic.

PAYOFF TABLES AND EXPECTED MONETARY VALUES

Much of modern decision theory had its beginnings at the gambling table some 300 years ago. The elements in a gambling situation are closely analogous to those involved in many current business decisions. Therefore an initial illustration using a game of chance is appropriate both historically and practically. Suppose that you were offered the opportunity to play a version of an old carnival game called chuck-a-luck. You pay $1 for the opportunity to roll two dice. If you roll two sixes, you get your $1 back plus $2. If you roll a six and a "not-six," you get the $1 back plus $1. If you roll two not-sixes, you lose your original entry fee.

Before you play, you clearly have two alternatives—either to accept the conditions of the game and play or to choose not to play. But which of these alternatives is the "best bet" *before* the dice are rolled?

One point should be made here. The decision to play or not to play obviously has to be made before the dice are thrown. This is what is meant by decision making under uncertainty. If one could roll the dice and then decide after looking at them whether or not he should play, the decision would be pretty simple.

Most business problems also contain an element of uncertainty and decisions must be made *before* this uncertainty is resolved. Therefore one of our major concerns will be to formulate systematic procedures to help us decide what course of action is the "best bet" before the outcome is known. There is little reward in business for being a good Monday morning quarterback.

Back to our decision problem. We can summarize the situation thus far by constructing a payoff table. This table lists the net profit that will be made for every possible combination of acts and events. In our case the acts are to play or not to play, and the events are the outcomes of the roll. The payoff table is shown in Table 2.1.

Using this table, we can formulate several sorts of rules that may help us come to a decision. If we are pessimistic and assume that the worst will happen to us regardless of the act we choose, we observe that the worst outcome (no sixes), if we choose to play would result in a loss of $1, while the worst result if we choose not to play would be no loss (and no profit). Following the reasoning of choosing the act that will

Table 2.1 Payoff table for chuck-a-luck

	Acts	
Events	*Play*	*Not play*
2 sixes	$ 2	$0
1 six	1	0
0 sixes	−1	0

minimize our maximum loss would result in our preference for the act "not play." This rule is known as a *minimax rule:* choosing the best act, assuming that the least favorable event will occur. If we were optimistic rather than pessimistic, we might formulate a *maximax rule:* assuming that the most favorable event will occur, and choosing the act that maximizes profit given this event. For the problem at hand the maximax rule would lead us to play since the best outcome is a $2 profit, given that we play and roll two sixes.

While rules of this sort are useful for certain types of decision problems, it is apparent that they are not very satisfactory here since neither rule takes into consideration how *likely* the various events are. If the odds were overwhelmingly in favor of at least one six occurring, most of us would not hesitate to play. On the other hand, if the odds of no sixes were very high, most of us would figure that the odds were too much against us to warrant playing.

The next problem, then, is to find the odds of the various outcomes. One tedious but precise method of evaluating the odds is to list all the possible combinations of faces that might turn up. This enumeration is shown in Table 2.2.

Note that there are 36 possible combinations, only one of which results in two sixes, so the odds of two sixes are 1/36. Similarly, there are 10 ways of obtaining one six and one not-six for odds of 10/36, while the odds of obtaining no sixes are 25/36.

Although an assessment of these odds is helpful, they alone are not enough to form an adequate basis for a decision any more than were the payoffs alone. Even though the odds of two sixes are only 1/36, the game would have considerable appeal if the payoff for two sixes were $200 rather than $2.

It seems that a realistic decision rule must somehow consider both the odds and the payoffs. The most satisfactory method of combining odds and payoffs is simply to weight each payoff by the odds that it

Table 2.2 Combinations of faces that could be obtained in rolling two dice

Die 1	*Die* 2	*Die* 1	*Die* 2	*Die* 1	*Die* 2	*Die* 1	*Die* 2	*Die* 1	*Die* 2	*Die* 1	*Die* 2
1	1	1	2	1	3	1	4	1	5	1	6
2	1	2	2	2	3	2	4	2	5	2	6
3	1	3	2	3	3	3	4	3	5	3	6
4	1	4	2	4	3	4	4	4	5	4	6
5	1	5	2	5	3	5	4	5	5	5	6
6	1	6	2	6	3	6	4	6	5	6	6

Table 2.3 Calculation of expected profit, chuck-a-luck

		Acts			
		Play		*Not play*	
Events	*Odds*	*Payoff*	*Weighted payoff*	*Payoff*	*Weighted payoff*
2 sizes	1/36	\$+2	\$+ 2/36	\$0	\$0
1 six	10/36	+1	+10/36	0	0
0 sixes	25/36	−1	−25/36	0	0
Weighted average =			−13/36		0

will occur, add the weighted payoffs for each act, and choose the act that has the highest weighted average. Following this process, we obtain Table 2.3.

We have finally arrived at a rule that will guide us to rational decisions under uncertainty. In the case of chuck-a-luck with two dice the weighted average or expected value of not playing (\$0) is greater than the weighted average of playing (−\$13/36 or approximately −36 cents), and the better decision is to choose not to play.

PROBABILITY AND EXPECTED VALUE

What we have called "odds" up to this point can also be termed probabilities. A *probability* is a number between 0 and 1. The sum of the probabilities of a set of mutually exclusive (nonoverlapping) and collectively exhaustive (completely enumerated) elements must add to 1. Note that the odds we just calculated meet the two conditions above. When one rolls two dice, only three things can happen with respect to the occurrence of sixes; namely zero sixes turn up, one six turns up, or two sixes turn up. Thus these events are collectively exhaustive. They are also mutually exclusive; one could not possibly obtain no-sixes and one six on the *same* roll of a pair of dice.

The probabilities for obtaining sixes that we just used could be regarded as the relative frequency of occurrence of the various events in the long run under constant conditions. That is to say, if we were to roll these dice a large number of times, we could *expect* that 1/36 of the time we would obtain two sixes, 10/36 of the time one six and one not-six, and 25/36 of the time two not-sixes. On the other hand, we could regard these probabilities simply as the odds at which we should be willing to bet on the next toss of the same dice. The implications of these interpretations of probability will be brought out in the next chapter.

Since we can regard the odds of Table 2.2 as probabilities using either of the interpretations above, the "weighted averages" that were obtained for each act can be called *expected values* or mathematical expectations.[1] In the rest of the text we shall use the term *expected monetary value* rather than the term "weighted payoff" that we have used up to this point.

UTILITY FOR MONEY

The astute reader might have voiced some reservation regarding our statement that the best decision for this problem was not to play. A logical case could be made for playing if, for example, the pleasure of playing the game more than compensated for the unfavorable expected monetary value of playing. In a situation like this the decision maker's utilities are not linear with money.

To understand what is meant by the phrase "utility is not linear with money," let us consider the attitude several different people might have toward the risk of losing or gaining various amounts of money.

First consider the person with limited means and his reaction to a situation in which he had to choose between accepting or rejecting a business deal in which the odds of gaining $10,000 were 6 in 10 and the odds of losing $10,000 were 4 in 10.

We can calculate the expected monetary values (EMV) for accepting or rejecting the deal as we did for the chuck-a-luck problem, by weighting the payoff for each event by its probability and summating the weighted payoffs for all the events. For the act "accept the deal," the EMV is $.6(10{,}000) + .4(-10{,}000) = \$2000$. The EMV for rejecting the deal (doing nothing) is $0.

In spite of the fact that the EMV of accepting the deal is higher than that of rejecting it, this person, like most of us, would probably reject the opportunity because the loss of $10,000 would hurt him more than the gain of $10,000 would help him.

If we were to plot the utility for various amounts of money against the dollar value of money for such a person, we should get a curve convex

[1] Formally, an expected value is defined as $\Sigma XP(X)$, where X is a value of a discrete random variable, $P(X)$ is its probability and Σ (capital sigma) means "the sum of all of the $XP(X)$ values." These terms will be explained fully in Chap. 3. At this point we merely want to note that the process we used to obtain the weighted average corresponds to the definition of an expected value, where X is the payoff for a particular act-event combination, $P(X)$ is the probability of that payoff, and $\Sigma XP(X)$ is the sum of the weighted values for a particular act.

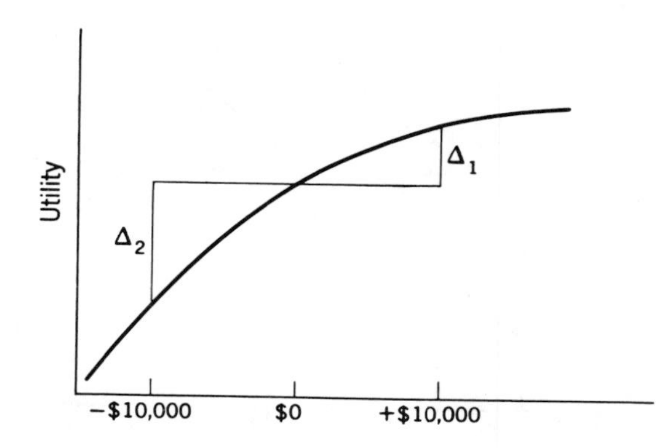

Fig. 2.1 Utility–money curve *A*.

to the *X* axis as in Fig. 2.1. Note that a gain of $10,000 produces a gain in utility of Δ_1, which is considerably smaller than the loss in utility suffered from a loss of $10,000, or Δ_2.

Now let us consider how a person in different circumstances might react to a slightly different opportunity. Assume that this person had to pay a creditor $10,000 by tomorrow and would have to declare bankruptcy if he didn't. He is confronted with another deal, where the probability of gaining $10,000 is .4 and the probability of losing $10,000 is .6. The *EMV* of accepting is $.4(10{,}000) + .6(-10{,}000) = -\$2000$, while the *EMV* of rejecting is 0. It is very likely that this person would accept the deal in spite of the fact that the *EMV* of accepting is lower than that of rejecting, because the loss of $10,000 would hurt him less than the gain of $10,000 would help him.

The utility versus money curve for this person would be concave to the *X* axis, as shown in Fig. 2.2.

Note that for this person the gain in utility of a gain of $10,000, or Δ_1, is greater than the loss in utility of a loss of $10,000, or Δ_2.

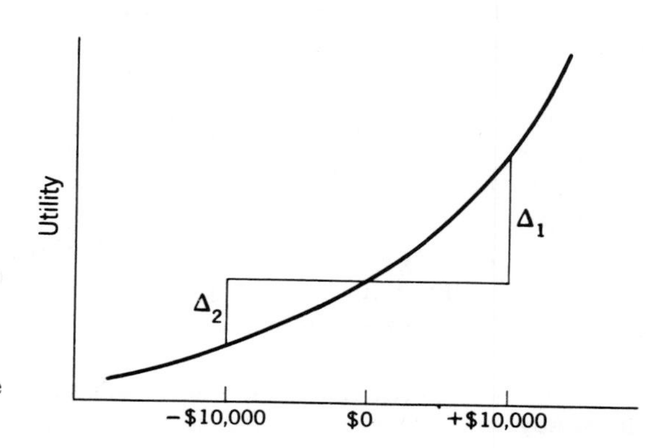

Fig. 2.2 Utility–money curve *B*.

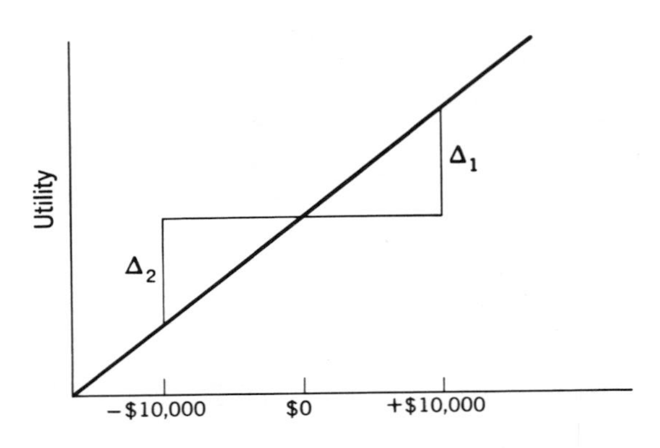

Fig. 2.3 Utility–money curve *C*.

The third kind of person we shall consider is one for whom a loss of $10,000 would be undesirable but not fatal and for whom a gain of $10,000 would be nice but would please him no more than the equivalent loss would have hurt him. Such a person's utility for money curve would be linear. (This expression is often abbreviated by saying that the person's utility is linear with money.) The appropriate curve is shown in Fig. 2.3.

At any point on the curve, $\Delta_1 = \Delta_2$, that is, a gain of $10,000 gives him as much pleasure (gain in utility of Δ_1), as a loss of $10,000 hurts him (loss in utility of Δ_2). Such a person, if he wants to be consistent with his utilities, will always choose the act with the highest *EMV*.

Since most business decisions involve dollar amounts small enough (relative to the size of the business) to represent neither a bonanza nor a catastrophe, the utility for money curve for such decisions may generally be considered linear. Therefore, we shall accept the criterion of maximization of expected monetary values as a valid guide to decision making under uncertainty throughout the remainder of the text.

In some business decisions (e.g., a small firm drilling for oil) the dollar amounts may be very large (relatively), and utility may not be linear with money. To properly analyze such a problem, one would have to determine his specific utility for money curve,[2] convert dollar values to utilities, and choose the act which maximized expected utility rather than expected monetary value. While this process could be difficult, it is by no means impossible.

We shall now investigate the calculation of expected monetary values and related statistics in greater detail, using a simple but reasonably realistic business problem.

[2] This can be achieved through a process called the "standard gamble" technique, devised by Von Neumann and Morgenstern.

DEVELOPMENT OF FURTHER CONCEPTS

STATEMENT OF THE PROBLEM

The owner of the small sporting goods store can take advantage, if he wishes, of a special opportunity to buy skis. If he buys in lots of 20 pairs, he can get the skis for $60 per pair rather than his usual cost of $80. The retail price for the skis is $120. However, if he overstocks, he will have to clear his inventory at the end of the season by selling the skis at $50 per pair, at which price all leftover skis will be sold. If he understocks, he can order skis as he needs them at his regular cost of $80 a pair.

Let us assume that his best estimate of the demand for skis at the regular price is as follows:

Demand, pairs	*Probability*
20	.2
40	.4
60	.3
80	.1

In other words, he figures that the odds of selling 20 pairs are 2 in 10, 40 pairs 4 in 10, 60 pairs 3 in 10, and 80 pairs 1 in 10 and that there is no chance that the demand will be less than 20 or more than 80. For convenience, we have assumed that demand will be in whole lots of 20.

The question, of course, is how many skis the dealer should order.

DETERMINATION OF CONDITIONAL PROFITS

The first step in analyzing a problem of this sort is to determine entries in the payoff table, that is, to determine the profits that will be realized for every combination of stock and demand. These profits are, of course, dependent or conditional on the level of demand and on the level of stock, and are called conditional profits.

Table 2.4 shows the calculation of conditional profits for the payoff table in question.

Although the calculations in Table 2.4 are straightforward, it might help to review them briefly and suggest a generalization. In any case where stock and demand are equal, the conditional profits will equal the number of pairs of skis stocked times the net profit per pair. This relationship could be expressed either as $CP = D(120 - 60) = 60D$ or as

Table 2.4 Determination of conditional profits for ski problem

Demand, D	*Stock,* S	*Stocking states*	*Conditional profit*	
20	20	$D = S$	$CP = 20(120 - 60)$	$= \$1200$
20	40	Overstocked	$CP = 20(120 - 60) + 20(50 - 60)$	$= 1000$
20	60	Overstocked	$CP = 20(120 - 60) + 40(50 - 60)$	$= 800$
20	80	Overstocked	$CP = 20(120 - 60) + 60(50 - 60)$	$= 600$
40	20	Understocked	$CP = 20(120 - 60) + 20(120 - 80)$	$= 2000$
40	40	$D = S$	$CP = 40(120 - 60)$	$= 2400$
40	60	Overstocked	$CP = 40(120 - 60) + 20(50 - 60)$	$= 2200$
40	80	Overstocked	$CP = 40(120 - 60) + 40(50 - 60)$	$= 2000$
60	20	Understocked	$CP = 20(120 - 60) + 40(120 - 80)$	$= 2800$
60	40	Understocked	$CP = 40(120 - 60) + 20(120 - 80)$	$= 3200$
60	60	$D = S$	$CP = 60(120 - 60)$	$= 3600$
60	80	Overstocked	$CP = 60(120 - 60) + 20(50 - 60)$	$= 3400$
80	20	Understocked	$CP = 20(120 - 60) + 60(120 - 80)$	$= 3600$
80	40	Understocked	$CP = 40(120 - 60) + 40(120 - 80)$	$= 4000$
80	60	Understocked	$CP = 60(120 - 60) + 20(120 - 80)$	$= 4400$
80	80	$D = S$	$CP = 80(120 - 60)$	$= 4800$

$CP = S(120 - 60) = 60S$. If stock is greater than demand, an overstocking exists. In all these cases (labeled "overstocked" in the stocking-states column) the conditional profits are equal to $60 per pair of skis stocked initially, minus the loss suffered in selling the overstocked skis late in the season. The appropriate equation if $S > D$ (when stock is greater than demand), is

$$CP = D(120 - 60) + (S - D)(50 - 60) = 70D - 10S$$

The conditional profit of the entries marked "overstocked" could be determined by substituting appropriate levels of D and S in the equation above.

If $S < D$, the stock is less than the amount demanded and the dealer is understocked (labeled "understocked" in the stocking states column). This necessitates the dealer's buying skis during the season at a higher cost, and the resulting conditional profit can be determined through the relationship

$$CP = S(120 - 60) + (D - S)(120 - 80) = 20S + 40D$$

Note that if demand equals stock, both the CP equations for overstocking and for understocking reduce to $60 times the number of skis involved. Thus all the entries in the payoff table could have been determined by using the following equations:

$$CP = 70D - 10S \qquad \text{if } S \geq D \tag{2.1}$$
$$CP = 20S + 40D \qquad \text{if } S < D \tag{2.2}$$

Equations such as these will be called *conditional profit functions.* As we shall see in later chapters, it is often advantageous in more complex problems to derive the equations from the conditions of the problem and then determine the conditional profits from these functions.

Now that all the conditional profits can be determined, we can arrive at the optimal number of skis to stock by weighting the conditional profits for each act by the probabilities attached to each level of demand and summating the products for each act, just as we did for the chuck-a-luck example.

The weighting is accomplished in Table 2.5.

The optimal act (marked with an asterisk) is to stock 60 pairs since such an act produces the highest combination of probabilities times payoffs. Since the calculation is in terms of money, as opposed to units of utility, the expected values are called expected monetary values, and EMV^*, that is, $2560, is known as the expected monetary value of the optimal act.

OPPORTUNITY LOSSES

Sometimes it is simpler to determine optimal acts through the use of *conditional opportunity losses* (*COL*) rather than conditional profits. An *opportunity loss* is defined as the difference between the conditional

Table 2.5 Determination of optimal act, ski problem

		Acts							
		Stock 20 *pairs*		*Stock* 40 *pairs*		*Stock* 60 *pairs*		*Stock* 80 *pairs*	
Events Demand of:	*Probability of event (weight)*	*CP*	*CP* × *probability*	*CP*	*CP* × *probability*	*CP*	*CP* × *probability*	*CP*	*CP* × *probability*
20 pairs	.2	$1200	$ 240	$1000	$ 200	$ 800	$ 160	$ 600	$ 120
40 pairs	.4	2000	800	2400	960	2200	880	2000	800
60 pairs	.3	2800	840	3200	960	3600	1080	3400	1020
80 pairs	.1	3600	360	4000	400	4400	440	4800	480
		EMV =	$2240		$2520		$2560*		$2420

Table 2.6 Optimal conditional profit for each event, ski problem

	Acts			
Events *Demand of:*	*Stock* 20 *pairs*	*Stock* 40 *pairs*	*Stock* 60 *pairs*	*Stock* 80 *pairs*
20 pairs	$1200*	$1000	$ 800	$ 600
40 pairs	2000	2400*	2200	2000
60 pairs	2800	3200	3600*	3400
80 pairs	3600	4000	4400	4800*

profit of the optimal act, *given a particular event,* and the conditional profit of any other act, given the same event.

The meaning of opportunity loss can most easily be illustrated by converting a table of conditional profits to a table of conditional opportunity losses. The first step is to examine the conditional profits to determine the optimal act for each event. Table 2.6 shows the conditional profits from Table 2.5, with the optimal act for each event marked with an asterisk.

Note that the highest conditional profit for any level of demand occurs, as we should expect, where the amount stocked is equal to the amount demanded.

The table of conditional opportunity losses can be obtained by subtracting the *CP* for the act in question from the optimal *CP* for that event. Thus the first row of the *COL* table (*COL* for demand 20) is obtained by subtracting each entry for that row from $1200. The complete *COL* table is shown in Table 2.7.

Two observations can be made regarding the entries in Table 2.7. First, the conditional opportunity losses form a pattern. For every 20 pairs that the dealer is overstocked, the opportunity loss grows by

Table 2.7 ***COL*** **table, ski problem**

	Acts			
Events *Demand of:*	*Stock* 20 *pairs*	*Stock* 40 *pairs*	*Stock* 60 *pairs*	*Stock* 80 *pairs*
20 pairs	$ 0	$200	$400	$600
40 pairs	400	0	200	400
60 pairs	800	400	0	200
80 pairs	1200	800	400	0

increments of \$200, while for every 20 pairs he is understocked, the opportunity loss grows by increments of \$400. These relationships can be determined directly from the facts of the problem in the form of equations, rather than deriving the COL table from a table of conditional profits. These relationships are:

$COL = 10(S - D) \quad \text{if } S > D$
(The dealer loses \$10 on each pair of skis that is overstocked.)

$COL = 20(D - S) \quad \text{if } S < D$
(The dealer loses the opportunity to increase his profit by \$20 for each pair of skis understocked.)

$COL = 0 \quad \text{if } S = D$
(The dealer has optimized his profits.)

These equations can be summarized as:

$$COL = 10(S - D) \quad \text{if } S \geq D \tag{2.3}$$
$$COL = 20(D - S) \quad \text{if } S < D \tag{2.4}$$

Second, the equations and the COL table illustrate the fact that opportunity losses measure either the regret of suffering an out-of-pocket loss (for overstocking) or the regret of not taking advantage of an opportunity for gain (for understocking). Opportunity losses always measure positive amounts of regret and can *never* be negative. If one acts optimally, he suffers no regret; if one does not act optimally, he suffers a positive amount of regret. (The conditional profit of the optimal act *minus* the conditional profit of any other act for the same event can never be negative.)

Since conditional profits and conditional opportunity losses are so intimately related, one might hypothesize that the optimal act could be identified by minimizing expected opportunity losses as well as by maximizing expected profits. Calculation of the optimal act through minimizing expected opportunity loss is accomplished in Table 2.8.

The optimal act is to stock 60 pairs, with an expected opportunity loss of \$200.

COST OF UNCERTAINTY

The expected opportunity loss of the optimal act, EOL^*, is called the *cost of uncertainty*. If a person had a perfect forecasting device, he would always know what event would occur. He would then choose the best act for that event, and his opportunity losses would be 0. Therefore the EOL^* is the price he has to pay for having to make a decision in the face of uncertainty and is called the cost of uncertainty.

EXPECTED VALUE OF PERFECT INFORMATION

If the perfect forecasting device mentioned in the preceding paragraph could be bought, how much would it be worth? Since a perfect forecast would reduce expected opportunity loss to 0, it would be logical to pay any amount up to EOL^* for the forecasting service, but no more. Thus EOL^* provides a measure of what perfect information would be worth, and can be called the expected value of perfect information ($EVPI$).

COST OF IRRATIONALITY

When faced with uncertainty, a person who wants to be rational will choose the optimal act. If he chooses another act instead, he is acting irrationally. This, of course, is his option, but the difference between EOL^* and the larger EOL for the act he chooses measures the cost of his irrationality. The difference between EOL^* and the EOL of any other act is the same as the difference between EMV^* and the EMV for that same act except that the sign is reversed.

EXPECTED PROFIT UNDER CERTAINTY

Assume that a forecasting service could tell the ski dealer any time he was confronted with the opportunity to make a special purchase of skis what the demand would be for that season. If the forecaster said the demand would be for 20 pairs of skis the dealer would stock 20 pairs, with a profit equal to the conditional profit for the act-event combination demand 20, stock 20, namely, $1200. If the forecast were for 40 skis, he would stock 40, sell them all, and make a profit of $2400, and so on, for all levels of demand. These values could be called profits

Table 2.8 Calculation of expected opportunity losses, ski problem

		Acts							
		Stock 20 pairs		*Stock 40 pairs*		*Stock 60 pairs*		*Stock 80 pairs*	
Events Demand of:	*Probability of event (weight)*	*COL*	*COL × probability*	*COL*	*COL × probability*	*COL*	*COL × probability*	*COL*	*COL × probability*
20 pairs	.2	$ 0	$ 0	$200	$ 40	$400	$ 80	$600	$120
40 pairs	.4	400	160	0	0	200	80	400	160
60 pairs	.3	800	240	400	120	0	0	200	60
80 pairs	.1	1200	120	800	80	400	40	0	0
		EOL =	$520		$240		$200*		$340

Table 2.9 Calculation of expected profit under certainty, ski problem

Events Demand of:	*Probability of event (weight)*	*CP of optimal act, given demand*	*CP × probability*
20 pairs	.2	$1200	$ 240
40 pairs	.4	2400	960
60 pairs	.3	3600	1080
80 pairs	.1	4800	480
			EPC = $2760

under certainty. They are the conditional profits marked with asterisks in Table 2.6.

Now if the dealer used this forecaster's services every time he was confronted with this opportunity and if the odds of the various demands were as originally stated, he could calculate his average profit by weighting the profits under certainty by the odds of their occurring. This calculation, performed in Table 2.9, produces a measure called the expected profit under certainty (*EPC*).

Under conditions of certainty the *EOL*, as mentioned previously, would be 0, and the sum of *EPC* and *EOL* under certainty would be equal to $2760 + 0 = $2760. Note that this same value can always be obtained for problems under certainty by adding the *EMV* for the act in question and the *EOL* for that same act.

In the ski problem, the *EMV* for the act "stock 20," for example, was $2240 (Table 2.5), and the *EOL* for that act was $520 (Table 2.8). Their sum is $2760, the *EPC*. This value of $2760 could thus be obtained by adding the *EMV* for *any* act to the *EOL* for that same act.

SUMMARY

THE MEANING OF EXPECTED MONETARY VALUE AND EXPECTED OPPORTUNITY LOSS

We began this chapter by defining an optimal decision as one that looks like the "best bet" *before* action is taken. We saw that there were two elements to what made a particular act the "best bet," namely, the payoffs associated with all the act-event combinations, and how likely the events were to occur. We defined the act having the greatest weighted payoff, that is, the highest expected value, as the optimal act or "best bet."

It should be made perfectly clear that while the act with the highest expected value identifies for us the act with the most promise before the fact, the amount of EMV^* is not how much we shall make if we take that course of action. Once an act is taken, profits are no longer conditional, they are determined. In the chuck-a-luck problem, for example, the only possible monetary outcomes of playing the game once are $-\$1$, $+\$1$, or $+\$2$. The expected monetary value is the amount we can expect to average if we play the game a large number of times. What we are saying, then, is that *the act that maximizes the average profit over a large number of trials is the best act to choose before the fact, regardless of the number of times we shall be confronted with the situation.*

It should be emphasized again that maximization of expected value is not the only guide to action. However, it is a guide for making decisions under uncertainty which when followed will lead the decision maker to act in a manner consistent with his beliefs about the situation. Thus, procedures followed in this chapter constitute a systematic way to bring to bear on the decision all the information the decision maker has about the situation. We assume in this chapter that the decision maker does not have the opportunity to sample in order to secure more information about the problem before having to make a decision. How sampling procedures can be used to reduce the cost of uncertainty in decision problems will be discussed at length in later chapters.

After the preceding discussion, it should be clear that expected opportunity losses are interpreted in the same manner as other expected values. Thus, the expected opportunity loss of the optimal act is not the amount of money (or utility) a person will lose on taking the optimal act. The expected opportunity loss of the optimal act shows, on the average, the amount the decision maker pays for having to make his decision under uncertainty.

PROBLEMS

2.1 (*a*) Define each of the following:

(1) Conditional profit
(2) Expected profit (EMV)
(3) EMV^*
(4) Opportunity loss
(5) Expected opportunity loss
(6) EOL^*
(7) $EVPI$
(8) Expected profit under certainty
(9) Cost of uncertainty
(10) Cost of irrationality

(*b*) Show, wherever you can, the identities or relationships that exist among the terms in part (*a*) of this question, and explain them in your own words.

2.2 Assume that you are given the following payoff table:

	Acts		
	(1)	(2)	(3)
Events	*Conditional profit*	*Conditional profit*	*Conditional profit*
A	\$20	\$10	\$ 0
B	35	40	30
C	50	55	60

You are told that the probability of events *A*, *B*, and *C* are .5, .3, and .2, respectively.

(*a*) Calculate the *EMV* for each act, and identify the optimal act.

(*b*) Draw up a table of conditional opportunity losses, calculate the *EOL* for each act, and identify the optimal act.

(*c*) Calculate the expected profit under certainty.

(*d*) Calculate the cost of irrationality for each of the nonoptimal acts.

(*e*) What is the cost of uncertainty?

(*f*) What is the expected value of perfect information?

2.3 Suppose the newsboy in Prob. 1.9 attaches the following probability weights to various levels of demand for newspapers on a particular day:

Demand, number of papers	*Probability*
18	.1
19	.1
20	.2
21	.3
22	.2
23	.1

Assuming that unsold newspapers are worthless,

(*a*) How many papers should he purchase?

(*b*) How much does he expect to make on the day in question?

(*c*) If he believed the demand situation would stay the same, how much would he expect to make in 30 days?

(*d*) How much could he afford to pay for a perfect forecast of demand?

2.4 You run a concession at football games in a small town. A question you must resolve is how many hot dogs to stock on a typical night. You can buy buns for 48 cents per dozen and weiners for 60 cents per dozen. If they are not sold, the weiners are a total loss, but the buns can be returned, in which case you receive 12 cents per dozen for them. Catsup, mustard, etc., average 2 cents a hot dog (24 cents per dozen) for hot dogs *sold*. Hot dogs sell for 20 cents *each*. Assume that the only possible levels of demand are 10, 20, and 30 dozen, and that these levels have probabilities of .2, .5, and .3 respectively.

(*a*) Determine the conditional profit functions.
(*b*) Make a table of conditional profits.
(*c*) Determine the optimal number to stock, using conditional profits.
(*d*) Determine the opportunity loss functions.
(*e*) Make an opportunity loss table from the conditional profit table.
(*f*) Check the opportunity loss table using the conditional opportunity loss functions.
(*g*) Determine the optimal number to stock, using the opportunity loss table.
(*h*) Determine the cost of uncertainty.
(*i*) Determine the expected value of perfect information.
(*j*) Determine the expected profit under certainty.

2.5 Do you think *your* utility for money curve over the range of −$1000 to +$1000 looks like that in Fig. 2.1, 2.2, or 2.3? Why do you feel that way?

If you received a windfall profit of $10,000 tomorrow, might your utility for money curve change? Explain.

2.6 Occasionally, corporations or individuals may decide to self-insure against certain kinds of risks. A large chain store, for example, might self-insure against the risks of fire and theft, although an independent (one store) operator would be very reluctant to do so.

(*a*) On a per store basis, are the expected losses as a result of these risks different in the two situations?

(*b*) Why else might the decision makers' optimal acts be different in the two situations?

2.7 Would you rather play the chuck-a-luck game (with two dice) described in the text once with a $1000 bet or 1000 times making a $1 bet each time? Why? Does your answer have any relationship to Prob. 2.6*b*?

2.8 Inspired by entrepreneural spirit, you agree to operate a lemonade stand for the 100-day summer season at a tourist resort. Your predecessor provides you with the following data from last season's operations:

Approximate number of lemonades sold	*Number of days*
0	19
10	6
20	8
30	10
40	13
50	20
60	12
70	10
80	2
	100

You decide to use last season's selling price of 10 cents per glass, and you anticipate a similar sales pattern. The lemonade costs you 2 cents per glass and the paper cup 1 cent. The only thing that keeps you from fabulous riches from this operation is the cost of the ice. You can purchase it for 75 cents a bag from an ice truck that comes through each morning. Due to melting—you have no place to keep it frozen—you average only 15 cups per bag of ice, losing whatever ice is left at the end of the day. Of course, you can't sell the lemonade at all without ice, but since most of your customers are one-time only, you lose no *future* sales by running out of ice.

(*a*) What are the possible acts or strategies in this decision problem?

(*b*) What are the states of nature, or events? What assumptions must be made to utilize last year's sales data in weighting the events?

(*c*) Construct a payoff table based on incremental cash flows, utilizing any strategies you consider "reasonable," and determine their *EMV*.

(*d*) Construct an opportunity loss table for your strategies, and compute *EOL*s.

(*e*) Is the *EOL* of the optimum act the same as if *all* possible strategies had been included in the matrix? Why?

(*f*) How much could you expect to make in a season?

(*g*) What is the source of uncertainty in this problem? How could it be removed?

(*h*) How much would the ability to forecast demand exactly each day be worth to you?

(*i*) How much would you pay to rent a refrigerator that would prevent any ice losses? (Assume that you could still get 15 cups per bag, but extra ice could be carried over.)

2.9 You have a part-time job in a shoe department and have a chance to show off your knowledge of statistics by solving the following problem: Children's shoe boots (size 5B) cost you $5 each ($60 per dozen); they sell for $8 each ($96 per dozen) during the winter but must be marked down to $3 each ($36 per dozen) in the spring to clear the stock. You have determined the following distribution of demand:

Dozen	*Probability*
10	.5
20	.3
30	.2

Determine the optimal number of boots to stock using a table of conditional profits.

2.10 Kostplus Corporation, a manufacturer of aerospace subsystems, is under government contract to produce 5000 assemblies, each of which requires a delicate component that must meet rigid specifications. These components can be purchased in any quantity from a subcontractor, who will guarantee that their quality meets the specifications, at a cost of $15.80 each. Company engineers estimate that the components could be produced internally at a lower cost, but the nature of the production process is such that a high proportion—perhaps as high as 50%—of the components will not meet specifications. Based on previous experience with processes involving similar technology, the following estimates are made:

Fraction of parts not meeting specifications	*Probability*
0	.05
0.10	.40
0.20	.25
0.30	.15
0.40	.10
0.50	.05

The fixed setup cost involved in the production process is $20,000, and the variable costs are $10 per unit. Defective components can be discovered, reworked and replaced in the course of the assembly operation at a cost of $8 each.

(*a*) What is the expected cost of supplying the 5000 components internally (including the cost of defectives)?

(*b*) What are the anticipated savings (or losses) from producing versus purchasing the 5000 components?

(*c*) What is the cost of uncertainty in this decision problem?

(*d*) Are your answers to parts (*b*) and (*c*) the same? Explain why or why not.

(*e*) What is the *EVPI*?

(*f*) Are your answers to (*c*) and (*e*) the same? Explain why or why not.

(*g*) Interpret the meaning of the *EVPI* in this problem.

2.11 Suppose, in the situation described in Prob. 2.10, that Kostplus discovers that it is not possible to rework defective components to meet the necessary specifications. Components can be tested at a cost of 20 cents each, but any component found defective must be considered worthless and must be replaced by a new one. This implies that a decision to produce might involve more than 5000 units, and/or that some components might be purchased to supplement the internal production. Units in excess of the 5000 acceptable components required have a net resale value of $6 each.

(*a*) What are the possible acts (decision strategies) under these conditions?

(*b*) Write a generalized conditional payoff equation for this problem.

(*c*) Should Kostplus produce any components? If so, how many?

(*d*) Is the cost of uncertainty higher or lower than in Prob. 2.10*c*? Rationalize this difference.

2.12 Suppose defensive common stocks return an average 7% in years of economic expansion and 4% in recession years. Growth stocks return 30% in expansion years but may be expected to lose 40% in value in recession years. Of the last 25 years 7 have been recession years, as the term is used here.

(*a*) Over the long term, would you expect growth stocks or defensive stocks to perform better? (Assume, for purposes of this problem, that there is no particular pattern to the spacing of the recession years over the period.)

(*b*) How sure would you have to be that a recession was going to occur in the coming year to warrant shifting a portfolio from growth stocks to defensive stocks?

2.13 A man has the opportunity to buy $30,000 of term life insurance covering a 1-year period. The probability that he will survive the year is .995. His utility is linear with money.

(*a*) Draw up a payoff table showing the conditional profits of each act-event combination.

(*b*) What is the maximum amount he would be willing to pay for such a policy?

2.14 You are given the opportunity to play chuck-a-luck with three dice. The rules of the game are as follows:

You pay $1 to play.
You roll the dice once.

If you roll three sixes, you get $3 and your $1 back
If you roll two sixes, you get $2 and your $1 back.
If you roll one six, you get $1 and your $1 back.
If you get zero sixes, you lose your $1 entry fee.

(*a*) Draw up a table of conditional profits. Be sure to show all the act-event combinations.

(*b*) Calculate the expected monetary values for the acts "play" and "don't play."

(*c*) If your utility were linear with money, would you play the game or not? Explain.

2.15 The E. Z. Pay Co. has annual fixed costs of $1,000,000, variable costs of $10 per unit of product, and a selling price of $25 per unit. The company has an opportunity to make additional credit sales without increasing its fixed costs of operation, but the potential customers are poor credit risks. Some of the proposed accounts could be collected in a reasonable time, but many could not be collected at all. Unfortunately, the company has no adequate means for predicting in advance which customers will pay and which will default.

(*a*) What percentage of the proposed credit sales must create collectible accounts in order to make the additional sales profitable?

(*b*) Does your answer to (*a*) suggest any generalization about credit policy and its relationship to the utilization of productive capacity?

(*c*) According to generally accepted accounting procedures, the *net* accounts receivable figure shown on a firm's balance sheet is actually an *expected* value. Explain.

3
Probability Concepts

INTRODUCTION

At the heart of statistics and decision making lies a concept called "probability." Probability is a most pervasive idea. It creeps into our everyday life at innumerable points. It permeates every scientific enterprise. As we have seen in the previous chapter, it can become a determining factor in decisions made by businessmen.

Probability is frequently used in everyday language. We would not be surprised to hear a politician say, "Taxes will probably go up after the election," a banker assert that "The prime rate of interest will probably fall next year," or a student say, "I'll probably pass statistics—after two more semesters."

In the biological, social, and physical sciences the use of probability has become indispensable. We discover in genetics that the occurrence of a specific characteristic, given a cross of plants or animals, is essentially a matter of probability. We find in physics that it is impossible to predict a particle's specific momentum and position except on a probability basis. Virtually all predictions made in the social sciences have measures of probable error attached to them.

In Chap. 2 we illustrated the application of probability to business problems by weighting the conditional profit associated with a given level of demand by the probability that such a level of demand would occur, finally comparing the sum of the weighted values to find the best act under uncertainty.

Although our illustrations concerning the use of probability hint at a definition of the term, its meaning is not altogether clear. There is disagreement among statisticians, mathematicians, and philosophers about the precise definition of probability. As one noted philosopher pointed out, despite the fact that man has invented probability, he cannot agree on precisely what it is. In this chapter we shall consider two definitions of probability. Although our own preference will no doubt show through, the reader may choose the point of view that best suits his purposes.

OBJECTIVE PROBABILITY

The objective point of view considers *probability* as the ratio of successful outcomes of an experiment to the total number of outcomes possible, or as the "relative frequency" of successful outcomes. The experiment, whether in the laboratory or in the field, produces facts on which everyone can agree. It is these objective facts which form the basis of the probability statement. If, for example, out of a particular group of 10,000 people age 30 years, 9800 survive to age 35, the probability of survival of a member to age 35 equals .98.

Now we all know that a particular person can't be 98% alive at age 35, though some of us might feel that way or worse at times. The person picked will either be alive or dead at 35. The .98 simply means that if we know no more about the person in question than that he is a member of this particular group out of which 9800 will survive, we assign the group's relative frequency of survival to him. Or, if you prefer, we can give a slightly different interpretation to this objective probability and say that 98 to 2 are the best odds that we shall give that this person will survive to age 35.

SUBJECTIVE PROBABILITY

According to the subjective view, a probability is simply a number representing a degree of belief concerning the occurrence of a future event. The only limitation regarding this number is that it be between 0 and 1. Complete certainty that a particular event will occur is equated with a probability of 1. Complete certainty that the event will not occur is equated with a probability of 0. Less than complete certainty con-

Table 3.1 Calculation of expected monetary value, Packers bet

Event	*Probability*	*Payoff*	*Probability × payoff*
Packers win	.75	$+10	$+7.50
Packers lose	.25	−30	−7.50
			EMV = 0

cerning the event must then be characterized by a probability somewhere between 0 and 1.

A useful way of viewing subjective probabilities is to relate them to betting odds. If you were willing—just barely willing—to give 3 to 1 odds that the Green Bay Packers would win next season's National Football League championship, you implicitly assess the probability that they will win as 3 out of 4, or .75.[1] We can demonstrate this by showing that this probability makes the *EMV* of a bet of, say, $10 (against $30) equal to 0, as shown in Table 3.1.

Note that while the success of the Packers in previous years might be a factor in assessing these odds, it can hardly be the sole determinant. You know very well that neither the Packers nor their opponents will be exactly the same teams next year as in years past, nor will they be meeting under the same conditions.

In much the same way the businessman, on the combined basis of historical record, current conditions, and perhaps hunch, may formulate the probability of success of a business undertaking. A subjectivist would argue that the basis of this probability, called subjective or personal probability, does not lie in an irresponsible subjectivity but rather in a subjectivity based on a realistic appraisal of the empirical world. Thus in a business context, we might view the basis of subjective probability as "informed business judgment" regardless of the exact source.

OBJECTIVE AND SUBJECTIVE PROBABILITY: A RESOLUTION

Whether these views are contradictory from a philosophical viewpoint has still to be settled. For us, however, the crucial question is whether they are contradictory from the perspective of the decision maker in business. We do not think so. If a businessman has encountered a particular problem enough times to have available the relative frequencies of past events to use as probabilities of similar events occurring in the future, he would be foolish not to use them. On the other hand, if no such relative frequencies are available because the situation is

[1] This assumes that your utility is linear with money over a range of values representing the maximum gain or loss from the bet (see the discussion of utility in Chap. 2).

new or unique, he must rely on whatever related and general experience he has had in addition to whatever specific observations he can make to formulate the odds of possible outcomes.

THE MATHEMATICAL THEORY OF PROBABILITY

Whether the probabilities are objective or subjective, we shall often need to manipulate them to obtain useful empirical results. For example, if a man bets on horse A of race number 2 and horse D of race number 3, what is the probability that he has at least one winner? Or consider the plight of a politician who must decide whether or not to run for election before his opponent is determined by an opposing party's primary. He may rightfully believe that his probability of getting elected depends in part on who his opponent is. How is his probability of getting elected related to the various probabilities of success attached to the contestants in the other primary? In a business context, consider a firm's decision about whether or not to market a new product. The firm, through a market survey, gains some new information with respect to attitudes toward the product. How can this new information be combined with the firm's accumulated past experience and judgment in introducing new products to assess the probability of the product's success?

The kind of questions posed above can often be answered by utilizing a type of mathematical calculus called mathematical probability. The questions are real in the sense that they do have an empirical context. The mathematical structure used to manipulate these empirical probabilities, however, is purely formal. As it turns out, many empirical processes can be described well by this formal mathematical structure. In the remainder of this chapter we will develop a few simple but important probability concepts.

VENN DIAGRAMS AND FREQUENCY TABLES

To develop some important notions related to the manipulation of probabilities, consider the following example: A group consists of ten people, four men and six women. Three of the four men smoke, as do two of the six women. In formal terms we can call the group a sample space which includes ten elements. The sample space or universal set, U, can be broken down into four subsets, men, women, smokers, and nonsmokers. Note that the subsets "men" and "women" are nonintersecting and may be defined as *mutually exclusive;* in practical terms this means that there can be no single element that has both the characteristics "male" and "female." The same is true of the subsets "smoker" and "nonsmoker." However, other subsets such as "male" and "smoker,"

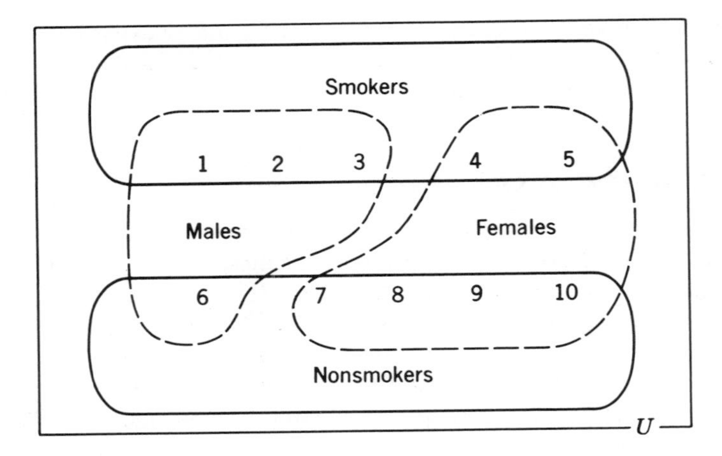

Fig. 3.1 Venn diagram, smoking example.

for example, are not mutually exclusive since one person can possess both characteristics.

The situation described above can be seen much more readily by drawing a Venn diagram which shows the relationships among the subsets, or by constructing a table showing the number of people in each category, as in Fig. 3.1 and Table 3.2.

Persons number 1, 2, and 3 in the Venn diagram can be identified as the three male smokers counted in the M,S cell of the frequency table. Similarly, person number 6 is the one male nonsmoker in the M,NS cell, etc. It is not necessary to identify each element in a Venn diagram with a specific number, but such a procedure will help us identify specific persons in the discussion that follows.

MARGINAL PROBABILITY

From the frequency table one can easily find, for example, the probability of choosing a male from the group by a method where every person

Table 3.2 Frequency table, smoking example

	Male, M	*Female, F*	*Total*
Smoker, S	3	2	5
Nonsmoker, NS	1	4	5
Total	4	6	10

in the group has an equal chance of being chosen. Since four of the ten people are males, the odds would be 4 in 10 that a person so selected would be male. To familiarize the student with the symbols that are used in probability calculations, let us summarize the previous sentence as:

$$P(M) = \frac{n(M)}{n(U)} = 4/10$$

Thus the probability of a male is the number of elements in the subset M divided by the number of elements in the universal set U. This probability, and any other one that includes the number of elements in a single category of classification, i.e., male, female, smoker, or non-smoker, in the numerator of a fraction and the number of elements in the universal set in the denominator, is known as a *marginal probability.* The term "marginal" has nothing at all to do with economic theory—it merely relates to the fact that the numbers in the numerator are to be found at the margins of the frequency table. Other marginal probabilities from the table are therefore:

$$P(F) = \frac{n(F)}{n(U)} = 6/10$$

$$P(S) = \frac{n(S)}{n(U)} = 5/10$$

$$P(NS) = \frac{n(NS)}{n(U)} = 5/10$$

JOINT PROBABILITY

A joint probability is one that relates to more than one category of classification, as the name indicates. The probability of M *and* S is the number of individuals who are male and smokers divided by the number in the universal set. Since there are three male smokers,

$$P(M \text{ and } S) = \frac{n(M \text{ and } S)}{n(U)} = 3/10$$

Similarly,

$$P(F \text{ and } S) = \frac{n(F \text{ and } S)}{n(U)} = 2/10$$

$$P(M \text{ and } NS) = \frac{n(M \text{ and } NS)}{n(U)} = 1/10$$

$$P(F \text{ and } NS) = \frac{n(F \text{ and } NS)}{n(U)} = 4/10$$

Note that whether the expression $n(M \text{ and } S)$ or $n(S \text{ and } M)$ is used, one still is referring to those three persons who have *both* the characteristic of being male and that of being a smoker. Therefore:

$$P(M \text{ and } S) = P(S \text{ and } M) = 3/10$$

CONDITIONAL PROBABILITY

A conditional probability is contingent upon or conditioned by prior knowledge. Suppose that someone picked a person from the group of ten and said, "The person I picked is a male; what is the probability that he is a nonsmoker?" Looking at the frequency table down the column headed "male," one observes that only one of the four males is a nonsmoker. Therefore the odds that the person picked would be a nonsmoker *given* that he was male would be:

$$P(NS \mid M) = \frac{n(NS \text{ and } M)}{n(M)} = 1/4$$

The vertical line dividing NS from M may be read as "given." Thus the probability of a nonsmoker given male is equal to the number of elements in the intersection of "nonsmoker" and "male" divided by the number of elements in "male."

Similarly,

$$P(NS \mid F) = \frac{n(NS \text{ and } F)}{n(F)} = 4/6$$

$$P(M \mid S) = \frac{n(M \text{ and } S)}{n(S)} = 3/5$$

. . .

RELATIONSHIPS AMONG MARGINAL, JOINT, AND CONDITIONAL PROBABILITIES

A conditional probability can be defined solely in terms of the corresponding joint and marginal probabilities. Using the male smoker illustration, the following relationship holds:

$$P(M \mid S) = \frac{P(M \text{ and } S)}{P(S)} = \frac{P(S \text{ and } M)}{P(S)}$$

The proof of this relationship follows from the definition of joint and marginal probabilities.

If

$$P(M \text{ and } S) = \frac{n(M \text{ and } S)}{n(U)}$$

and

$$P(S) = \frac{n(S)}{n(U)}$$

then

$$\frac{n(M \text{ and } S)/n(U)}{n(S)/n(U)} = \frac{n(M \text{ and } S)}{n(S)} = P(M \mid S)$$

The formulas we have employed thus far have all been developed in terms of the smoker-sex example. In more general terms, the relationships can be expressed as follows: for any two categories of classification A and B, consisting of four subsets A_1, A_2, B_1, and B_2,

marginal probabilities

$$P(A_1) = \frac{n(A_1)}{n(U)}$$

$$P(B_2) = \frac{n(B_2)}{n(U)}$$

$$\vdots \qquad \vdots$$

joint probabilities

$$P(A_1 \text{ and } B_1) = \frac{n(A_1 \text{ and } B_1)}{n(U)}$$

$$P(A_1 \text{ and } B_2) = \frac{n(A_1 \text{ and } B_2)}{n(U)}$$

$$\vdots \qquad \vdots$$

conditional probabilities

$$P(A_1 \mid B_1) = \frac{n(A_1 \text{ and } B_1)}{n(B_1)} = \frac{P(A_1 \text{ and } B_1)}{P(B_1)}$$

$$P(A_1 \mid B_2) = \frac{n(A_1 \text{ and } B_2)}{n(B_2)} = \frac{P(A_1 \text{ and } B_2)}{P(B_2)}$$

$$\vdots \qquad \vdots$$

THE GENERAL LAW OF MULTIPLICATION

The law of multiplication is simply a restatement of the definition of conditional probability. Defining conditional probability as

$$P(A \mid B) = \frac{P(A \text{ and } B)}{P(B)}$$

we can multiply both sides of the equation by $P(B)$, obtaining the relationship called the *law of multiplication:*

$$P(A \text{ and } B) = P(B)P(A \mid B) \tag{3.1}$$

It also follows that

$$P(A \text{ and } B) = P(A)P(B \mid A) \tag{3.2}$$

This law says that the joint probability of two subsets is the product of the conditional probability of those subsets times the marginal probability of the subset which is given as the condition.

Students usually think of the law of multiplication as some unfamiliar symbolic generalization, even though they may have actually used it many times unknowingly. Some simple examples should illustrate this fact. The probability of drawing two aces in succession from a well shuffled deck of cards is:

$$P(A_1 \text{ and } A_2) = P(A_1) \times P(A_2 \mid A_1)$$

$$\begin{pmatrix}\text{Probability of an}\\ \text{ace on draw 1}\\ \text{and draw 2}\end{pmatrix} = \begin{pmatrix}\text{Probability of an}\\ \text{ace on draw 1}\end{pmatrix} \begin{pmatrix}\text{Probability of an}\\ \text{ace on draw 2}\\ \textit{given} \text{ an ace}\\ \text{on draw 1}\end{pmatrix}$$

$$= 4/52 \times 3/51 = 12/2652$$

The marginal probability of an ace on the first draw is 4/52 since there are four aces in the deck of 52 cards. The conditional probability of an ace on the second draw *given* an ace on the first is 3/51 since there are three aces left among the 51 remaining cards.

Similarly, the probability of drawing four aces in succession is

$$\begin{aligned} P(A_1 \text{ and } A_2 \text{ and } A_3 \text{ and } A_4) &= P(A_1) \times P(A_2 \mid A_1) \times P(A_3 \mid A_1 \text{ and } A_2) \\ &\quad \times P(A_4 \mid A_1 \text{ and } A_2 \text{ and } A_3) \\ &= (4/52)(3/51)(2/50)(1/49) \\ &= 24/6{,}497{,}400 \end{aligned}$$

The probability of being dealt a royal flush (A, K, Q, J, 10 in any one suit in any order) in five-card stud poker is

$$(20/52)(4/51)(3/50)(2/49)(1/48) = 480/311{,}875{,}200$$

where 20/52 is the *marginal* probability of drawing an A, K, Q, J, or 10 in any suit out of the 52 cards, 4/51 is the *conditional* probability of drawing any one of the four necessary cards in the suit established by the first draw from the 51 remaining cards, etc.

THE SPECIAL LAW OF MULTIPLICATION: INDEPENDENT EVENTS

An event B is said to be independent of an event A if $P(B \mid A) = P(B)$. This situation occurs when event A has no effect whatsoever on event B, in which case knowledge that event A has occurred gives one no edge in predicting the occurrence of event B. You may have learned from hard experience that since slot machines have no memory and therefore don't run hot and cold (only the players have memories and run hot and

Table 3.2 (Repeated) Frequency table, smoking example

	Male, M	*Female, F*	*Total*
Smoker, S	3	2	5
Nonsmoker, NS	1	4	5
Total	4	6	10

cold), the probability of a payoff given a payoff on the preceding trial is exactly the same as the overall (marginal) probability of a payoff.

In the case of statistical independence, the law of multiplication

$$P(A \text{ and } B) = P(A \mid B)P(B)$$

reduces to

$$P(A \text{ and } B) = P(A)P(B) \tag{3.3}$$

since by the definition of independence $P(A \mid B) = P(A)$ for this case.

To solidify the notion of statistical independence, consider again the frequency matrix classifying smokers by sex as shown in Table 3.2.

Converting to a probability table by dividing each element by the sum of all the elements, we obtain joint probabilities in each cell and marginal probabilities at each margin as shown in Table 3.3.

From Table 3.3 it is evident that status as a smoker is *not* independent of sex. If it were, the product of the marginals would equal the corresponding joint probabilities. In Table 3.3 the product of the marginals "smoker" and "male," (.5)(.4), does *not* equal the joint probability of "smoker and male" of .3, and so on.

If the propensity to smoke were in fact independent of sex, the proportion of male smokers to total males would be the same as the proportion of female smokers to total females, as in Table 3.4.

Table 3.3 Probability table, smoking example

	Male, M	*Female, F*	*Total*
Smoker, S	.3	.2	.5
Nonsmoker, NS	.1	.4	.5
Total	.4	.6	1.0

Table 3.4 Probability table, smoking example with independent events

	Male, M	*Female, F*	*Total*
Smoker, S	.2	.3	.5
Nonsmoker, NS	.2	.3	.5
Total	.4	.6	1.0

In this case, the product of each pair of marginals is equal to the corresponding joint probability, proving independence. Thus the knowledge of a person's sex would be of no value in determining the probability that he smoked since $P(S \mid M) = P(S \mid F) = P(S)$.

THE GENERAL LAW OF ADDITION

The *law of addition* is used to calculate the probability that a number of events will occur, either separately *or* jointly. Thus $P(S \text{ or } M)$ means the probability that a person selected at random is a smoker *or* a male *or* both. Referring to the Venn diagram presented earlier (repeated here as Fig. 3.2), the probability that a person is a smoker *or* a male is equal to $n(S \text{ or } M)/n(U) = 6/10$. The specific persons in either of the subsets "smoker" and "male" are those numbered 1, 2, 3, 6, 4, and 5 in the shaded area of the Venn diagram.

For more complex problems it is convenient to calculate this proba-

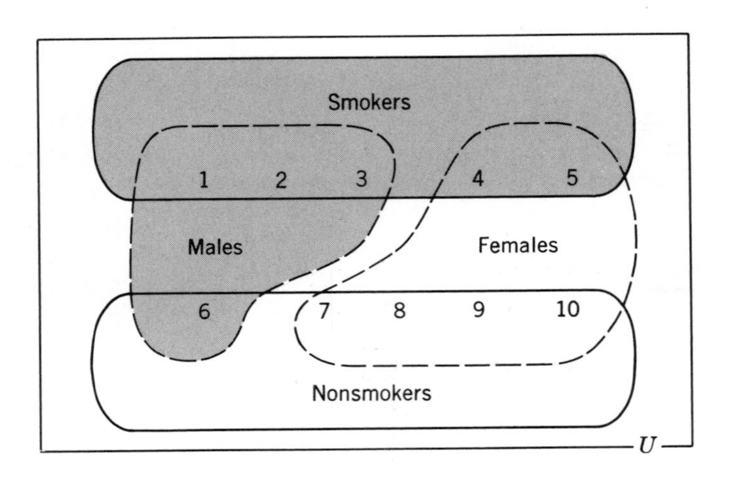

Fig. 3.2 Venn diagram, smoking example.

bility using probabilities already calculated. If we look carefully at the Venn diagram, we note that this can be accomplished as follows:

$$\begin{aligned} P(S \text{ or } M) &= P(S) + P(M) - P(S \text{ and } M) \\ &= \frac{n(S)}{n(U)} + \frac{n(M)}{n(U)} - \frac{n(S \text{ and } M)}{n(U)} \\ &= 5/10 + 4/10 - 3/10 = 6/10 \end{aligned}$$

This equality is known as the law of addition. We have to subtract $P(S \text{ and } M)$ from the sum of $P(S)$ and $P(M)$ to avoid double counting. If we added the number of smokers to the number of males, we should count the three persons who are *both* smokers and males twice.

In general, the law of addition for two events A and B is

$$P(A \text{ or } B) = P(A) + P(B) - P(A \text{ and } B) \tag{3.4}$$

THE SPECIAL LAW OF ADDITION: MUTUALLY EXCLUSIVE EVENTS

If two events are mutually exclusive, there are no elements common to both events. In such a case $P(A \text{ and } B) = 0$, and the general law of addition reduces to the special case,

$$P(A \text{ or } B) = P(A) + P(B) \tag{3.5}$$

Application of this special case can be demonstrated in relation to the smoking example. Suppose one were to calculate $P(S \text{ or } NS)$. Obviously one cannot be both a smoker and a nonsmoker (at least at the same time), and $P(S \text{ and } NS) = 0$. Therefore

$$P(S \text{ or } NS) = P(S) + P(NS) = 5/10 + 5/10 = 1$$

(When there are more than two mutually exclusive categories in a particular problem, the either-or probabilities of any two will not, of course, add to 1, as they do for the example above.)

BAYES' RULE

In the eighteenth century a Scottish pastor, the Reverend Mr. Thomas Bayes, manipulated the laws of addition and multiplication to form a rule which has proved to be a cornerstone of modern decision theory. His rule makes it possible to determine a conditional probability in terms of the complementary or reverse conditional probability and the relevant marginal probabilities. Suppose for instance in the smoking example that we are given $P(S \mid M)$, $P(S \mid F)$, $P(M)$, and $P(F)$ and wish to find $P(M \mid S)$. Let us derive Bayes' rule for this illustration. We know that a conditional probability can be found by:

$$P(M \mid S) = \frac{P(S \text{ and } M)}{P(S)} = \frac{P(M \text{ and } S)}{P(S)}$$

but it is also true that

$$P(S \text{ and } M) = P(S \mid M)P(M) \qquad \text{(law of multiplication)}$$

so that

$$P(M \mid S) = \frac{P(S \mid M)P(M)}{P(S)}$$

If we do not know $P(S)$, we may derive it as the sum of mutually exclusive joint probabilities which include the event S

$$P(S) = P(S \text{ and } M) + P(S \text{ and } F) \qquad \text{(law of addition, mutually exclusive events)}$$

also,

$$P(S \text{ and } M) = P(S \mid M)P(M)$$

and (law of multiplication)

$$P(S \text{ and } F) = P(S \mid F)P(F)$$

so that

$$P(S) = P(S \mid M)P(M) + P(S \mid F)P(F)$$

Therefore, Bayes' rule is

$$P(M \mid S) = \frac{P(S \mid M)P(M)}{P(S \mid M)P(M) + P(S \mid F)P(F)} \tag{3.6}$$

To use this last expression, which is known as Bayes' rule, to get a numerical result, recall that $P(M) = 4/10$, $P(S \mid M) = 3/4$, $P(F) = 6/10$, and $P(S \mid F) = 2/6$. Therefore

$$P(M \mid S) = \frac{(3/4)(4/10)}{(3/4)(4/10) + (2/6)(6/10)} = \frac{3/10}{5/10} = 3/5$$

We can check the results of Bayes' rule from the original frequency table for the problem, where we observe that

$$P(M \mid S) = \frac{n(M \text{ and } S)}{N(S)} = 3/5$$

Since the various conditional and joint probabilities in the smoking example were either known or apparent, Bayes' rule may have seemed of little use. Let us consider another example to show its usefulness.

Suppose you were asked to determine which of two dice, which appear identical, is loaded. Assume you know that one is "fair" with a probability of a one-spot of 1/6 and that the other is loaded to make the probability of a one-spot 1/4. You choose one die and examine its physical characteristics closely, but you can detect nothing. As far as you are concerned at this point, the odds that the die you have chosen is the fair one are simply 50-50; that is, the probability that the die is fair is 1/2. Suppose further, however, that you are allowed to test the die you have chosen by rolling it just twice. You do so and obtain a one-spot and a non-one on the two rolls. Now, given this experimental outcome, what are the odds that the die is fair?

The answer to the question is a conditional probability, namely, $P(F \mid O)$, the probability that the die is fair, given the outcome we observed from rolling the die twice (which was one one-spot and one non-one). There is no direct way to calculate this probability. However if we summarize the information available to us, we shall see that the desired probability can be found using Bayes' rule.

We can first calculate the conditional probability of obtaining the particular outcome of the experiment *if* we knew whether the die were fair or unfair.

$P(O \mid F)$, the probability of getting a one-spot and a non-one, *given* that the die is fair is equal to $(2)(1/6)(5/6) = 10/36$. This result can be explained as follows: the probability of rolling a one-spot on the first roll is 1/6; the probability of rolling a non-one on the second roll is 5/6. Therefore, using the special law of multiplication (since the two rolls are independent events), the probability of the joint occurrence of a one-spot on the first roll followed by a non-one on the second roll is $(1/6)(5/6)$. Similarly, we could just as well have obtained the non-one on the first roll and the one-spot on the second. The probability of this sequence is $(5/6)(1/6)$. Since we do not care if the one-spot occurs on the first or the second roll, we find the probability of a one-spot on the first and a non-one on the second *or* a non-one on the first and a one-spot on the second by using the special law of addition, obtaining $(1/6)(5/6) + (5/6)(1/6) = (2)(1/6)(5/6) = 10/36$.

In a similar fashion the probability of observing the same outcome if the die were unfair is $P(O \mid U)$, the probability of the outcome (one-spot and non-one) *given* that the die is unfair, which equals $(2)(1/4)(3/4) = 6/16$.

Now we are in a position to apply Bayes' rule:

$$
\begin{aligned}
P(F \mid O) &= \frac{P(O \mid F)P(F)}{P(O \mid F)P(F) + P(O \mid U)P(U)} \\
&= \frac{(10/36)(1/2)}{(10/36)(1/2) + (6/16)(1/2)} \\
&= \frac{40}{94} \\
&= .426
\end{aligned}
$$

Thus before rolling the die, we should have bet with even odds that the die was fair. After the experiment, we should be less sure that the die was fair (since the outcome we observed is less likely if the die were fair than if it were unfair), and we should reduce the odds from 500 in 1000 to 426 in 1000.

Note that what we have really done in this example is to revise a set of probabilities to reflect the outcome of an experiment. This revision process will prove to be extremely useful to us later as we incorporate the evidence from samples (experiments) into our calculation of expected monetary values and expected opportunity losses in business decision problems.

BINOMIAL PROBABILITY

In the dice problem of the last section, we found it necessary to compute the probability of the experimental outcome "one one-spot in two tosses of a fair die." This is a *binomial probability*, defined as such because of the following characteristics:

1. The experiment could be viewed as a sequence of separate and distinct "trials" (in this case the two successive tosses of the die).
2. Each "trial" could result in either of two possible outcomes, which, for convenience, are referred to as "success" and "failure." (The outcome "one-spot" may be arbitrarily defined as success, and the outcome "non-one" as failure. It makes no difference which is which as long as we are consistent.)
3. The probability of success on any given trial remains constant throughout the sequence of trials. (The probability of obtaining a one-spot is 1/6 on each toss.)
4. The trials are statistically independent; i.e., the outcome of any given trial does not depend on the outcome of other trials in the sequence. (The outcome of the second toss of the die is unaffected by the outcome of the first toss. The die has no memory!)

Trials which meet the conditions set forth in conditions 2 through 4 are referred to as *Bernoulli trials*. Binomial probabilities measure the probability of obtaining a given number of successes in a given number of Bernoulli trials. Successive tosses of a particular coin, or even simultaneous tosses of identical coins, represent Bernoulli trials, and the probability of obtaining 7 heads out of 10 tosses is a binomial probability.

Examples of Bernoulli processes and the use of binomial probabilities are by no means limited to dice- and coin-tossing experiments. Many empirical processes of importance to business decision makers can be described by classifying a series of distinct elements on an either-or, "go or no-go" basis. Each unit of a product coming off an assembly line might be classified as defective or not defective. Persons comprising the potential market for a particular product might be classified as buyers or nonbuyers. Vouchers examined by an auditor may be viewed as correct or in error.

In many business-related illustrations such as these, the conditions described above for a Bernoulli process may not be met precisely. The probability of a defective output from a manufacturing process may change over time (violating condition 3) as a result of mechanical wear on a machine. Errors in invoices may occur in clusters (violating condition 4) because of the effect of fatigue on clerical employees. Very often, however, the effect of departures from theoretical conditions on the solutions of practical problems is minor, and the assumption of Bernoulli processes may make difficult problems tractable. In any case, the uses of binomial probabilities are so widespread as to justify some particular attention to their calculation.

THE CALCULATION OF BINOMIAL PROBABILITIES

To illustrate the calculation of binomial probabilities, let us expand our dice-tossing experiment to include four successive tosses. Assuming that the die is fair, i.e., that the probability of a one-spot on any roll is 1/6, what is the probability of obtaining exactly two one-spots (successes) on four tosses (trials)?

Now if these two successes were to occur on the first two tosses, to be followed by two failures, i.e., *SSFF*, we could easily calculate the probability of occurrence according to the law of multiplication for independent events.

$$P(SSFF) = (1/6)(1/6)(5/6)(5/6) = 25/1296$$

Usually, however, we are not concerned about the ordering of the outcomes, but only the likelihood of two successes out of four trials in any order. All in all, we must consider all the following possible orderings:

SSFF	*FFSS*
SFSF	*FSFS*
SFFS	*FSSF*

In total, there are *six* possible orders in which the two successes (coupled with two failures) can occur. Each of these orderings has a probability of occurrence of 25/1296, obtained as the product of two factors of (1/6) and two factors of (5/6) in some order. Since they are mutually exclusive, the probabilities are additive, and

$$P(2S,\ 2F,\ \text{in any order}) = (6)(25/1296) = 150/1296$$

In order to eliminate the rather clumsy notation used so far, we can formalize it:

Let n = the number of trials
r = the number of successes in n trials
$n - r$ = the number of failures in n trials
p = the probability of success in any trial
$(1 - p)$ = the probability of failure in any trial

The probability of r successes in n trials in a particular order is

$$(p)^r(1 - p)^{n-r}$$

The number of possible orderings of successes and failures is given by the combinatorial formula for the combination of n elements taken r at a time:

$$C(n,r) = \frac{n!}{r!(n - r)!}$$

The ! symbol stands for *factorial*. For $n = 4$, $n!$ means $4 \times 3 \times 2 \times 1$. Note that the number of orderings of two successes in four trials, as given by this formula, is:

$$C(4,2) = \frac{4!}{2!(4 - 2)!} = \frac{4!}{(2!)(2!)} = \frac{4 \times 3 \times 2 \times 1}{(2 \times 1)(2 \times 1)}$$
$$= \frac{24}{4}$$
$$= 6$$

This checks with the result we obtained by enumeration or brute force.

The generalized formula for a binomial probability can now be written by combining the term describing the probability of the desired outcome in a particular order with the combinatorial term which "counts" the number of possible orderings:

$$P(r \mid n,p) = \frac{n!}{r!(n - r)!}\,p^r(1 - p)^{n-r} \tag{3.7}$$

This is read as the binomial probability of r successes, given n trials and probability of success p on any given trial.

To demonstrate the use of this formula, let us consider some further examples.

Example 1: What is the probability of obtaining exactly 8 heads out of 10 tosses, assuming a fair coin?

$$P(r = 8 \mid n = 10, p = .5) = \frac{10!}{8!2!}(1/2)^8(1/2)^2 = .0440$$

Example 2: For an assembly line product past experience indicates that 5% of the product is defective. If 15 units are drawn from the assembly line, what is the probability that exactly 2 are defective?

$$P(r = 2 \mid n = 15, p = .05) = \frac{15!}{2!13!}(.05)^2(.95)^{13} = .1348$$

THE BINOMIAL DISTRIBUTION

Actually, the general binomial distribution is a family of probability distributions describing the probabilities of the possible experimental outcomes for all possible combinations of n and p. Since n can be any positive integer and p any value between 0 and 1, the size of the family is unlimited. The values n and p which determine a particular binomial distribution are called *parameters* of the distribution. For purposes of explanation, let us calculate the binomial probabilities for a particular member of this family with parameters $n = 4$ and $p = 1/6$, the combination describing the four tosses of our fair die.

$$\begin{aligned} P(r = 0 \mid n = 4, p = 1/6) &= \frac{4!}{0!4!}(1/6)^0(5/6)^4 \\ &= 1(625/1296) = 625/1296 \end{aligned}$$

(The student may need to recall that $0! = 1$, by definition, and $k^0 = 1$.)

$$\begin{aligned} P(r = 1 \mid n = 4, p = 1/6) &= \frac{4!}{1!3!}(1/6)^1(5/6)^3 \\ &= 4(125/1296) = 500/1296 \\ P(r = 2 \mid n = 4, p = 1/6) &= \frac{4!}{2!2!}(1/6)^2(5/6)^2 \\ &= 6(25/1296) = 150/1296 \\ P(r = 3 \mid n = 4, p = 1/6) &= \frac{4!}{3!1!}(1/6)^3(5/6)^1 \\ &= 4(5/1296) = 20/1296 \\ P(r = 4 \mid n = 4, p = 1/6) &= \frac{4!}{4!0!}(1/6)^4(5/6)^0 \\ &= 1(1/1296) = 1/1296 \end{aligned}$$

Specifically, it is the summarization of these results for all possible outcomes $r = 0$ through $r = 4$ given in Table 3.5 that is called a binomial probability distribution. Note that since the listed outcomes are mutually exclusive and collectively exhaustive, the sum of the proba-

Table 3.5 Binomial probability distribution for $n = 4$, $p = 1/6$

Number of successes, r	*Probability*	
0	625/1296 =	.482
1	500/1296 =	.386
2	150/1296 =	.116
3	20/1296 =	.015
4	1/1296 =	.001
	1296/1296	1.000

bilities is equal to 1.0. This is characteristic of all probability distributions, about which we shall have more to say in subsequent chapters.

BINOMIAL TABLES

Fortunately, a great many binomial probabilities have been calculated for various values of p and n and published in tables. These tables conserve considerable effort, for even though the computation of binomial probabilities is conceptually straightforward, the arithmetic involved in many practical problems could be overwhelming.

The calculation problem is even more formidable when questions concerning *cumulative* probabilities are asked. For example, the probability that *at least* 3 people out of 20 have birthdays on a particular day is a cumulative probability. "At least three people" means three or more, so that we should be forced to calculate not only $P(3)$, but $P(4)$, $P(5), \ldots, P(20)$ and to sum over all these terms. Or, a relevant question might be: What is the probability that *less than* two defectives appear in a sample of 10 with a given p?

All questions of this sort can be answered by summing over the relevant individual, or point probabilities. In the case of the birthdays it would be easier to calculate $P(0)$, $P(1)$, and $P(2)$ and then to subtract their sum from 1 to get $P(3 \text{ or more})$. However, in the case of the two defectives it appears that the quickest and easiest procedure to get $P(\text{less than } 2)$ is to calculate $P(0)$ and $P(1)$ and then add them. At any rate, to answer these questions, at least some, and sometimes many individual probabilities would have to be calculated. For this reason most published binomial tables give cumulative probabilities, from which the individual point probabilities can be easily determined. Appendix A is such a table.

Let us examine the table in Appendix A. First of all, we must remember that the binomial distribution is a family of distributions depending on combinations of p and n. The table considers values of n from 1 through 20, at 50, and at 100. For each n we can find probabilities for p values from .01 to .99 at increments of one hundredth. The table is cumulative. It deals with the *upper* end of the distribution for $p \leq .50$ and the *lower* end of the distribution for $p > .50$. For example, with $n = 50$ and $p = .4$, the probability that r is equal to 19 *or more* is given as .6644. Remember that by r we mean the number of successes in a given number of trials. Thus, for this illustration, $P(r \geq 19 \mid n = 50, p = .4) = .6644$. The .6644 is the sum of the point probabilities for all the values of r from 19 through 50.

To determine a point probability, i.e., the probability of exactly r, we merely need to subtract two successive cumulative probabilities. For example, with $n = 20$ and $p = .3$, the probability of $r \geq 5 = .7625$. Given the same n and p, the probability of $r \geq 6 = .5836$. Some reflection will show that $(r \geq 5) - (r \geq 6)$ defines $(r = 5)$. Thus the point probability that r is the integer 5 is $.7625 - .5836 = .1789$. To get the probability that r is less than some particular number Y at a given n and p combination simply involves subtracting $P(r \geq Y)$ from 1. Although the student would do well to practice a bit with these tables at this point, we shall have occasion to illustrate their use at numerous points as we go along.

SOME CHARACTERISTICS OF PROBABILITY DISTRIBUTIONS

RANDOM VARIABLES

A *random variable* is defined as a quantity that has a definite value for each possible event (or state of nature). These values may be thought of as the outcomes of a probability experiment, or random generating process. Although the values of the random variable are unknown prior to the outcome of the experiment, the probability that the random variable will take on specific values may be known in advance.

This definition is perhaps better understood by reference to an earlier illustration. In the die-tossing example, the number of one-spots appearing in four tosses of a fair die is a random variable. Although we cannot say with certainty how many one-spots will appear in any particular experiment (set of four tosses), the binomial probability distribution constructed earlier does give us the likelihood that the random variable will take on the specific values 0, 1, 2, 3, and 4. To generalize, the number of successes r is the random variable of any binomial probability distribution. Recall that n, the number of trials, and P, the probability of success on any given trial, are parameters, or characteristics, of the distribution which serve to determine the probabilities of various outcomes, or values of the random variable.

The concept of a random variable is not restricted to binomial probability distributions. In fact, *any* listing of all the possible values of a random variable together with the probability of each is called a *probability distribution*. Other probability distributions which we shall consider later simply describe a different functional relationship between a random variable and a set of probabilities than that given by the binomial formula.

Random variables and their associated probability distributions can be *discrete* or *continuous*. A variable is discrete if it can take on only a restricted set of values. The random variable r in the die-tossing example is discrete since it can take on integer values, 0, 1, 2, 3, 4. A continuous variable, on the other hand, is capable of assuming *any* value within a given interval. More will be said about continuous variables later, in Chaps. 8 to 12. In the first portion of this book, however, we deal only with discrete variables, not because they are more common or useful in business application, but because the necessary statistical apparatus is less involved.

Concern regarding random variables is quite appropriate to a discussion involving business decision theory because it is lack of certainty regarding the value of a random variable that characterizes many business problems. For example, the correct quantity of a good to stock would be easy to determine if demand, measured in terms of units that might be sold, were known with certainty. If demand could take on a number of possible values and thus be considered a random variable, the problem of how many to stock becomes a significant one of decision making under uncertainty.

The quantitative nature of values of random variables is a distinguishing characteristic. There is a definite value or number such as demand of 1, 10, 25, etc., that characterizes each state of nature or event. Events described in qualitative, rather than quantitative, terms cannot be random variables, e.g., sweater size would not be a random variable if the sizes were small, medium, and large. (However, if sizes were measured according to inches such as 36, 38, 40, 42, etc., sweater size could be considered a random variable.) This quantitative characteristic is important for it allows for the summarization of distributions of random variables through the use of expectations, or expected values.

EXPECTATIONS

An expected value, or expectation, is obtained by multiplying each possible value of a discrete random variable by the probability of that value and adding all the weighted values. This is exactly what we did in Chap. 2 in calculating expected monetary values and expected opportunity losses. In the examples of Chap. 2, conditional profits or opportunity losses met the definition of a random variable used in the previous section. Each had a specific value that could be represented as the outcome of a probability experiment, and each had a probability associated with it. These variables were mutually exclusive, and the sum of their probabilities added to 1. (In the case of the stocking problem the conditional profits or opportunity losses were random variables derived as linear functions of the basic random variable "demand," and therefore their probabilities were the same as those for the random variable "demand.") You will remember that we found the expected value in these problems by weighting each value of the random variable by its probability and adding the weighted values.

In general, an expected value is denoted by the symbol E followed by the random variable in question in parenthesis. Thus if X is a random variable, its expected value is

$$E(X) = \Sigma XP(X) \tag{3.8}$$

Where X is a particular value of the random variable, $P(X)$ is its probability and Σ (upper case Greek sigma) means the summation of the $XP(X)$ values for all the values of X.

A CONCLUDING COMMENT

The final sections of this chapter have served merely to formalize some of the concepts already employed in the decision situations of Chap. 2. Recall that the decision process developed to solve those problems made no use of sample information, or experimental evidence. The decision maker had only historical relative frequencies or subjective estimates (or some combination of both) with which to assess the probabilities of various states of nature.

Earlier portions of this chapter concerned with probability calculations and binomial probabilities may have seemed at times to be unrelated to the practical world of business affairs. Actually, they serve as a base for the extension of decision theory into the important class of practical business problems in which sample information *does* (actually or potentially) play a role. We are now ready to turn to the study of sampling and the process of statistical inference.

PROBLEMS

3.1 Give two definitions of the word "probability."

3.2 Give three examples of situations in which the assessment of a probability might be expected to affect a business decision. Do not use situations described in the text.

3.3 You work for a car dealer and are interested in the relationship between the sex of the buyer and the color of the car. Tabulation of past sales results in the following table:

	Sex		
Car color	*Male*	*Female*	*Total*
Dark	100	40	140
Light	100	60	160
Total	200	100	300

(*a*) Determine the marginal probability of light.
(*b*) Determine the joint probability of male and dark.
(*c*) Determine the conditional probability of dark given female.
(*d*) Is color of car independent of sex? Prove your answer numerically.

3.4 Assume that you have determined the following relationships between income level and number of TV sets owned by families:

Family income	0 *TV sets*	1 *TV set*	2 *or more TV sets*	*Total*
$<\$5,000$	40	240	20	300
\$5,000–\$10,000	50	400	50	500
$>\$10,000$	10	160	30	200
	100	800	100	1000

(*a*) Find the marginal probability of less than \$5000 income, $P(<5000)$.

(*b*) Find the conditional probability of 0 sets given less than \$5000 income, $P(0 \mid <5000)$.

(*c*) Find the probability of the joint occurrence of 0 sets and less than \$5000 income, $P(0, <5000)$, using appropriate numbers from the table.

(*d*) Find $P(0, <5000)$ as in part (*c*), but using the general law of multiplication and your results from parts (*a*) and (*b*).

(*e*) Is TV ownership independent of income? Prove your answer using appropriate numbers.

3.5 Assume that you carry insurance on your house, your car, and your health. The probability of your filing a claim in any one year on your house is .05, on your car is .20, and on your health is .80.

(*a*) If these three types of claims are independent of each other, find:

(1) The probability of filing a health claim *and* a car claim but not a house claim in one year.

(2) The probability of filing either a health claim *or* a car claim or both but not a house claim in one year.

(3) The probability of filing all three types of claims in one year.

(*b*) Why is the assumption of independence made in part (*a*) not likely to be completely justified?

3.6 An appliance dealer has kept careful records on sales versus prospects for washers and dryers. (A prospect is a person who enters the store and asks a salesman about an appliance.) After some time he finds that the probability that a prospect will buy a washer is .10, the probability that a prospect will buy a dryer is .05, and the probability that a person will buy a matching washer and a dryer is .02.

(*a*) What is the probability that a prospect will buy either a washer or a dryer (but not a matching pair)?

(*b*) What is the probability that a prospect will buy a matching dryer, having bought a washer?

(*c*) What is the probability that a prospect will buy a matching washer, having bought a dryer?

(*d*) Is the buying of dryers independent of the buying of washers? Explain.

3.7 The women voters in a particular precinct are all married. Ninety percent of them invariably vote *differently* than their husbands vote. Sixty percent of the male voters are known to favor Miss Bubbles Cash for mayor over the alternate candidate.

(*a*) What percentage of the female votes can "Bubbles" expect to receive?

(*b*) In what percentage of the families will both spouses cast their vote for Bubbles?

Hint: A frequency matrix—expressed in percent—such as the one on page 39 may be helpful in solving this problem.

3.8 The New York Mets are leading in the World Series three games to two. The odds are 4 out of 10 that they will clinch the Series by winning the sixth game. Even if they lose the sixth game, there is a 3 out of 10 chance that they will win the seventh and deciding game. What are the odds that the Mets will win the World Series (best 4 out of 7 games)?

3.9 In a card game with which the adventuresome student may have had some contact, a flush is a reasonably good hand. It consists of any five cards of the same suit.

(*a*) What are the odds of drawing five straight spades in the original deal?

(*b*) Suppose the original deal gave you three spades, a heart, and a club, with no numerical combinations of any interest. What are your chances of obtaining two spades on a draw of two cards?

(*c*) In (*b*), did you need to make an assumption about the number of players in the game? Why?

3.10 To test severely your ability to manipulate probabilities (and to reason), calculate:

(*a*) the probability of drawing a straight in five cards, i.e., any numerical sequence, regardless of suit, such as 2, 3, 4, 5, 6 or 8, 9, 10, J, Q.

(*b*) the probability of drawing a full house, i.e., three of a kind plus two of a kind, such as three 9s and two 7s, in five cards.

(Should you have any interest, you should now be able to complete a table of probabilities for all poker hands, or for the likelihood of filling certain hands by replacing discards with a draw.)

3.11 Over a cup of coffee after class, a friend of yours claims that he can control the toss of a coin if allowed to spin it with his thumb, catch it in his hand, and flip it on the back of his other hand in the usual manner. In fact, he claims that he can obtain heads 9 times out of 10. You don't think he can, and offer him 4 to 1 odds that he can't get 5 heads in a row. (This is equivalent to saying that your prior probability that he can't control the toss is .8.)

He flips the coin 5 times and obtains 5 heads. At what odds would you be willing to bet that he can't do it again?

3.12 You know from comments made in class that your professor has two children and that at least one of them is a boy. When you deliver a term paper to his home, the door is answered by a small boy, who admits to being his son. What is the probability that his other child is also a boy?

3.13 Suppose a card game is played with a deck consisting of only the ace of spades, ace of clubs, deuce of spades, and deuce of clubs. The cards are shuffled, and two cards are dealt to an opponent. We are interested in the odds that he has both aces.

(*a*) Given no other information, what are the odds that he has both aces?

(*b*) Suppose we obtain a peek at one of the opponent's cards, noting that it is an ace (although we are unable to determine the suit). What is the probability that his hand contains both aces?

(*c*) If our peek discloses that one of his cards is the ace of spades, what is the probability that the opponent's hand contains both aces?

3.14 A salesman has a long history of making sales on about 60% of the calls he makes.

(*a*) What are the chances that on a particular day he will sell more than 6 of the 10 customers he visits?

(*b*) Did you assume statistical independence in (*a*)? Specifically, what does this assumption mean here? Is it a valid assumption? If not, is your answer to (*a*) too high or too low? Why?

(*c*) What are the chances that he will sell exactly 6 out of 10 (assuming independence)?

(*d*) What are the chances that he will sell 4 or less out of 10?

3.15 Give some examples, drawn from a business context, of situations which could be considered as Bernoulli processes. Distinguish between cases where the trials involved meet the theoretical requirements and those where the Bernoulli assumption would represent a good approximation for practical purposes.

3.16 For each of the following binomial probabilities, make a simple sketch showing enough of the binomial distribution to illustrate the probability in question. Then find the probability, using the binomial tables.

(*a*) $P_b(r \geq 12 \mid 20, .3)$
(*b*) $P_b(r = 12 \mid 20, .3)$
(*c*) $P_b(r < 12 \mid 20, .3)$
(*d*) $P_b(r = 0 \mid 10, .4)$
(*e*) $P_b(r \geq 1 \mid 10, .4)$
(*f*) $P_b(r \geq 55 \mid 100, .6)$
(*g*) $P_b(r = 55 \mid 100, .6)$
(*h*) $P_b(r \leq 45 \mid 100, .6)$

3.17 (*a*) Assuming a Bernoulli process, *calculate* the probability of obtaining 4 defective parts from a sample of 10 parts if the proportion of defectives in the population were .2.

(*b*) *Calculate* the probability of obtaining 1 or fewer defective parts from a sample of 10 parts if the proportion of defectives in the population were .2.

(*c*) Check your answer to (*a*), using the binomial tables.

(*d*) Check your answer to (*b*), using the binomial tables.

3.18 A component for an assembly is purchased from three subcontractors, companies A, B, and C.

Company A supplies 50% of the total of this component.
Company B supplies 30% of the total of this component.
Company C supplies 20% of the total of this component.

The probability that Company A will produce a defective component is .01, Company B .03, and Company C .05. Since the parts all look exactly alike and have no company identification, it is impossible to identify a component after the assembly is completed. Upon final assembly one of the parts is found to fail because of a defect in the component subcontracted. What is the probability that the defective part was produced by Company A? by Company B? by Company C?

4

Statistical Inference and Some Uses of Samples

THE MEANING OF STATISTICAL INFERENCE

The remainder of this text involves, in one way or another, the process of statistical inference. It is this process which enables the decision maker to *infer* what is true about a *population* from the results of a *sample* drawn from it. Population, used in this context, may be defined simply as *all* the elements in a set under consideration; a sample is merely a subset of the population. Populations may be finite (containing a definite number of elements) or infinite. The concept of an infinite population derives from the notion of a process that may be expected to continue indefinitely, thereby producing an infinite series of population elements. The output of parts from a production process might be considered an infinite population if no termination of the process itself is in sight.

Note that a population may be defined in any way that best suits the needs of a particular decision problem, identifying only those elements of interest. A population could be defined as all college students in the United States, all students attending a particular university, all students enrolled in a statistics course, or all students patronizing a local pizza parlor, depending on the problem at hand. Likewise, next year's output of manufactured parts, the next shipment, or any other subset of parts produced from a process may be defined arbitrarily as a population. Thus the definition may take any form that is convenient or meaningful as long as consistency is maintained.

Usually, precise statistical statements, or inferences, are made with respect to a particular characteristic, or parameter, of a population. Although in later chapters we shall make inferences regarding other population parameters, in this chapter we shall confine ourselves to inferences regarding the *proportion of items in a population* that possess a certain attribute. Specifically we shall consider the sort of statements that can be made regarding a population proportion, such as the proportion of defective parts in a process, from a knowledge of the proportion of successes or failures in the sample.

SAMPLING

RANDOM SAMPLING

There are many ways in which a sample from which inferences are to be made could be selected. A decision maker could select a sample of items which he considered to be representative of the population on the basis of his own judgment. Certainly items purposefully selected by a knowledgeable individual can make up a sample that yields a considerable amount of useful information. Unfortunately, however, precise statistical inferences cannot be made from *judgment* samples subjectively selected in this manner. Rather, the considerable body of statistical theory that has been developed to enable one to make statistical inferences depends on the assumption that the sample in question has been selected *at random.*

Now "random" has a very special meaning in statistics that is quite different from its use in common language. In ordinary terms, "random" often means "without thinking" or "haphazard." In statistics a *simple random sample* is a sample obtained by a process such that each possible combination of items that could make up a given size sample has an equal chance of being selected. To get a better feel for the meaning of this definition observe that a necessary (but not sufficient) condition of simple random sampling is that *every item in the population has an equal chance of being included in the sample.*[1] Although statisticians have developed a variety of more complicated sampling plans that also rely on the concept of randomness, random sampling in this text will refer to simple random sampling as defined above.

To obtain a simple random sample requires a great deal of care. Data cannot be grabbed because they are convenient. Some systematic device such as a table of random numbers must be used to ensure that every possible combination of items in the sample does in fact have an equal chance of being selected. This process of randomization prevents bias from entering into the selection of the items in a sample. Moreover, as mentioned earlier, all the theory relating to statistical inference is predicated on the fact that the samples have been taken at random.

SAMPLE VERSUS CENSUS

Considering the problems involved in selecting a random sample and the sometimes formidable difficulties of mastering the theory and concepts of statistical inference, one might reasonably raise the question: "Why take a sample?" If indeed a knowledge of some population characteristic is necessary to make a decision, why not take a *census* of the population? One answer is that a census, meaning a complete enumeration of the characteristics of every item in the population, may be impossible or at least prohibitively expensive.

If a manufacturer of flash bulbs wants to know the proportion of defective bulbs in his production process, he can hardly resort to testing every one of them. In this case the testing process is destructive and a complete census would use up the population, leaving no bulbs to sell. In other cases, although a census may not be destructive, obtaining the necessary information on an item by item basis may be extremely costly. Under these circumstances, it may be economical to resort to sampling.

SAMPLING ERROR

It should be intuitively clear to the student, even in the absence of any formal knowledge of statistical inference, that any time a sample is used to estimate a population characteristic the possibility of an estimating error is introduced. Of course, if all items in the population are identical,

[1] The reason this is not a *sufficient* condition to define simple random sampling can best be explained by an example. Suppose it is required to sample 1% of the names in a telephone book. A sample could be obtained by selecting every hundredth name. If the starting point were randomly selected from the first 100 names in the book, every name in the book would have, before the selection begins, an equal chance of appearing in the final sample. However, this would not be a simple random sample, as defined here, since a sample combination involving say the fiftieth and fifty-first names would have *no* chance of being selected. From a practical point of view such a departure from the ideal of simple random sampling *might* be desirable, but we make no attempt to deal with such considerations here.

e.g., if the flash bulbs are all good or all bad, then different samples will also have identical characteristics, and there will be no sampling error. Usually, however, variability abounds, and population items are not identical. A production run of flash bulbs will contain some good and some bad bulbs, and different random samples drawn from the same process will contain different proportions of good and bad, leading to different statistical inferences about the population. Thus, any time we infer from a particular sample something about the population, we must recognize that the sample will not, in general, be exactly representative of the population. No sample is a microcosm of the population from which it was drawn, and the fact of sampling error must be reckoned with in any problem of statistical inference.[2] Fortunately, the problem is not hopeless, for a variety of procedures for analyzing and dealing with sampling error has been developed. Indeed, in subsequent chapters we shall incorporate the dollar costs associated with sampling error directly into the decision process. First, however, we shall examine some concepts of estimation that are generally regarded as fundamental elements in the field of classical statistical inference. In this chapter, as indicated previously, we confine ourselves to the specific problem of inferences regarding the true proportion of "successes" in a population. As a result, the present discussion will be concerned solely with what is called binomial sampling.

BINOMIAL SAMPLING

The process of drawing a sample is referred to as *binomial sampling* whenever the sample may be considered to represent a number of trials, n, in a Bernoulli process. Recall that a Bernoulli process has: (1) only two possible outcomes on each trial, (2) a constant probability of success on each trial, and (3) statistically independent trials.

Actually, examples of binomial sampling have already been discussed. In the loaded-die example in Chap. 3, we were allowed to roll the die in question twice to assist in deciding whether or not it was loaded. This may be considered a sample of two from a Bernoulli process, i.e., a binomial sample of size 2. Later in Chap. 3 we computed the probability of various possible outcomes of rolling a fair die four times using the binomial formula. This is equivalent to a binomial sample of size 4. We then calculated the binomial probability distribution for the die-

[2] Actually, sampling errors may or may not be more serious than other sources of error in an estimation problem. In some cases, measurement errors may render a census less accurate than a sample estimate. If, for example, you wanted to know the number of e's in the text, a total count might be less accurate than an estimate based on a careful count of the number of e's on one randomly selected page multiplied by the number of pages in the text (because of the clerical errors you are almost certain to make in attempting a complete enumeration).

Table 4.1 Binomial probability distribution for $n = 4$, $p = 1/6$

Number of successes, r	*Probability*	
0	625/1296 =	.482
1	500/1296 =	.386
2	150/1296 =	.116
3	20/1296 =	.015
4	1/1296 =	.001
	1296/1296	1.000

rolling problem for $n = 4$ and $p = 1/6$ which is repeated as Table 4.1. This listing of all the possible outcomes of samples together with their respective probabilities of occurrence is called a *sampling distribution.*

The binomial distribution was applicable in the case of tossing a die four times because each toss could be regarded as a "draw" from a potentially infinite sequence of trials. Many business processes, such as the one which produced flash bulbs mentioned earlier, can likewise be usefully regarded as infinite sequences. If the other two conditions prerequisite to a Bernoulli process are also met, i.e., that one of only two possible states must occur and that the probability of a success is constant throughout the process, then the binomial sampling distribution can be used to make statistical inferences for these processes.

SAMPLING FROM A FINITE POPULATION: THE HYPERGEOMETRIC DISTRIBUTION

Many other types of business problems deal with the occurrence of one of two states, success or failure, but involve finite rather than infinite populations. In a market research investigation, the customers in a particular trade area may be classified as buyers or nonbuyers. Similarly, a flash bulb from a shipment of 10,000 bulbs can be good or defective, orders can be filled or unfilled, employees may be male or female, etc. In any of these cases a decision maker may be concerned with the proportion of successes, p, or failures, $1 - p$, in a sample and with how this proportion relates to the proportion in the population.

Strictly speaking, the binomial distribution does not describe the sampling in these examples because the populations are not infinite. This means that removal of one item from the population, such as one flash bulb from a shipment, changes the proportion of defectives in the bulbs remaining. Of course, if the population is reasonably large, the removal of one item is not going to change the probability of success on the next draw, or trial, very much. Still, recall that a requirement of binomial sampling (from a Bernoulli process) is that the probability of success remains constant from trial to trial and that the trials be statistically independent. If sampling takes place *without replacement* (i.e., by removing items selected for the sample so that there is no chance of their reselection), the requirement is violated and the binomial distribution does not apply theoretically. For example, if three consecutive black cards are drawn from an ordinary deck without replacement, the probability of a black card on the next draw is not 1/2, but 23/49.

The sampling distribution that *is* theoretically applicable in the situation of sampling without replacement from a finite population is called the hypergeometric distribution. Hypergeometric probabilities can be derived in a straightforward manner using the law of multiplication for probabilities and the rules of counting developed earlier in conjunction with the binomial.

For example, the probability of drawing three black cards from a well shuffled deck without replacement is:

$$P(B,B,B) = (26/52)(25/51)(24/50)$$

Similarly, the probability of two black and one red (in that order) is:

$$P(B,B,R) = (26/52)(25/51)(26/50)$$

If we are not concerned about where the one red card falls in the sequence, we recognize that there are three possible sequences (*BBR*, *BRB*, and *RBB*), so that

$$P(\text{2 black and 1 red, any order}) = (3)(26/52)(25/51)(26/50)$$

In the same way, the probability of one black and zero black cards in three draws could be derived, giving the complete sampling distribution for three draws without replacement from an ordinary deck of cards, which is shown in Table 4.2.

Table 4.2 Hypergeometric sampling distribution for the occurrence of black cards in three draws without replacement from an ordinary deck of cards

Event	*Probability*	
3 black, 0 red	(1)(26/52)(25/51)(24/50) =	.1176
2 black, 1 red	(3)(26/52)(25/51)(26/50) =	.3824
1 black, 2 red	(3)(26/52)(26/51)(25/50) =	.3824
0 black, 3 red	(1)(26/52)(25/51)(24/50) =	.1176
		1.0000

The formula for the hypergeometric probability of exactly r successes in n trials is given by

$$P_H(r \mid n) = \frac{C(Np,r) \times C(Nq, n - r)}{C(N,n)} \tag{4.1}$$

where r is the number of successes, n is the number of trials, N is the size of the population, p is the proportion of successes in the population, and q is the proportion of failures ($q = 1 - p$).

Although the hypergeometric distribution has been tabulated for certain values, the tables required are much more extensive than for the binomial. This is the case because there is a different hypergeometric distribution for every combination of sample size, *population size,* and number of successes in the population, whereas the binomial sampling distribution involves only the two parameters n, sample size, and p, proportion of successes.

Fortunately, we do not need to use the hypergeometric in most practical problems since the more manageable binomial provides a very adequate approximation. In fact, unless a sample from a finite population is a substantial proportion of that population—a useful rule of thumb is 20%—the assumption of binomial sampling introduces only insignificant errors in the decision process and is justified on the basis of greater simplicity. Somewhat paradoxically, *most* applications of the binomial sampling distribution in this text and in practice occur where the distribution is not theoretically applicable, but a good approximation.

ESTIMATION

ESTIMATION OF A POPULATION PROPORTION

Having developed the concept of the binomial as a sampling distribution, let us apply it to a specific problem in statistical inference suggested earlier: the estimation of the proportion of successes in a population p from the proportion of successes in a sample r/n. Suppose, for one reason or another, that the flash bulb manufacturers wished to estimate the proportion of defective bulbs in the production process. We saw earlier that a census was impractical in such a situation; instead the estimate might be based on the testing of 100 bulbs selected at random from the process.

Assume that 7 of the sample of 100 bulbs tested proved defective. What can be inferred about the proportion defective in the population?

POINT ESTIMATES

Naturally, it is by no means certain that the population p is the same as the proportion defective in the sample, 7/100, or .07. Different random samples of 100 would yield different proportions defective, no one of which was necessarily equal to the true p for the population. Nevertheless, in the absence of any additional evidence, .07 is the *best* estimate of p that we can make. There is certainly no incentive to place a higher likelihood on, say, .04 or .09 or any other value. An estimate equal to the sample proportion, r/n (for which we use the symbol $\bar{p}$), is called a *point estimate* of p: Note that it consists of a single value with no accompanying information to indicate the reliability of the estimate.[3]

INTERVAL ESTIMATES

It is quite likely that a statistician or anyone else recognizing the possibility of sampling error will wish to hedge his point estimate of p. The statistician, at least, would typically prefer to express his estimate as an *interval*, containing the point estimate but allowing for error on either side. A statement to the effect that the true proportion of defective bulbs in the population is *between* say .05 and .09 would represent an *interval estimate.*

Now if a statistician estimating p were to assert, "p is between 0 and 1," he would be very safe indeed. In fact, we could say that he is 100% *confident* that his interval estimate contains the true value of p. Of course, such an estimate really says nothing that isn't obvious and is of little use to anyone. A much more useful statement would instead establish an interval that was *reasonably* sure to contain the true value of p. With 7% defective bulbs in the sample, for instance, it is highly unlikely intuitively that the true p for the population is as high as 90%, or 50%, or even 25%. The interval estimate need not contain these values. It turns out that it is possible to ascertain specifically how wide the interval must be to provide us with any stated level of confidence that the true p is contained within it.

Suppose we construct what is called a 95% *confidence interval* for estimating p. This means that we shall find an interval that we are 95% confident contains the true p. It follows that there is a 5% chance that it does not. The customary procedure is to split this 5% equally and to assume that there is a 2.5% chance that the stated interval is too high to include the true p and a 2.5% chance that it is too low.

The problem is to find the limits of such an interval. This can be accomplished by using the binomial tables in a reverse fashion. To illustrate the procedure, a portion of the binomial table for $n = 100$ is reproduced here, namely, portions of the *rows* of the table for $r \geq 7$ and $r \geq 8$. (The need for these particular rows is related to the fact

[3] This particular estimate of p has the desirable statistical property of being *unbiased*, which technically means that if the estimating procedure were repeated a very large number of times, the mean of the estimates so obtained would equal the true p.

Table 4.3 Binomial table excerpt, $n = 100$

r \ p	.01	.02	.03	.04
7	.0001	.0041	.0312	.1064
8	.0000	.0009	.0106	.0475

r \ p	.11	.12	.13	.14
7	.9328	.9633	.9808	.9903
8	.8715	.9239	.9569	.9766

that *exactly* 7 defectives were found in the sample of 100.) Remember that the entries in this abbreviated table give the probability of 7 *or more* and 8 *or more* defectives for various values of p. Ideally, the lower limit of a 95% confidence interval could be found by searching across the $r \geq 7$ row for a probability equal to .0250. The *column* in which we find this value is associated with a particular p value. This p value is the lower limit of the confidence interval. In other words, the trick is to locate the p value such that $P(r \geq 7 \mid n = 100, p) = .0250$.

It would take a more detailed table to locate such p values exactly, but an approximate result can be obtained with the table at hand. Note that in the $r \geq 7$ row the nearest probability to .025 is .0312, the value for $p = .03$. If we wish to be conservative, however, and obtain a confidence level of *at least* 95%, we should look for the probability in the table that is closest to *but smaller than* .025. In this case, that probability is .0041, corresponding to a $p = .02$. Thus .02 is the lower limit of the confidence interval.

For the upper limit, we need to find a p so that

$$P(r \leq 7 \mid n = 100, p) = .025$$

An inspection of the $r \leq$ column at the right margin of the binomial table shows that for any value of $p > .50$ the probability of $r \leq 7$ is less than .0001 (the smallest r value shown is 31). Therefore the appropriate value of p must be less than .50, and we must use the $\geq$ column at the left margin. Now if $r \leq 7$, it cannot be ≥ 8, so we can get $P(r \leq 7)$ by taking $1 - P(r \geq 8)$. We need to identify the p so that $P(r \geq 8 \mid n = 100, p) = 1 - .025 = .975$. Thus, using the $r \geq 8$ row and searching for the probability that is closest to *but greater than* .975, we can determine that the upper limit of the confidence interval is

$p = .14$. We are now prepared to state that the 95% confidence interval for the population proportion defective p is .02 to .14.

SOME GENERALIZATIONS CONCERNING INTERVAL ESTIMATES

The student is probably painfully aware at this point that the reasoning involved in the construction of a confidence interval is tortuous. This is so even though no attempt was made to "prove" that the interval constructed is 95% reliable in estimating p. The difficulty is not for the most part with the concept of interval estimation but with the nature of the binomial distribution used. While more complete binomial tables would have made the job easier, it is still a somewhat sticky one. In Chap. 9, when the student has a few more statistical tools in his kit, we shall return to the matter of confidence intervals. There methods are discussed not only for obtaining approximate confidence interval estimates for p (without using binomial tables) but for other population parameters as well. Here, greater benefit can be obtained from forming some generalizations about interval estimation that may shed some light on the entire process of statistical inference.

First, let us review the semantics involved in the estimation problem. The sample proportion defective, .07, is called a *point* estimate of p. The range .02 to .14 is a *confidence interval;* and the .95, or 95%, may be referred to as a confidence level or *confidence coefficient.* The confidence interval, confidence coefficient, and sample size are intimately related. Their relationship is worthy of generalizing: For any given sample size, the confidence interval will widen as the confidence coefficient increases. Therefore, if we want a very high level of confidence that p is included in the estimating interval, we must accept a relatively wide interval. If we construct a narrow interval estimate, our confidence that the interval really contains p must be relatively low. The only way to have our cake and eat it, too, in this situation is to increase the size of the sample, which in practice can be done only at an increased cost.

A little experimenting with the binomial tables—and the problems at the end of this chapter force the student to do just that—will show that increases in sample size do not provide *proportional* decreases in the confidence interval or proportional increases in the confidence coefficient. For now, a good rule to remember is that to cut a confidence interval in half (with the confidence coefficient remaining the same) generally requires increasing the sample size about fourfold.

It is also worth remembering that unless the sample itself represents a substantial (more than 20%) fraction of the population, it is the *absolute* size of the sample that matters, rather than its size relative to the population or the percentage of the population that is covered. These somewhat counterintuitive results will be demonstrated with specific examples in Chap. 9. Let us turn here to some relevant questions concerning the interpretation of confidence intervals and their use in decision making.

INTERPRETATION OF THE CONFIDENCE INTERVAL

A strict interpretation of the type of confidence interval constructed above would be as follows: If a very large number of interval estimates were constructed on the basis of successive samples, at least 95% of these intervals would contain the true value of p; the other 5% (or less) would fail to include it.[4] Now it would be much less cumbersome to interpret the interval as simply meaning that we are 95% certain (or the probability is .95) that the true p value falls somewhere between .02 and .14. Although this latter statement is intuitively appealing, classical statisticians frequently object to it on the grounds that it is simply not proper to make probability statements about p, a population parameter. Putting it roughly, they argue that p is what it is and that a statement giving the probability that it is more or less than some limit is meaningless. While it is quite all right to talk of the probability of obtaining a given *sample* result via some sampling procedure, the population p, even if unknown, is fixed.

This argument hits close to the issues raised earlier in connection with objective versus subjective interpretation of probabilities (Chap. 3). It certainly may be useful to the business decision maker to view unknown population parameters such as p as if they were random variables, even if they are in fact already fixed or determined. Indeed, as we have seen in Chap. 2, the betting odds that the decision maker assigns to possible values of such parameters become the weights which, along with conditional payoffs, determine the optimal action.[5]

A homely illustration may serve to sharpen the issues involved in the argument. Suppose a friend tosses a presumably fair coin onto a table and covers it with his hand without allowing you to observe the outcome. If this friend now asks you, "What is the probability that the coin shows tails?" would you answer, "One-half"? From a strictly objective point of view, the outcome is already determined and the question is meaning-

[4] No effort is made here to prove that the method used here to obtain a confidence interval gives these results. A readable but involved discussion is given in Robert Schlaifer, "Introduction to Statistics for Business Decisions," McGraw-Hill Book Company, New York, 1961, pp. 217–219.

[5] Some diagrams which may serve to explain the difference between objective and subjective interpretations of confidence intervals are given in Chap. 11, p. 211, for continuous variables. That approach is probably not helpful at this point.

less or at best trivial. The probability of a tail is either 0 or 1 depending on the predetermined outcome. However, from your own subjective point of view, it seems perfectly reasonable to assess the *odds* that the coin is tails as 50-50, even if you know the outcome is already determined. This is a little like betting on a videotape rerun of last year's Rose Bowl game. If two people had no knowledge of the outcome, there is no reason they couldn't engage in some spirited wagering, complete with cheering on their favorites. At many points later on in this text, we shall proceed to treat population parameters as if they were random variables, adopting the subjective view of the decision maker.

INTERVAL ESTIMATES AND DECISION MAKING

To the business manager, the probability or odds that some key decision variable lies within specified limits *is* a meaningful concept. The confidence interval—at least the subjective interpretation of it—is a convenient way of summarizing the state of available knowledge concerning an unknown quantity. However, its direct usefulness in *decision* problems is not so well established. In the first place, it is not clear what part of the interval is to be used in the decision process: The point estimate or "best guess" within the interval, the limits, or some value in between. Certainly a decision would be based on the point estimate from a particular sample only in the total absence of any other information pertinent to the decision. One would hardly conclude, for example, that an associate was dishonest if he won, say, 7 out of 10 times in an apparently "even" coin-tossing game. An interval estimate, which also fails to incorporate the previous knowledge of the decision maker, has limits which depend on the choice of a level of confidence. This choice is essentially arbitrary, and arbitrary inputs are certainly to be avoided in decision making.

We conclude this section on confidence intervals with the observation that they are useful and widely used in conveying a certain kind of information, but per se they are of little value in the decision-making process. This is not to say that sample information has no use in decision making. A further development of the concepts of statistical inference will show quite the contrary. We proceed with this development in the next three chapters, beginning with a study of classical statistical decision theory.

PROBLEMS

4.1 Suppose that you wish to estimate the proportion of your firm's six employees who carry their own health insurance. Assume that the situation is actually as shown in the following table:

Employee	*Carries health insurance*
Able	Yes
Baker	No
Charles	Yes
Davis	No
Evans	No
Farr	No

You select a random sample of two employees on which to base your estimate.

(*a*) What is the probability that your sample will contain 100% successes (i.e., employees who *do* carry their own insurance)?

(*b*) What is the probability that your sample will contain 50% successes?

(*c*) What is the probability that your sample will contain 0% successes?

(*d*) Tabulate your answers to parts (*a*) through (*c*). What is this tabulation called?

(*e*) What is the probability that your sample proportion will differ from the true population proportion by more than .25?

(*f*) Can you use the binomial distribution (or binomial tables) to answer the preceding questions? Why or why not? Would it make any difference if you were sampling from a population of 6000 employees?

4.2 Obtain the sampling distribution of the proportion of employees having health insurance in samples of size 3, drawn from the population in Prob. 4.1.

4.3 Define statistical inference. Give several examples of situations in which a decision maker might want to make an interval estimate for a population proportion. For each example, would the decision maker be more interested in the lower limit or the upper limit of the interval estimate? Why?

4.4 If an interval estimate made for a population proportion proves to be too large to be of practical use, what alternatives do you have to reduce it?

4.5 (*a*) About how many heads would you expect to get on tossing a *fair* coin 100 times?

(*b*) How likely is it that you would get 60 or more heads?

(*c*) The probability is .95 (i.e., you can be 95% confident) that the proportion of heads will be between ________ and ________.

(*d*) Will the answer to (*c*), stated in proportions, be the same if the coin is tossed 1000 times? If not, how will it differ? (You should be able to answer this question qualitatively, even though you do not have binomial tables for $n = 1000$.)

4.6 Testing of a random sample of 50 flash bulbs reveals 3 defectives.

(*a*) Make a point estimate of the process (population) fraction defective.

(*b*) Make an interval estimate of the process fraction defective.

(*c*) Why is there no *single* correct answer to (*b*)?

4.7 Suppose you decide to test five parts from a Bernoulli process. Derive the sampling distribution for the proportion of defectives in the sample if the population proportion of defectives is .4.

4.8 Suppose there are 10 persons qualified for a certain job, 4 men and 6 women. A random sample of 5 persons is selected. Derive the sampling distribution for the proportion of men in the sample.

4.9 Why does the distribution in Prob. 4.7 differ from that in 4.8?

4.10 Suppose that you test 10 parts from Bernoulli process and find 4 defectives.
(*a*) Make a point estimate of the proportion of defectives in the population.
(*b*) Make an interval estimate for the proportion of defectives in the population, using a 90% confidence coefficient.

4.11 Suppose that you test 20 parts from a Bernoulli process and find 8 defectives.
(*a*) Make a point estimate of the proportion of defectives in the population.
(*b*) Make an interval estimate for the proportion of defectives in the population, using a 90% confidence coefficient.

4.12 Suppose that you test 50 parts from a Bernoulli process, and find 20 defectives.
(*a*) Make a point estimate of the proportion of defectives in the population.
(*b*) Make an interval estimate for the proportion of defectives in the population, using a 90% confidence coefficient.

4.13 Summarize your answers to Probs. 4.10 through 4.12, and show that the accuracy of the interval estimate is inversely related to the square root of the size of the sample.

4.14 Analyze the following statement: "I don't see how we can tell much about how 50 million people are going to vote just from interviewing 750 of them."

4.15 One hundred of a city's registered voters are selected at random to assess their preferences regarding a proposed stadium-financing plan. Fifty-seven of those interviewed express disfavor of the plan; the other forty-three favor it.
(*a*) Make an interval estimate of the proportion of voters favoring the plan.
(*b*) If you had to bet on the outcome of the election concerning the proposed plan, which way would you bet?
(*c*) What odds could you afford to give and still have a "good bet"?

4.16 You need to know the proportion of homes in a particular area that house teenage children. You hope to estimate this proportion to within .02 with 95% confidence but have only a $50 budget.

A market research organization gives you an estimate of 75 cents per home to obtain this information by sampling. Can your $50 provide the desired estimate? (State any assumptions you make in solving this problem.)

5

Classical Statistical Decision Theory

TESTS OF HYPOTHESES

Point and interval estimates, as indicated in the previous chapter, are in themselves of little direct use in decision-making processes. Sample information must therefore be used in a different way by the decision maker. A procedure of classical statistical inference which does incorporate sampling in the decision process is known as *hypothesis testing*. Actually, the test of a hypothesis involves a particular type of decision situation in which there are three alternative decisions or courses of action which can be followed: (1) to *accept* the hypothesis in question, (2) to reject it as inconsistent with the evidence, or (3) to postpone judgment pending collection of additional information. The third alternative is considered in depth in subsequent chapters. Here we shall confine the discussion to situations where an immediate selection between the first two alternatives, acceptance or rejection, must be made.

The hypothesis to be tested may be any unambiguous statement concerning a population characteristic. Here again, as in the previous chapter, discussion will concern only hypotheses about a population proportion p. For example, a manufacturer might hypothesize that a new product will capture at least 30% of the existing market for similar items, i.e., that $p \geq 30$. Such a hypothesis might be tested by a sampling from a carefully conceived test market. The flash bulb distributor of Chap. 4 might use sample evidence to test the hypothesis that the fraction of defective bulbs in a shipment is no greater than .05, that is, $p \leq .05$. A hypothesis of this type, by its nature, is either right or wrong. Note that if we reject it—i.e., conclude that it is wrong—we implicitly *accept* an alternative hypothesis. Rejection of the hypothesis that $p \leq .05$ *implies* that we believe that $p > .05$.

Acceptance or rejection of the hypothesis in question depends upon whether the particular sample results observed are consistent with the hypothesis that has been advanced. If, in a coin-tossing experiment, 52 heads were obtained out of 100 tosses of a coin, the student would probably agree that these sample results are consistent with the hypothesis that the coin is fair, that $p = .5$. It is, after all, rather unlikely that even a perfectly fair coin would produce *exactly* 50 heads in 100 tosses.[1] On the other hand, obtaining 97 heads out of 100 tosses of a different coin would cause almost anyone to reject the hypothesis of fairness. These results do *not* appear consistent with the hypothesis.

But what is really meant by a statement that a sample result is consistent with a hypothesis or that it is not? Although the conclusions seemed obvious in the coin-tossing examples, can the intuitive process by which one arrives at these conclusions be formalized?

It can be, by proceeding as follows: Assuming that the hypothesis *is* true, calculate the probability that the sample result actually observed or any "even more extreme" sample result could occur. Obviously, if this probability is very small, we should be justified in labeling the hypothesis as inconsistent with the sample result and rejecting it. The probability of obtaining 97 *or more* heads out of 100 tosses of a *fair* coin, $P_b(r \geq 97 \mid n = 100, p = .5)$ is so small that it doesn't even appear in the binomial table. (That is, rounded to the fourth decimal place, the probability is .0000.) While 97 heads *could* occur with a fair coin, it is so unlikely that the hypothesis that the coin was fair loses credibility.

Conversely, if the probability of obtaining a value equal to or more extreme than the sample result is reasonably large, the disparity between the sample result and the hypothesis is attributed to chance and the hypothesis is accepted. If 52 heads were observed rather than 97, one would be likely to accept the hypothesis that the coin was fair since the

[1] The student can use the binomial table to verify that $P_b(r = 50 \mid n = 100, p = .5) = .5398 - .4602 = .0796$.

probability of tossing 52 or more heads using a fair coin is

$$P_b(r \geq 52 \mid n = 100, \ p = .5) = .3822$$

More will be said shortly about how one decides what "reasonably large" means in this context.

Perhaps a better feel for the sort of reasoning involved here can be obtained from the following example: Several years ago in a western city a large bakery chain was sued by a customer who claimed that he had bitten into a piece of bread baked by that bakery, had struck a bolt, and had broken a tooth. The jury examined the evidence and established the facts that the tooth had indeed been broken, that the bolt was of a type used in the baking machinery, and that there was a small but finite probability that such a bolt could have fallen into a batch of dough and subsequently could have been embedded in a loaf of bread offered for sale. On the basis of its deliberations the jury awarded the plaintiff damages.

A month later a rather strange coincidence occurred. Another bakery was sued on exactly the same grounds. This case never got to court. It happened that the same insurance company insured both bakeries, and an insurance adjuster had noticed that the victim of the second accident was also the plaintiff in the former case.

The insurance company figured that the odds of a bolt being embedded in a loaf of bread were probably no greater than 1 in 100,000. However, this meant that perhaps once out of every 100,000 loaves on the average some unfortunate consumer would get more iron in his bread than would be healthy, and the jury was not being unrealistic when it awarded damages to the plaintiff. But how likely would it be that one person would get two such loaves in a relatively small period of time? Assuming independence and that the person in question bought fifteen loaves a month, the binomial probability of getting two bad loaves in his sample of fifteen *by chance* would be $105(1/100{,}000)^2\,(99{,}999/100{,}000)^{13}$ which is about 1 in 100,000,000.

Now the important point of this example is that while it would be possible for a sample like this to occur by chance, it is *very* unlikely. The hypothesis that this consumer's situation was the result of plain bad luck was simply not tenable. The insurance company concluded that these events happened not by chance but by cause. Either someone was salting our victim's loaves of bread with bolts, or he was onto what he thought was a profitable though painful way of making money. When confronted with the insurance adjustor's calculations, our hard-bitten hero confessed to the latter.

So far, the examples considered all represent extreme situations. The case for rejection or acceptance of the hypothesis is clear-cut, and the decision is intuitively obvious. But what of the gray area in-between?

Suppose a coin gives 59 heads in 100 tosses. Would this result be consistent with the fair-coin hypothesis? The binomial table shows $P_b(r \geq 59 \mid n = 100, p = .5) = .0443$. Remember that this means that about 4 1/2% of the time, or roughly 1 time in 23, a coin that really *is* fair would fall heads 59 or more times in 100 tosses *just as a result of pure chance or sampling error.*

Now in the bread-baking example, the 1 in 100,000,000 odds were viewed as too long, and the chance hypothesis was rejected. Should 1 in 23 odds also be regarded as long odds, or should we accept the fair-coin hypothesis on the grounds that the sample results could very well have occurred "by chance"? The answer to this question involves some very subjective consideration. Different persons might answer differently depending on the circumstances and even, to some extent, on their personality characteristics.

A good way for the student to answer where he himself would "draw the line" is to imagine that he is playing what he considers to be a fair game of chance. (To keep it simple, suppose a coin is being tossed to determine who buys coffee.) Now two or three successive losses at this sort of game would not be surprising. Even four straight losses might not result in any great distrust of one's opponent. After all, the probability of four losses in four plays of a *fair* game is $(1/2)^4 = 1/16$, so one could expect to be this unlucky every so often. But how about five straight losses, $P = 1/32$, or six, $P = 1/64$. Would you believe 19? The point is that although anyone can be unlucky, even very unlucky, there is some point at which he is no longer willing to attribute his misfortune to Lady Luck. The odds connected with this point may be relatively great or very small depending on the circumstances. If your wife ran into your car with hers as you were driving downtown, you might attribute the first incident to chance. But if it happened three days in a row, you wouldn't need a larger sample to have a disquieting feeling that your domestic relations could be improved. On the other hand, if the odds on winning a sweepstakes were one in a million, you would hardly say it was rigged if you happened to win. Even though the odds of one *particular* person's winning are very small, the probability that *someone* would win is 1.

SIGNIFICANCE LEVELS

In formal hypothesis testing, the point at which the sample results will be considered inconsistent with the hypothesis is identified *in advance* of obtaining the sample. It is actually a probability level, referred to as the *level of significance* at which the hypothesis is tested. The hypothesis will be accepted as long as the probability of obtaining the observed sample result, given that the hypothesis *were* true, is *greater* than the level of significance selected. It is rejected if the probability that the sample result occurred by chance is *less* than the significance level. For example, testing a hypothesis at a 5% or .05 level of significance means that the hypothesis will be rejected only if there is a 5% chance or less that results as extreme as those in the sample could have occurred as a result of sampling error. Note that 59 heads out of 100 would lead to rejection of the fair-coin hypothesis at the 5% level of significance, since $P(r \geq 59) = .0443 \leq .05$, but *acceptance* at the 2%, 1%, or other lower levels.

Thus it is clear that whether a particular hypothesis is accepted depends not only on the results of a sample but also on the significance level chosen for the test. This level of significance, customarily represented in statistical notation as the Greek letter alpha, α, is most often taken as .05, .01, or .001. Often, a sample result which leads to rejection at the .05 level (i.e., $\alpha = .05$) is called significant evidence against a hypothesis; rejection with $\alpha = .01$ would imply highly significant and with $\alpha = .001$ very highly significant evidence. These terms, like the selection of the α levels themselves, are of course arbitrary.

SELECTION OF THE APPROPRIATE HYPOTHESIS FOR A TEST

If a hypothesis is typically tested at α levels such as .05 or .01, the burden of proof is put on rejecting it. That is, the hypothesis is accepted unless relatively strong evidence against it appears. For this reason, if the traditional procedures are to be applied, some care must be taken in selecting the hypothesis for the test. Remember that acceptance of a hypothesis implies rejection of an alternate, converse hypothesis. Since the deck is stacked in favor of the hypothesis being tested, it is customary to choose that hypothesis in such a way that it represents the accepted norm or the status quo. This kind of hypothesis is called a *null hypothesis;* the other hypothesis whose acceptance is implied by rejection of the null is simply referred to as the *alternate hypothesis.*

In the coin-tossing examples, the null hypothesis would be the accepted norm, namely, that the coin was fair; in this case the alternative conflicts with the generally held view that an ordinary coin is fair.

Because the sample proportion was .59 in the specific coin-tossing experiment discussed, we found an *upper tail* area corresponding to $P_b(r \geq 59 \mid n = 100, p = .5)$ to test the null hypothesis that the coin was fair. At the 5% level of significance, we conclude that the coin diverged from fairness in the direction of producing *more* heads than a fair coin would. If we had observed, say, 45 heads, we would have tested the null hypothesis that the coin was fair by finding the *lower* tail area corresponding to $P_b(r \leq 45 \mid n = 100, p = .5)$. If this probability turned out to be less than the level of significance we chose for the problem, we should conclude that the coin diverged from fairness in the direction of producing *fewer* heads than a fair coin.

Tests of this kind are called *one-tailed tests* because only one end of the cumulative binomial distribution is used. The tests were concerned with departures in only one direction from the accepted norm.

Before an experiment begins, one might very well be interested in departures by the sample proportion from the expected value in *either* direction. Too many heads *or* too many tails might lead to rejection of the hypothesis that the coin was fair (or that $p = .5$ exactly). Here a *two-tailed test* could be used, with the only real difference being that the significance level α is cut in half before comparing it with the probability of the sample result. The null hypothesis would be rejected if the probability of obtaining the actual sample result or one farther from .5 in the direction observed in the sample were less than $(1/2)\alpha$.

A two-tail test is thus like a one-tail test in concept and operation except for a difference in the way the significance level is interpreted. The difference, however, is a subtle one, and even statisticians do not always agree on one- versus two-tailed interpretations. Fortunately, we need not be concerned here with these subtleties and philosophical issues since for purposes of business decision making *one-tailed tests* are nearly always appropriate. Even though the decision maker may be interested in deviations in both directions from a norm, any decision leading to action is almost certain to be based on deviations in one direction *or* the other.

For example, an advertiser may be interested in knowing whether or not a new series of ads produced a change in sales, but before he could act, he would need to know whether the change increased sales or decreased them. The specific act might be to put more money into the new series if an increase were observed or to drop the new agency if a decrease were observed. For this reason one-tailed tests will be emphasized in this text.

Let us consider the application of a one-tail test of a hypothesis to a specific business problem. Returning to the flash bulb example, suppose that for economic reasons the distributor would find the shipment of bulbs acceptable if he were convinced that it contained no more than 4% defective bulbs. If his experience with previous shipments had been favorable, he might formulate the hypothesis that $p \leq .04$ and test it against sample evidence. Taking the sample result discussed earlier, 7 defectives out of a sample of 100 bulbs, let us subject this hypothesis to a test of significance at, say, an α level of .05.

Now if the hypothesis were indeed true, with an actual fraction defective in the *population* of exactly .04, the probability of 7 defectives or more in a sample of 100 would be $P_b(r \geq 7 \mid n = 100, p = .04) = .1064$.

Since this probability is considerably greater than .05, the hypothesis that $p \leq .04$ should be accepted. Although 7% of the *sample* bulbs are defective, this is not sufficient evidence to reject the hypothesis and refuse the shipment. Based on the prescribed test, the bulbs would be rated as acceptable.

ERRORS IN HYPOTHESIS TESTING

It should be clear that nothing is ever proved (in the literal or mathematical sense of the word) by a statistical test of a hypothesis. The test described in the previous paragraph does not *prove* that the hypothesis is true and that the true proportion of defective bulbs in the population is $\leq .04$. In fact the 7 out of 100 defectives in the sample points in the opposite direction. Thus the sample results do not confirm the null hypothesis in a positive way in this case, they are just insufficiently strong to negate it. Even in cases where the sample evidence does lead to rejection, it does not prove that the hypothesis is false. It merely establishes the falsity beyond some reasonable doubt.

Samples can lead to incorrect inferences, and sampling error can lead us to wrong decisions regarding the acceptance or rejection of hypotheses. It is worth observing that the errors that can be made are of two distinct kinds. We can (1) erroneously *reject* a null hypothesis that is in fact *true* or (2) erroneously *accept* a null hypothesis that is in fact *false.* In standard statistical nomenclature these are referred to as "type I" and "type II" errors, respectively. The situation is perhaps clarified by examining the four possibilities in a hypothesis test in the form of a 2×2 table (see Table 5.1). Accepting a null hypothesis that is in fact true or rejecting a false one are of course correct decisions. It is the other combination of possibilities that produces incorrect decisions. The maximum risk of a type I error, α, has already been identified as the level of significance in the test of a hypothesis. The risk of a type II error is known as the beta risk, β.

This analysis should not lead the student to infer that the two types of error are in any sense equivalent or that they are equally likely to

Table 5.1

Decision is made to:	Null hypothesis is in fact:	
	True	False
Accept	Correct decision	Type II error
Reject	Type I error	Correct decision

occur. Since tests at the customarily low level of significance α require relatively strong evidence against a hypothesis to reject it, type I errors occur relatively infrequently. In fact one way to choose the null hypothesis from the alternate when the choice is not obvious is to assign the null in such a way that the most serious or expensive potential errors are made type I errors and therefore involve an incorrect rejection of the null hypothesis. For example, it might be appropriate to call the hypothesis that a medicine was *not* of acceptable quality the null hypothesis and to test with a low level of significance, α. This would be logical because the consequences of accepting the medicine if it were really not up to quality standards could result in the death of persons taking it, making the cost of this type of error very large. Assessment of the risks of the two kinds of error and the means for adjusting these risks are considered in the following sections.

STATISTICAL DECISION RULES

A *statistical decision rule* is nothing more or less than a procedure for testing a hypothesis where the accept-reject decision has been determined in advance for all possible sample outcomes. For example, in the flash bulb–testing problem, a decision rule might be formulated as follows: "Take a simple random sample of 100 bulbs; if 8 or more bulbs are defective, reject the shipment; otherwise, accept the shipment."

Notice that the decision rule leaves nothing to judgment. Once such a rule had been formulated, anyone could carry out the instructions provided without knowledge of statistical inference. Formulation of the proper rule, however, is a more difficult matter. The statistician or the decision maker must be concerned with the *error characteristics* of the rule, which requires an assessment of how likely it is that the rule will lead to rejection of a good shipment of bulbs (a type I error) or acceptance of a bad shipment (a type II error).

Now the likelihood that use of the rule will lead to a particular error depends on the true fraction of defective bulbs in the population. Recall that the null hypothesis being tested was that the shipment contained no more than 4% defective bulbs, i.e., $p \leq .04$. If p were really greater than .04, the null hypothesis would be false and there would be *no* chance of making a type I error since we should *correctly* reject the null hypothesis. The null hypothesis (and the shipment) could be incorrectly accepted, but this would be a type II error.

Thus the type of error that can be made as well as the probability of an error depend on the true p for the population. A thorough study of the error characteristics of a decision rule must therefore consider all possible values for the parameter p. We shall begin the analysis by determining the probability that the null hypothesis $p \leq .04$ will be rejected for various values of p. These probabilities can be obtained from the binomial table.

Suppose $p = .02$. Then the probability that the decision rule stated earlier (based on 8 or more defectives) will lead to rejection is

$$P_b(r \geq 8 \mid n = 100, p = .02) = .0009$$

This result agrees with the intuitive observation that a sample of 100 drawn from a "good" population containing only 2% defectives is very unlikely to contain 8 or more defective bulbs. If $p = .04$,

$$P_b(r \geq 8 \mid n = 100, p = .04) = .0475$$

For other values of p:

$$P_b(r \geq 8 \mid n = 100, p = .06) = .2517$$
$$P_b(r \geq 8 \mid n = 100, p = .08) = .5529$$
$$P_b(r \geq 8 \mid n = 100, p = .10) = .7939$$
$$P_b(r \geq 8 \mid n = 100, p = .12) = .9239$$
$$P_b(r \geq 8 \mid n = 100, p = .14) = .9766$$
$$P_b(r \geq 8 \mid n = 100, p = .16) = .9939$$

A convenient way to represent this information, as well as that for other values of p not listed, is to graph the probability of rejecting the null hypothesis versus possible values of the population parameter p. Such a graph is called a *power curve*. The S-shaped curve shown in Fig. 5.1 is

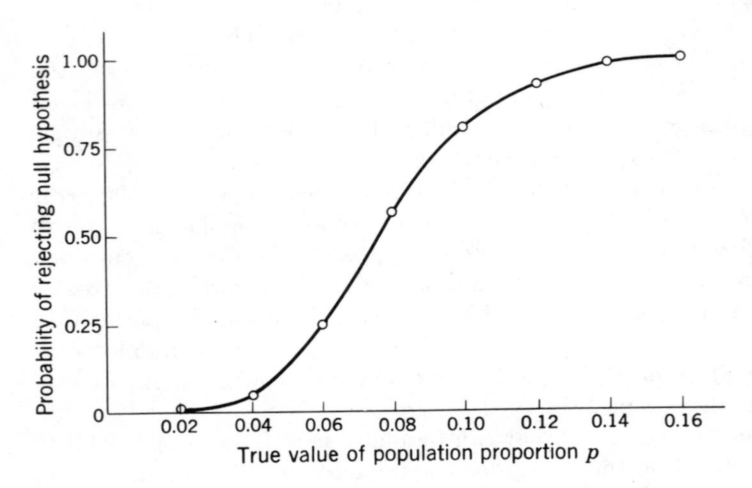

Fig. 5.1 Power curve for the decision rule $n = 100$ (if $r \geq 8$, reject; if $r < 8$, accept). (H_N: $p \leq .04$.)

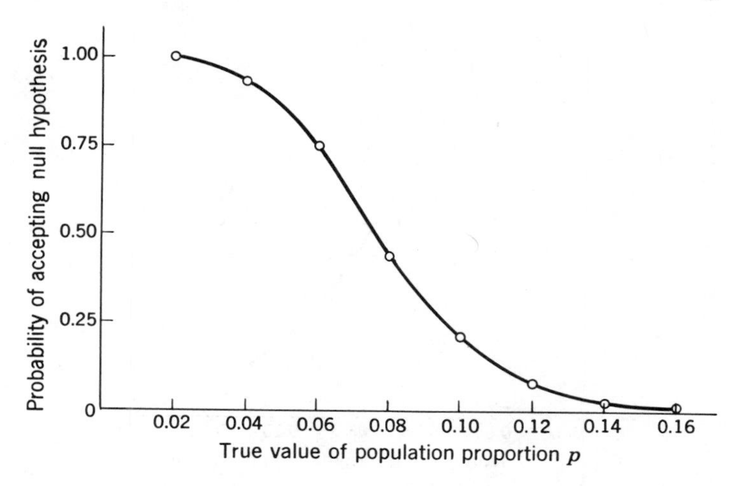

Fig. 5.2 *OC* curve for the decision rule $n = 100$ (if $r \geq 8$, reject; if $r < 8$, accept). (H_N: $p \leq .04$.)

characteristic in problems where the area of rejection is an upper tail. However, it should be noted that in problems where the rejection of the null hypothesis involved a lower tail area, the curve would descend from left to right.

A similarly derived curve that gives the probability of *accepting* the null hypothesis rather than rejecting it is called an *operating characteristic curve,* or simply *OC* curve (see Fig. 5.2). Since the probability of accepting the null hypothesis for any assumed value of p is 1 minus the probability of rejecting, the *OC* curve is a sort of upside-down mirror image of the power curve. Obviously, both curves provide essentially the same information regarding the decision rule they describe.

Actually, neither the power nor the *OC* curve is as useful as a third curve which combines them, showing the probability of a *wrong decision* for any value of p. It is called, appropriately, an *error curve.* It consists of that portion of the power curve (the probability of rejecting the null) in the range where *rejection* is a wrong decision and that portion of the *OC* curve (the probability of accepting the null) where *acceptance* is a wrong decision. The error curve for the decision rule under discussion is given in Fig. 5.3. Notice that the lower left-hand tail of the curve is identical to the power curve in Fig. 5.1, up to $p = .04$, since if the true proportion is really .04 or less, rejection of the null hypothesis is a type I error. For p values greater than .04, it is the *acceptance* of the null hypothesis (a type II error) that represents a wrong decision. Thus each point in the right-hand portion of the curve is 1.0 *minus* the corresponding ordinate on the

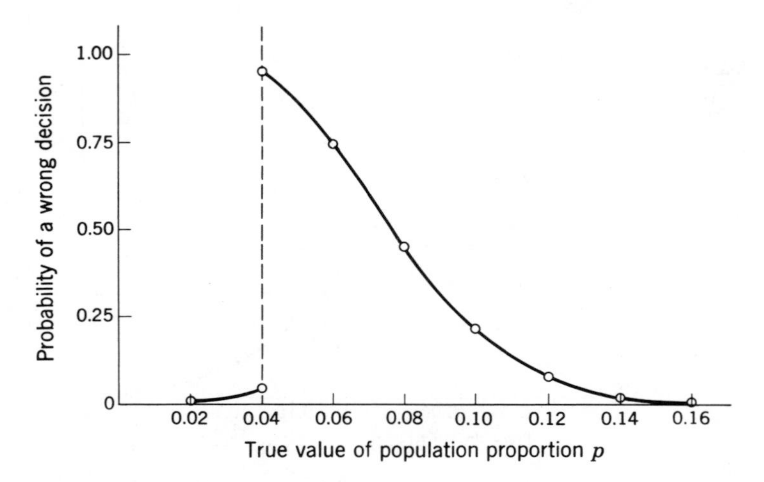

Fig. 5.3 Error curve for the decision rule $n = 100$ (if $r \geq 8$, reject; if $r < 8$, accept). (H_N: $p \leq .04$.)

power curve, making the curve beyond $p = .04$ identical to that portion of the *OC* curve shown in Fig. 5.2.

MAXIMUM RISK OF A TYPE I ERROR

It is common to characterize the entire error curve on the basis of the maximum risk of a type I error. This maximum risk or probability of a type I error will occur when a true hypothesis is just on the borderline of becoming false. One would be more likely to conclude in error that a shipment of flash bulbs is of poor quality if the proportion of defectives in the population were .04, the highest proportion of defectives that is acceptable, than if the population proportion defective were smaller than .04. Note that if p, the proportion of defectives in the population, were .02, the risk of a type I error as calculated on page 78 would be .0009, whereas if p were .04, the α risk would be .0475. If the proportion of defectives in the population were any value greater than .04, it would no longer be possible to make a type I error in interpreting sample results since the hypothesis is in fact false and rejecting the shipment would be a correct decision. Therefore, this risk for this decision rule, which is also called the level of significance, is .0475.

Conversely, the maximum risk of a type II error would occur for a p value just barely past .04. This is the case because if the true proportion of defectives in the population were greater than .04, the shipment should be rejected and the only error that could be made would be to accept the shipment, which is a type II error. The larger the proportion of defectives in the population, the less likely the decision rule would lead one to make a type II error. For practical purposes, therefore, we can say that the maximum risk of a type II error is $1 - .0475 = .9525$.

ERROR CURVES FOR OTHER DECISION RULES

So far we have studied but one particular decision rule, making no value judgments as to its merits. One of the important uses of error curves is to study the error characteristics of *different* decision rules that test the null hypothesis (hereafter denoted as H_N) for the purpose of choosing among them. This study is facilitated by adopting some shorter notation. For example, the rule studied earlier (rejection based on 8 or more defectives) could be written in symbolic form as

$H_N\colon p \leq .04$
$n = 100$
If $r \geq 8$, reject H_N
If $r < 8$, accept H_N

The number 8, on which the action to be taken depends, is called the *criterion number*, c. The rule can be written in still shorter form as simply ($n = 100$, $c = 8$).

Effect of changes in the criterion number Consider first the alternative of leaving the sample size fixed at $n = 100$, and changing the criterion number c. What will be the error characteristics of, say, the rule ($n = 100$, $c = 6$), where rejection is based on only 6 or more defectives? Figure 5.4 shows the error curve for ($n = 100$, $c = 6$) superimposed on the ($n = 100$, $c = 8$) curve given earlier in Fig. 5.3. At this stage, the student should be able to validate points on the new curve.

Some observations concerning Fig. 5.4 are in order. While the probability of a type I error is *higher* for any given level of p using the $c = 6$ rule with an α risk of .2116, it gives a *lower* probability of type II errors over the entire relevant range of p. This observation can be generalized as follows: For any given sample size changes in the criterion number can only reduce the risk of one kind of error at the expense of the other; a change in c alone cannot simultaneously reduce the risks of both types of error.

Effect of changes in the sample size The only way in which both error risks *can* be simultaneously reduced is by increasing the size of the sample. Since this text does not contain a binomial table for sample sizes larger than 100, let us consider the effect of a change in the opposite direction, say, cutting the sample to $n = 50$. The error curve from the ($n = 100$, $c = 8$) rule (Fig. 5.3) is reproduced in Fig. 5.5 to contrast with a compara-

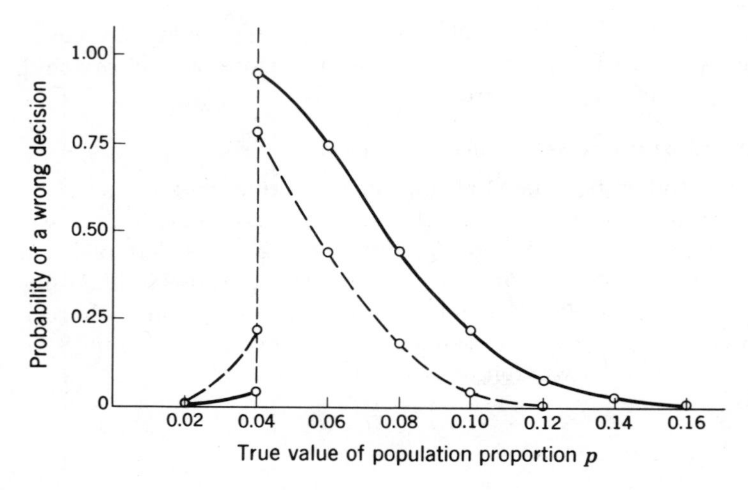

Fig. 5.4 Comparison of error characteristics for decision rules ($n = 100, c = 8$), indicated by solid line, and ($n = 100, c = 6$), indicated by dashed line. (H_N: $p \leq .04$.)

ble rule for the smaller sample ($n = 50$, $c = 5$). The criterion number $c = 5$ is chosen as comparable with $c = 8$ for the larger sample because it provides approximately the same maximum risk of type I error (.0490 versus .0475).

Note that the risks of type I *and* type II errors are generally larger

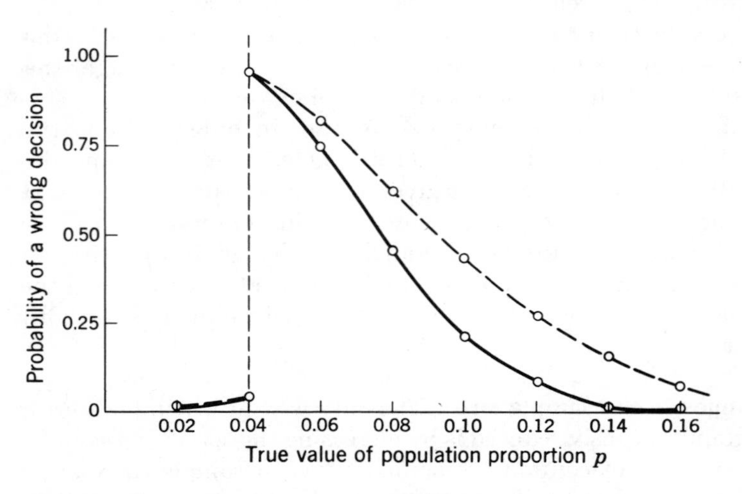

Fig. 5.5 Comparison of error characteristics for decision rules ($n = 100, c = 8$), indicated by solid line, and ($n = 50, c = 5$), indicated by dashed line. (H_N: $p \leq .04$.)

for the smaller sample over all ranges of p. We can generalize to the effect that a decision rule can be made more efficient, in the sense that both types of error risk are reduced, by increasing the size of the sample. Of course larger samples are available in practice only at higher costs, so that the increased efficiency of the rule must be balanced against the increased costs of employing it.

THE PROBLEM OF SELECTING THE "BEST" DECISION RULE

To this point we have studied the error characteristics of alternative decision rules, avoiding the question of which rule should be used in a given decision situation. We shall consider first the problem of how to select the best criterion number c for a given sample size. It has been observed that with n fixed, changes in c merely "trade off" one type of error risk for another. Let us examine the specific implications of this fact in the context of the flash bulb–testing problem.

It was assumed earlier that the distributor would regard the shipment of bulbs as "acceptable" if the proportion of defective bulbs were no greater than 4%, that is, $p \leq .04$. Now if whatever decision rule used leads to rejection of the shipment, there is still some chance that a truly "acceptable" shipment has been mistakenly rejected and perhaps returned to the manufacturer. It is not surprising that the risk of this kind of mistake (a type I error) is often referred to as *producer's risk*. Conversely, the risk of the mistaken acceptance of a truly bad lot (a type II error) is called *consumer's risk*, based on the notion it is the purchaser who suffers from this mistake. Increases in the c value will make rejection less likely, decreasing the producer's risk but increasing consumer's risk; decreases in c will have just the opposite effect.

The problem of selecting the "best" decision criterion or c value to use is then a problem of deciding on an appropriate balancing of the risks involved. This balance is often determined on an essentially arbitrary basis, generally by specifying the maximum allowable risk of a type I error (producer's risk) or, equivalently, the significance level α. This risk, or α level, is often set at .05, .01, or some other relatively low level.

Setting α relatively low is consistent with establishing the null hypothesis so that type I errors are more serious. However, since the specification is often arbitrary, no explicit effort is made to determine how *much* more serious a type I error really is.

For some types of problems where dollar costs are not available or where the costs involve complexes of utilities that are extremely difficult to quantify, the decision regarding an appropriate level of type I and type II errors must be subjective and in a sense arbitrary. Even in these cases an effort should be made to appraise the relative seriousness of the errors before the selection of a decision rule. Then the appropriate sample size and decision rule can be determined by considering the α and β risks desired. These techniques will be considered in more detail in Chap. 10.

For a wide range of important business problems it *is* possible to measure the dollar costs or utilities associated with type I and type II errors, not only for the maximum risks of these errors but for the entire continuum over which the errors can occur. These costs can then be used, together with the cost of sampling, to arrive at the optimal sample size and decision rule. Furthermore, it will also be possible to incorporate information obtained prior to the sample as well as the costs associated with the sample in question into the analysis. Within this framework, one can then decide whether or not to sample at all, how large a sample to take if sampling is desirable, and how to structure an optimal decision rule to interpret the sample results. The nature of this analysis is the subject of the next two chapters.

PROBLEMS

5.1 After extensive remodeling a supermarket takes a simple random sample of size 100 and determines that the proportion of residents in the sample who shop at their store is .08. The population of residents in their market area is very large.

(*a*) Make an interval estimate for the proportion of customers in the population, using a 90% confidence coefficient.

(*b*) Assume that before the store was remodeled, the management knew that the proportion of customers in the population who shopped there was .06. Test the hypothesis that the proportion of customers in the population has not increased since remodeling. Use a level of significance of .05.

(*c*) Discuss the relationship between your answers to (*a*) and (*b*). Does your interval estimate in (*a*) confirm your test in (*b*)? Explain.

5.2 You are requested to perform a survey to determine the percentage of time that your company's engineers and scientists spend in oral communication with their colleagues. In order to make the disruptive effect as small as possible, you institute a procedure known as "work sampling," whereby you observe the activities of randomly selected personnel at random times.

(*a*) You make 100 work sampling checks, finding your subjects engaged in oral communication in 24 cases. Is the percentage of time spent in oral communication significantly greater than 20%?

(*b*) Make an interval estimate of the percentage of time spent in oral communication, using a 90% confidence level.

(*c*) If you had answered part (*b*) first, could you have then answered (*a*) without additional calculations? Explain.

(*d*) Generalize the relationship between confidence intervals and hypothesis testing.

5.3 Instant Wealth, an investment advisory service, recommends a list of 20 common stocks each quarter which are selected to "outperform the market." In the last quarter, 8 of their selected stocks rose in price, while 12 declined. Of the 500 stocks comprising "Standard and Poor's 500," a list widely accepted as being representative of the market, 140 advanced and 360 declined over the period.

(*a*) Test the hypothesis that the Instant Wealth service does no better than you could do by throwing darts at the S. and P. 500 list—an investment technique recommended by many finance professors. Use a 5% level of significance for the test.

(*b*) On the basis of (*a*), would you spend $1000 per year for the Instant Wealth service? Why or why not?

5.4 Suppose a friend of yours claims to possess powers of extrasensory perception (ESP) which can be used to detect the color (black or red) of ordinary playing cards as they are drawn from a shuffled deck in an adjacent room.

(*a*) Design a test of hypothesis to confirm or deny his claim. (To make it simple, assume that after each card is drawn and checked against his "call" it is replaced and the deck reshuffled prior to the next draw. Also, use a sample size for which you have binomial tables).

(*b*) On what basis did you choose the null hypothesis in (*a*)? Did your choice have anything to do with your prior beliefs concerning ESP?

5.5 In the flash bulb–testing problem in the text, suppose a distributor is willing to increase the consumer's risk by increasing to .20 the maximum risk of a type I error (accepting a shipment of bulbs with a fraction defective of more than .04). Formulate the appropriate decision criterion for sample sizes of:

(*a*) $n = 100$
(*b*) $n = 50$
(*c*) $n = 20$

5.6 Define a power curve, an *OC* curve, and an error curve, and explain how they are related.

5.7 The point that distinguishes acceptable from nonacceptable performance is always the point at which the maximum risk of a type I error occurs and is also the point that separates type I from type II errors. Explain why this is true.

5.8 Assume that a large lot of flash bulbs is considered acceptable if .04 or fewer are defective.

(*a*) Plot the power curve
(*b*) Plot the *OC* curve
(*c*) Plot the error curve

for the decision rule: Take a simple random sample of 20 bulbs and test them. If 2 or more are defective, reject the lot, otherwise accept it.

Use values of the population proportion p of .02, .03, .04, .05, .06, .07, .10, .14, and .20.

5.9 Repeat Prob. 5.8, but use the following decision rule: Take a simple random sample of 50 bulbs, and test them. If 5 or more are defective, reject the lot, otherwise accept it. Plot the curves on the same grids as the corresponding curves for Prob. 5.8.

5.10 Compare the error curves for Probs. 5.8 and 5.9. How would you summarize the effect of increasing the sample size from 20 to 50?

5.11 Assume that a Norwegian student who is a classmate of yours is considering importing and selling hand-knit ski sweaters. He has decided to concentrate his selling efforts on sororities and calculates that if he can sell .05 of the girls, he can break even, including a reasonable return for time spent selling. He asks you to set up a sampling plan for him to test the market. You decide to investigate the characteristics of the following decision rule: Take a simple random sample of size 20. If the number of sales in the sample is greater than or equal to 1, get in the business, otherwise don't.

(*a*) Determine the ordinates of the error curve for the decision rule above for values of p of .01, .02, .03, .04, .05, .06, .08, .10, .15, and .20. Graph the error curve.

(*b*) What is the maximum risk of a type I error for this decision rule? For what value of p does it occur?

(*c*) What is the maximum risk of a type II error for this decision rule? For what value of p does it occur?

5.12 Redo Prob. 5.11, using an action limit (i.e., a criterion number) of 2 rather than 1, with everything else in the problem the same. Graph the error curve on the same grid as that for Prob. 5.11.

5.13 Compare the error curves for probs. 5.11 and 5.12. What has been the effect of increasing the action limit from 1 to 2? Which of these two decision rules do you feel would be better for this problem?

5.14 If the probability of committing a type I error is fixed at a certain level and the sample size is decreased, what is the effect on the risk of committing type II errors?

5.15 Given the error curve for a decision rule, state the general effects of:

(*a*) Altering the criterion number (action limit), leaving the sampling size fixed

(*b*) Increasing the sample size, and increasing the criterion number to maintain the same maximum risk of type I error

Illustrate your answers with rough sketches, identifying the regions of type I and type II errors.

6
The Economics of Decision Rules and Sampling

INTRODUCTION

From the outset, this book has been concerned with the selection among alternative strategies in the face of uncertainty. We now wish to consider an alternative not evaluated previously: *to take no action* based on the available information, delaying any action *until additional information is available.* Conceptually, the strategy "Buy additional information before making a final decision" should always be added to the list of strategies (or acts) in a decision problem, unless timing is such that an immediate final decision must be made. This is true because additional information, in the form of a sample, will generally reduce the cost of uncertainty inherent in the decision situation. If this cost can be reduced by more than the cost of obtaining the information, then it is economically desirable to sample before making a final decision.

Statistical decision rules, considered at length in the previous chapter, do provide us with the means for basing a decision on sample results. Until now, however, we have not attempted to evaluate the economic consequences of utilizing samples and decision rules in business situations. The first part of this chapter will deal with the selection of the *best* action limit or criterion number to use with a particular size sample in a business decision problem. The second part will consider the broader questions of the economics of sampling: whether information (a sample) should be purchased and, if so, how much (how large a sample) should be obtained.

SELECTION OF AN OPTIMAL CRITERION NUMBER

The error curves of the last chapter provided us with a graphic analysis of the properties of decision rules. That is, given any value for the true process parameter p, we could obtain the probability that the decision rule adopted would lead to an incorrect decision. Yet when we compared the error curves for several alternative decision rules, we were left at a loss as to how to select the "best" rule among them. It was suggested that decision rules are often selected so that the maximum risk of type I error is set arbitrarily at, say, 5%. Such a decision rule admittedly stacks the deck in favor of accepting the null hypothesis being tested. No justification was offered except that the null hypothesis selected for a test either represented in some sense the status quo or was strongly preferred on the basis of accumulated experience.

In some cases such a method of selecting a hypothesis may be well-founded. Under our judicial system a person accused of a crime is assumed innocent and must be proved guilty beyond some reasonable doubt. For moral and social reasons, we consider it justifiable to establish a hypothesis of innocence and to test it via legal proceedings in a manner that ensures that the risks of a type I error are relatively small. We do this because we believe the *costs* of making a type I error (sending an innocent person to jail) are relatively greater than the costs of making a type II error (allowing a guilty man to go free). Even though in this example the costs are intangible, it is clear that cost considerations provide the appropriate basis for selecting and testing a hypothesis.

In designing classical tests of hypotheses, the risk of a type I error *is* usually specified at a low level, say, .05. This seemingly arbitrary specification may not be unreasonable for certain types of scientific work. Indeed, it may be perfectly reasonable that we should put the burden of proof on a new scientific theory which contradicts established doctrines. Orderly scientific progress requires that new ideas bear the burden of proof. However, in most business decision-making situations there is no a priori reason for minimizing errors of the one kind at the expense of making errors of the other kind. Such a procedure could be justified only on the basis of *cost* considerations, where the costs of one kind of error are quite different from the costs of the other kind. There are many business problems in which type I errors are no more serious than type II.

Whenever possible we shall incorporate the economic consequences of the two kinds of wrong decisions in our procedure for selecting an appropriate decision rule. Of course, the business decision maker is concerned not only with the probability of making a wrong decision but also with the magnitude of the loss resulting from a wrong decision. Thus, it is really the *expected loss* resulting from use of a particular decision rule that is important to the selection process.

Unfortunately, the computation of this expected loss is not a simple matter. As we have seen from our earlier study, there is no *one* risk of a type I or a type II error. These risks depend upon the true value of the population parameter p. Likewise, there is no such thing as *the* cost of a type I or of a type II error. Generally these costs will also depend upon the value of the parameter p.

For purposes of making business decisions, we are not solely concerned with the question of whether a particular hypothesis is true or false (i.e., whether p is more or less than some specified value) but also with how far the true value of p may deviate from some economic break-even point. Suppose, for example, that the proportion p of a particular market that will buy a new product represents the source of uncertainty (the random variable) in a decision problem. It is potentially far more serious if actual sales fall far below the break-even level of profitability than if the sales are slightly below. On the other hand, we are not so concerned about failing to undertake the production of a new product whose sales would have been only slightly above the break-even level but are very much concerned about passing up a very high volume item.

Thus in assessing the merits of a decision rule to apply to a business situation, i.e., computing the expected opportunity loss resulting from its use, we must consider:

1. The probability that the particular decision rule will lead to an incorrect decision *for every given level of p*. We have referred to this earlier as the probability of type I or type II errors, and it has been shown by the error curve or (indirectly) by the power curve or the *OC* curve for the rule.
2. The opportunity loss that would result from a wrong decision *for every given level of p*.

Note that the probability of an incorrect decision and the loss from a wrong decision are both conditional upon a given level of p. That is to say, this probability and loss will generally be different for each value of p that is considered. A complication in assessing the expected loss resulting from the use of a decision rule arises from the fact that various values of the parameter p will not, in general, be equally likely. Therefore, in addition to the two factors listed above, we must consider a third:

3. The probability that various levels of p (states of nature) will occur.

To see specifically how these three factors enter into the selection of a decision rule, let us consider a particular business decision situation.

THE ECONOMICS OF A BUSINESS DECISION PROBLEM: NEW PRODUCT DEVELOPMENT

Suppose a firm selling to 20,000 industrial accounts is considering the addition of a new product to its line. Management is somewhat reluctant to make this proposed addition because its development costs are high. It is estimated that $500,000 would be required for full-scale development. Further, the management believes the proposed product to be a "one-shot" item, having virtually no possibility of repeat sales to the same customer. It is unique, so its addition can be expected to have no effect, either positive or negative, on sales of the existing line.

The product would add nothing to existing overhead expenses (above the $500,000 development costs) and could be produced at a variable cost of $1200 per unit. Variable selling expense would be approximately $300 per unit. Because of the nature of the item, it can be produced to order, so no inventory must be carried.

As a result of previous experience with similar products and interviews with company salesmen, the market research department believes the product could be most profitably priced at $2000. They are able to assign the probability distribution in Table 6.1 to the proportion of customers who will actually purchase the new product.

Table 6.1 Probability distribution for new product

Proportion purchasing	*Probability*
.02	.1
.04	.3
.06	.3
.08	.2
.10	.1
	1.0

CALCULATION OF AN ECONOMIC BREAK-EVEN POINT AND CONDITIONAL OPPORTUNITY LOSSES

A useful first step in the analysis of this problem will be to calculate the the economic break-even value of p, the proportion of the total population of customers purchasing the product. This calculation will involve no use of statistical analysis, only simple business arithmetic. Since the selling price per unit is \$2000 and the total of variable costs per unit are \$1500, we might consider the difference, or \$500, to be a contribution to profit and overhead. Since fixed development costs of \$500,000 are involved, 1,000 units of the product must be sold in order for the firm to break even (\$500,000/\$500 = 1000). Thus 1000 out of the firm's 20,000 customers, or a proportion p of .05, must buy the product in order for the firm to break even.

If the true proportion of customers who would ultimately purchase the product is less than .05, then the firm will experience an out-of-pocket loss if the product is produced; that is, the total contribution to profit and overhead will not be sufficient to cover the fixed development costs incurred. On the other hand, if p is greater than .05, an opportunity loss will be incurred if the product is *not* produced, as a result of the lost profit opportunity.

Of course, if $p \geq .05$ and the firm decides to produce or if $p \leq .05$ and the firm decides not to produce, a correct decision will have been made and the firm will incur no opportunity loss.

The conditional opportunity loss (*COL*) functions for these four possibilities are shown in Table 6.2.

To be sure that the equations are understood, let us "talk our way" through the equation in the cell "develop, if $p < .05$." If the decision is made to develop, a cost of \$500,000 will be incurred for development. Some of this cost will be recovered by selling units at a profit of \$500 each to a certain proportion of the population, p. The gross profit will be

Table 6.2 Conditional opportunity loss functions

	Develop	*Don't develop*
If $p < .05$	$COL = \$500{,}000 - \$500(p)(20{,}000) = \$10{,}000{,}000(.05 - p)$	$COL = 0$
If $p > .05$	$COL = 0$	$COL = \$500(p)(20{,}000) - \$500{,}000 = \$10{,}000{,}000(p - .05)$

$500(p)(20,000). However, if $p < .05$, the profit will not cover the development cost, and a measure of our regret would be the net cost, $500,000 − $500(p)20,000 = $10,000,000(.05 − p).

In order to calculate the *COL* for any act-event combination, one need only substitute the desired value of p in the appropriate equation in Table 6.2. For example, for the act "develop" and the event $p = .2$, *COL* = $10,000,000(.05 − .02) = $300,000. In a similar manner one could find all the other *COL*s shown in Table 6.3, below:

Table 6.3 Opportunity loss table

p	*Develop*	*Don't develop*
.02	$300,000	$ 0
.04	100,000	0
.06	0	100,000
.08	0	300,000
.10	0	500,000

EXPECTED OPPORTUNITY LOSS FOR AN IMMEDIATE DECISION WITHOUT SAMPLING

Now if an immediate decision as to whether or not to develop the product must be made, we could proceed as before to calculate the expected opportunity losses (*EOL*s) of the two decisions using as weights the probabilities of Table 6.1. This procedure is carried out in Table 6.4. The *EOL* of the decision to develop the product is $60,000 compared with

Table 6.4 Analysis of immediate decision (without sampling)

Events		*Acts*			
		Develop		*Don't develop*	
Proportion buying, p	*P(p)*	*COL*	*Weight × COL*	*COL*	*Weight × COL*
.02	.1	$300,000	$30,000	$ 0	$ 0
.04	.3	100,000	30,000	0	0
.05	.3	0	0	100,000	30,000
.08	.2	0	0	300,000	60,000
.10	.1	0	0	500,000	50,000
			EOL = $60,000		*EOL* = $140,000

an *EOL* of $140,000 for the decision not to develop. If no other information were available, we should decide to develop the product since that act has the lower *EOL*.

EOL WITH SAMPLING

Because of the sizable losses that could be incurred, an alert management might desire additional information before making a decision. Suppose that the firm's marketing research manager recommends an intensive survey of a random sample of customers to determine whether they would purchase the item in question. Since such a survey would be relatively expensive if definite commitments were to be obtained from the customers contacted, let us assume that the sampling is limited to 20 customers.

Deferring for the moment all questions regarding the economic desirability of sampling or the particular sample size of 20 that was chosen, let us address the problem of what the optimal decision rule should be. It is this rule that will tell us how to use the sample results once they are obtained.

We want to specify a rule of the form: If some number, c, or more out of the 20 prospective purchasers buy the product in question, then go ahead with development; if less than c express an interest but do not develop the product.

The selection of an appropriate value of c should involve consideration of all three of the elements listed on pages 89 and 90. Notice that the immediate decision without sampling involved only two of those elements, namely, the costs (or opportunity losses) of wrong decisions and the probabilities of various states of nature (values of p). In introducing the use of a decision rule utilizing sample evidence, we must consider the remaining element—the probabilities that the decision rule will lead us to an incorrect decision.

The probability of a wrong decision The probability that use of a particular decision rule will lead to a wrong decision, for any value of p, may be obtained from binomial tables. Consider, for example, the case of a decision rule ($n = 20$, $c = 1$). This rule says that if one or more of the prospective purchasers interviewed desires to buy the product, we shall develop it. The probability that this decision rule will lead to error, and even the nature of the error itself, depends upon the true value of p. Let us evaluate the probability of an error for each value of p using Fig. 6.1 as an aid to understanding.

If $p = .02$, the probability that the decision rule ($n = 20$, $c = 1$) will lead to a wrong decision is given by the binomial probability $P_b(r \geq 1 \mid n = 20,\ p = .02)$. This value, .3324, may be obtained

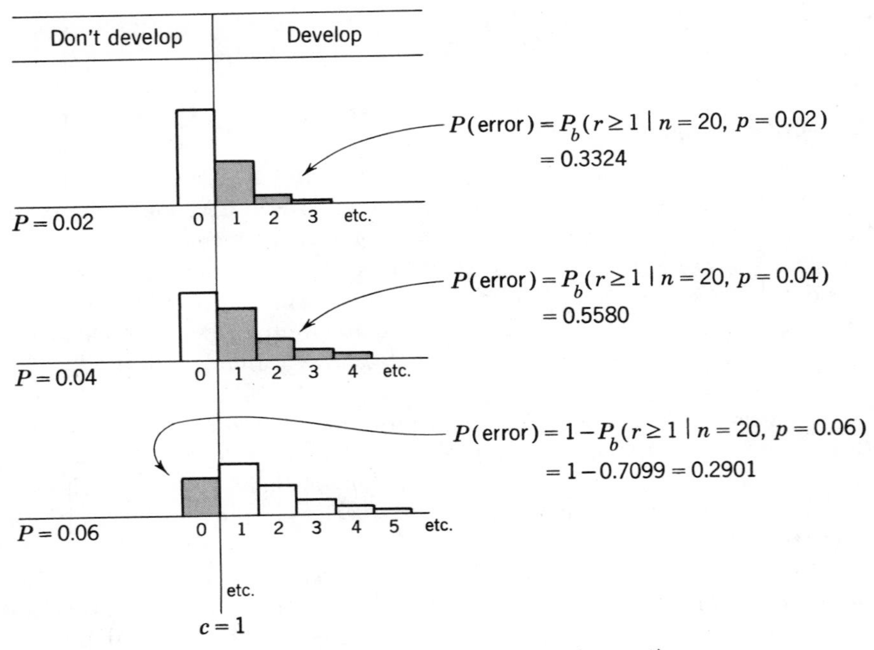

Fig. 6.1 Probabilities of error for decision rule ($n = 20$, $c = 1$).

directly from the binomial table. If $p = .04$, then the probability of a wrong decision from the decision rule will be given by $P_b(r \geq 1 \mid n = 20, p = .04)$. This probability, from the table, is .5580. Notice that as soon as p is more than .05 (the break-even point), we can no longer obtain the probability that the decision rule will lead to an incorrect decision directly from the binomial table. The reason for this is that for p values greater than .05, the wrong decision is not "to develop" but rather to *fail to develop* the product.

If, for example, $p = .10$, then the firm can make a substantial profit by developing the product. The only way that the decision rule could lead to the *wrong* decision (not to develop the product) is if the sample contains no positive responses (since any number of responses of one or more will lead to development, a *correct* decision). Given $p = .10$, the probability of no favorable responses in the sample can be obtained indirectly from the binomial table, as 1 minus the probability of one or more favorable responses, or $1 - .8784 = .1216$. In each case the probabilities in Table 6.5 represent the probability of making a wrong decision for a given level of p. However, it must be remembered that the character of the wrong decision changes from one side to the other as we pass over the break-even value of p. While the numbers in the upper part of the table are read directly from the binomial table, those in the lower portion (for values of p greater than .05) are obtained by subtracting the probability read in the binomial table from 1.

Note that for this particular decision rule ($n = 20$, $c = 1$) the action limit of 1 in 20 is equal to the break-even value of .05 This will not be the case for other possible decision rules, so we must remember to be careful not to confuse the action limit (which tells us how to interpret our sample) with the break-even value (which tells us which tail of the distribution represents the probability of an error).

***EOL* for a particular decision rule** We may now proceed with the computation of the *EOL* resulting from the use of the decision rule ($n = 20$, $c = 1$). For each of the given values of p there is a certain opportunity loss associated with a wrong decision. These losses are the non-zero entries in Table 6.3, which we calculated earlier.

Since each of these losses is a conditional loss, we need to know the probability that it will be incurred in order to compute the *expected* (or weighted average) opportunity loss. The probability in question is actually a *joint* probability. Specifically, it is the probability of the joint event that a particular value of p (state of nature) occurs *and* that the decision rule employed ($n = 20$, $c = 1$) leads to a wrong decision. This is best illustrated by a specific example.

We calculated earlier that if $p = .02$, a decision to develop (in that case a wrong decision) will result in an opportunity loss of $300,000. Note that this loss will actually be incurred only in the case where $p = .02$ *and* a wrong decision is made. The probability of the joint event "$p = .02$ *and* wrong decision" can be obtained by a straightforward application of the multiplication rule for probabilities, i.e., $P(p$ and wrong decision$) = P($wrong decision $\mid p) \times P(p)$. The probability of a

Table 6.5 Conditional probabilities of a wrong decision from the decision rule ($n = 20$, $c = 1$) for various values of p

p	*Probability of a wrong decision, given p*	*Source*
.02	.3324	Read directly
.04	.5580	Read directly
.06	.2901	1 − .7099
.08	.1887	1 − .8113
.10	.1216	1 − .8784

Table 6.6 Computation of probability weights for computing *EOL* resulting from the use of the decision rule ($n = 20$, $c = 1$)

(1)	(2)	(3)	(4)
p	$P(p)$	$P(wrong\ decision \mid p)$	$P(wrong\ decision\ and\ p)$
.02	.1	.3324	.03324
.04	.3	.5580	.16740
.06	.3	.2901	.08703
.08	.2	.1887	.03774
.10	.1	.1216	.01216
		P(wrong decision) =	.33757

wrong decision *given* that $p = .02$ is .3324, from Table 6.5. The marginal probability that $p = .02$, obtained from the subjective management estimate given in Table 6.1 is .1. Therefore, the joint probability of incurring an opportunity loss of $300,000 because of a wrong decision to develop is .3324(.1) or .03324. The probabilities of joint events involving other levels of p, calculated in a similar manner, are shown in column 4 of Table 6.6.

The sum of these joint probabilities, .33757, represents the marginal probability of a wrong decision from the decision rule. That is, the chances that use of the rule ($n = 20$, $c = 1$) will lead to a wrong decision are about 34 in 100, or 1 in 3. It is not, however, this overall probability of a wrong decision with which we are primarily concerned. In order to compute the *EOL* for our decision rule, we must weight the conditional opportunity losses of a wrong decision (From Table 6.3) by the probabilities that they will be incurred (the joint probabilities from column 4 of Table 6.6). This procedure is carried out in Table 6.7.

Note that we seem to be utilizing a set of probability weights which

Table 6.7 Calculation of *EOL* using the decision rule ($n = 20$, $c = 1$)

(1)	(2)	(3)	(4)
p	*COL of a wrong decision*	*Probability of incurring loss*	(2) × (3)
.02	$300,000	.03324	$ 9,972
.04	100,000	.16740	16,740
.06	100,000	.08703	8,703
.08	300,000	.03774	11,322
.10	500,000	.01216	6,080
		$EOL(n = 20, c = 1) =$	$52,817

Table 6.8 Computation of probability weights for computing EOL for the decision rule (n = 20, c = 2)

(1) p	(2) $P(p)$	(3) $P(wrong\ decision \mid p)$	(4) $P(wrong\ decision\ and\ p)$
.02	.1	.0599	.00599
.04	.3	.1897	.05691
.06	.3	.6605	.19815
.08	.2	.5169	.10338
.10	.1	.3917	.03917
		P(wrong decision) =	.40360

add to .33757 rather than 1, which would be inconsistent with our earlier method of computing expected value. This inconsistency is apparent rather than real. Omitted from the calculations in Table 6.7 is the fact that about two-thirds of the time (.66243), we shall be incurring an opportunity loss of 0, as a result of making the *correct* decision.

We shall designate the final figure in Table 6.7, $52,817, as $EOL(n = 20, c = 1)$, the EOL resulting from the procedure of employing a sample of 20 and a criterion number of 1 to make the decision.

***EOL* for different criterion numbers** We can compute the EOL of other decision rules in a similar fashion. For example, taking the sample size of 20 as fixed, we may consider other values of c that may lead to superior results, i.e., lower EOLs. Evaluation of the EOL for the rule ($n = 20$, $c = 2$), is carried out in Tables 6.8 and 6.9. The value of $77,902 obtained for $EOL(n = 20, c = 2)$ is substantially greater than that for $EOL(n = 20, c = 1)$, demonstrating the superiority of the use of $c = 1$ as the criterion number for a sample of 20. Higher c values, c = 3, 4, 5 . . . will give

Table 6.9 Computation EOL for the decision rule (n = 20, c = 2)

(1) p	(2) *COL of a wrong decision*	(3) *Probability of incurring loss*	(4) (2) × (3)
.02	$300,000	.00599	$ 1,797
.04	100,000	.05691	5,691
.06	100,000	.19815	19,815
.08	300,000	.10338	31,014
.10	500,000	.03917	19,585
		$EOL(n = 20, c = 2)$ =	$77,902

progressively worse results (larger *EOL*s), and of course $c = 0$ is meaningless as a criterion. (Zero or more favorable responses will always be found in any sample, rendering this sampling procedure useless.) Note that in the general case where some value of c other than 1 is optimal, we must obtain a higher *EOL* for a c value on each side of it to be sure it is the best.

A c value of 1 is thus the optimal decision criterion for use with a sample of size 20 in this problem. If the suggested survey of 20 of the firm's customers is made, development of the product should be undertaken if one or more of the customers "buys" it. Only if there are *no* favorable responses out of the sample of 20 should the firm decide not to develop the product.

Alternative methods of computation Before we leave the mechanics of computing the *EOL*s resulting from the use of particular decision rules, we should note that alternative computational schemes are available. Each of the figures in the final column of our computations of Table 6.7 or Table 6.9 is obtained as the product of the three factors considered earlier: (1) The conditional cost of a wrong decision, given p, (2) the probability of a wrong decision, given p, and (3) the probability of occurrence of a given level of p. As in any case where we multiply three figures together, the end result does not depend on the *order* of multiplication. For purposes of explanation, we chose to multiply the probabilities first, and then the joint probability obtained by the conditional costs. Other authors have chosen to first multiply the conditional costs by the conditional probabilities of error, obtaining a set of expected loss figures which are still conditional on various values of p, and which must finally be weighted by the $P(p)$ values. A third alternative is perhaps best of all for computational purposes, although not for understanding. Since the conditional probabilities of a wrong decision, $P(\text{wrong decision} \mid p)$ are the only numbers which change for different decision rules, it might be advantageous to multiply the other two constant factors [conditional cost $\times P(p)$] first, saving the changing conditional probabilities for the last step. This will result in only one *new* set of multiplications for each $EOL(n,c)$ evaluation, rather than two sets.

THE ECONOMICS OF SAMPLING

CALCULATION OF THE EXPECTED VALUE OF SAMPLE INFORMATION

The importance and usefulness of the foregoing analysis extends far beyond selection of the optimal decision criterion for a particular sample size. With the benefit of this analysis we may now consider questions relating to the economics of sampling. Earlier we saw that the expected value of *perfect* information (*EVPI*), in cases of decision making under uncertainty, was equal to the expected opportunity loss of the optimal act. This *EVPI*, while it placed an *upper limit* on the amount we should be willing to spend to gain additional information before making a decision, did not enable us to determine the desirability of obtaining the less than perfect information always provided by a sample. We could say only that if sampling were more costly than the *EVPI* calculated for the decision problem, the sampling should not be undertaken. However, should the cost of sampling be somewhat less than the *EVPI*, we are in no position to evaluate the relative desirability of obtaining a sample before a decision is made versus making an immediate decision without sampling.

In the product development problem considered in this chapter, the *EVPI* is $60,000, the *EOL* of the best act without sampling, which is to develop (see Table 6.4). This figure does place an upper bound on the amount we should be willing to spend for sample information, which is always less than perfect. Suppose, however, that the sampling of 20 customers proposed by the management could be conducted at a cost of $10,000, not an unreasonable figure for the type of depth investigation necessary to determine the customer's needs. We know that more than $60,000 should not be spent for sample information, but should we spend $10,000?

To evaluate the desirability of obtaining a sample before a decision is made, we need to know the *expected value of sample information*, which we will call *EVSI*. For any given sample size, the *EVSI* may be computed as the difference between the *EVPI* and the *EOL* resulting from the use of the best decision rule for the sample size in question. Thus, in the product development example, the *EVPI* is $60,000. From this we must deduct $52,817, the expected opportunity loss resulting from the use of the best decision criterion in conjunction with a sample of size 20, that is, $c = 1$. The difference, $7183, is the *EVSI* for a sample of size 20.

The *EVSI* may also be thought of as the reduction in the cost of uncertainty brought about by the use of the sampling procedure. *EVPI*, it was noted earlier, is identical to—in fact another name for—the cost of uncertainty in a decision-making situation. The *EOL* after sampling is similarly the remaining cost of uncertainty after the sample has been taken and the optimal decision criterion applied. It is reasonable that the reduction in the expected cost of uncertainty represents the value of sample information, *EVSI*. Having obtained this figure, we need only to compare it with the cost of actually obtaining the sample to ascertain the economic feasibility or desirability of sampling. In the present case, the sample of 20 should *not* be taken since its cost, $10,000, is greater than its expected value, $7183.

SELECTION OF AN OPTIMAL SAMPLE SIZE

***EVSI* for various sample sizes** The above comparison does *not* indicate that all possible sampling procedures are undesirable; it says only that a sample of size 20 costs more than its expected value. Other sample sizes may yield expected values in excess of their cost. Unfortunately (from the point of view of the student), the procedure involved in the calculation of *EVSI* must be repeated for all possible sample sizes. This is due to the fact that the reduction in uncertainty resulting from sampling will not necessarily be proportional to the size sample taken.

From our earlier study of sampling distributions, we might suppose that the reduction in uncertainty from increasing sample sizes is somewhat less than proportional to the increase in sample size. Also, the cost of obtaining the sample need not necessarily be proportional to the sample size. There may be some fixed costs associated with taking any size sample, and generally some variable costs may be directly related to the size of the sample taken. Determination of an optimal sample size can be accomplished only by subtracting the cost of obtaining the sample from the *EVSI*, obtaining the *net gain* that is achieved with various size samples.

Making this procedure even more cumbersome is the fact that the *EVSI* calculation for each sample size must be based on the use of an *optimal* decision criterion, or c value. Notice, therefore, that the determination of the optimal sample size in a practical case is strictly a trial and error procedure, involving many calculations such as those in Tables 6.6 to 6.9. We should need to determine not only the optimal decision criterion for each given sample size but would need to repeat this calculation for all possible sample sizes. Only then are we in a position to compare the *EVSI* resulting from the use of various (n,c) combinations to the costs of obtaining the samples and ultimately to determine an optimal arrangement.

Actually, all this is not quite as bad as it might seem at first sight. The optimal decision criterion number c will change only occasionally and systematically as the sample size increases. For example, suppose it is determined that $c = 1$ represents the optimal criterion number for a given small sample, as it does for $n = 20$ in the example. Then for the next larger size sample ($n = 21$ in the example), the optimal c will be either 1 or 2. It can be proved mathematically that if the *EOL* using the decision rule ($n = 21$, $c = 1$) is *less* than the *EOL* for ($n = 20$, $c = 1$), then $c = 1$ *is* an optimum for $n = 21$. If the *EOL* for ($n = 21$, $c = 1$) is *greater*, then $c = 2$ is the optimum for $n = 21$. Thus usually only one computation of an $EOL(n,c)$, and never more than two, must be made. Even if some sample sizes are skipped, proceeding in a systematic, commonsense fashion will limit the required number of computations.

As a practical matter, it is not necessary to consider every possible value of n, the sample size. Some very large values for n may be immediately ruled out because the cost of obtaining such a sample would exceed the *EVPI* in the decision problem. Since sampling information of any sort must necessarily be less than perfect, there would be no point in considering these sample sizes further.

Also, a rough idea of the optimal sample size might be obtained by considering only certain "round" sample sizes and omitting from consideration the possibilities in between. For example, one might proceed in a problem involving the determination of an optimal sample size to consider n values of 5, 10, 20, 50, 100, 200 . . . . Before many trials are made, it will probably be possible to "zero in" on some number which closely approaches the optimal sample size.

We are further assisted by the fact that generally in sampling size determinations the total cost curve (represented by the sum of actual sampling costs and the remaining cost of uncertainty after sampling) will be rather flat in the region of the optimum. That is, we can probably miss the true optimal sample size somewhat without seriously increasing our expected costs. In all cases it must be kept in mind that the cost of the time spent in analysis is another element that should be considered. Usually a fairly rough calculation to determine the amount of information that can profitably be purchased before making a decision will prove sufficient.

Net gain from sampling Let us return to the product development problem to consider whether the purchase of additional information before making a decision is economically desirable. We saw earlier that the use of the decision rule ($n = 20$, $c = 1$) was not desirable since the *EVSI* ($7183) was exceeded by the cost of obtaining the sample, $10,000. Suppose the $10,000 sample cost were composed of a $4000 fixed cost of setting up the sampling procedure and a $300 per customer variable cost. (In practice, these costs would probably not be known with certainty. However, as elsewhere in our analysis, we may work with the *expected* costs of sampling.) Using the methods of analysis outlined in this chapter, we can compute *EVSI*, sample cost, and the net gain from sampling for various sample sizes, thus determining the desirability of purchasing various quantities of information in the product development situation. Results of the computations, which the student should attempt to verify, are given in Table 6.10 for $n = 10$, 20, 50, and 100.

These results deserve some comment. Notice that for a sample of 10, the *EVSI* is *negative*, indicating that it is better to make an immediate decision without sampling rather than employ the decision rule ($n = 10$, $c = 1$) even if the sample of 10 were available at no cost. Because of the

Table 6.10 Net gain from sampling for various sample sizes

(1) Sample size, n	(2) Optimal criterion number, c	(3) $EVSI$ [\$60,000 − $EOL(n,c)$]	(4) Sample costs ($4000 + 300n$)	(5) Net gain from sampling (3) − (4)
10	1	\$−15,198	7,000	\$−22,198
20	1	7,183	10,000	−2,817
50	2	21,737	19,000	+2,737
100	5	32,436	34,000	−1,564

high probabilities of not developing a profitable product due to zero successes in the small sample, the $EOL(n = 10, c = 1)$ is \$75,198, which is greater than the \$60,000 cost of uncertainty in the decision problem. While a sample of 20 has positive value, this value, as noted earlier, does not exceed its cost. The same is true for the sample of size 100. The sample of 50, on the other hand, does promise informational value greater than its cost, when utilized with its optimal criterion number. From Table 6.10, it appears that a sample of size 50 represents the optimal sampling arrangement. Although there is probably some other sample size near 50 that would yield even greater net gain, the difference would be slight. If net gain from sampling were plotted against sample size, the net gain curve would be rather flat between $n = 20$ and $n = 100$. Thus as a practical matter, we might be satisfied to employ the decision rule ($n = 50$, $c = 2$).

Note that the \$2737 gain projected is an *expected* gain. As with other expected values, we have no assurance that this particular gain will be realized or even that the sampling procedure will save us from a wrong decision. Remember, also, that the expected gain is based on possible *opportunity losses* from wrong decisions, which have no necessary relationship with accounting profits. If the sample of 50 advocated by our analysis led to a decision not to develop the product, we would have nothing to show for our efforts, in an accounting sense, but a \$19,000 expense item (the cost of the sample). It does not show up on the company's books that the \$19,000 investment may have saved it from a substantial loss.

One additional point should be considered. We have seen earlier that where conditional values are large relative to the financial capacity of the decision maker, expected utilities may have to be substituted for expected monetary values as a decision criterion. In the product development example, the gain expected from purchasing additional information is relatively small (even though it is positive) compared with the cost of obtaining the sample. However, even though the $19,000 sample cost seems to be a large out-of-pocket expense (as opposed to lost opportunity), remember that much larger out-of-pocket losses are possible if a wrong decision to develop the product is made. We cannot be sure how the decision to purchase additional information might be changed without a repetition of the analysis using utilities rather than dollars.

SOME SUMMARY OBSERVATIONS

In this chapter we have considered the selection of sample sizes and accompanying decision criteria, basing our analysis on an explicit consideration of the costs involved in making wrong business decisions. Explicit consideration of these costs significantly modifies and extends the classical procedures involved in the selection of a decision rule. In defense of the classical procedures, it might be pointed out that they are often employed in situations where the consequences of a wrong decision are extremely difficult to measure (e.g., scientific-hypothesis testing). Many classical statisticians would further argue that cost considerations should be and are incorporated in this procedure even though the inclusion is implicit rather than explicit.

Aside from cost considerations, however, another fundamental question remains at issue. The Bayesian approach, including the procedures outlined in this chapter, utilizes a probability distribution describing the likelihood of occurrence of various possible states of nature. These probabilities may be based on objective evidence (perhaps historical relative frequencies) or purely subjective judgments such as the management estimates of our product development problem. It is the use of subjective probabilities with which classical statisticians are most apt to disagree. The classical approach considers all states of nature, as viewed before a sample is taken, to be equally likely. The authors believe that where prior evidence regarding the states of nature relevant to a business decision exists, whether in the form of objective frequencies or subjective judgments, a decision maker acts irresponsibly if he does *not* take it into account. We shall examine this point at somewhat more depth in the following chapter.

PROBLEMS

6.1 For the product development problem in this chapter, confirm the fact that for a sample of size 50 the optimum criterion number is $c = 2$.

6.2 Prior to formal publication, faculty members at two institutions are using a locally printed version of a text in their classes. The fixed cost of printing is $800. The variable cost is $1.50 per copy. Their estimate that 300 students will be in the course next semester can be considered an accurate point estimate. The major source of uncertainty is the proportion of students next semester who will order new texts (as opposed to buying used copies from former students). The authors sold the text last semester at a price of \$5.00 per copy (not including the bookstore's markup). The objective in pricing is to break even.

The authors find that information on the proportion of students who might order new books is hard to obtain. After conferring with the bookstore's manager and other knowledgeable persons, they arrive at the following distribution for the proportion of students who will order new texts.

Proportion	*Probability*
.5	.1
.6	.4
.7	.2
.8	.2
.9	.1

(*a*) Should the authors publish the text next semester, assuming that the price will be \$5.00 per copy and that an immediate decision must be made without sampling?

(*b*) If the correct decision in (*a*) is "not to publish at the same price" and they decide to publish, what price should be charged to obtain the break-even objective?

(*c*) Since the authors neither want to make money or to lose money on the venture and since the probability distribution on the proportion of students buying new texts is quite "flat," they devise the following sampling procedure.

The second term at one of the institutions, which is on the quarter system, starts about a month before the second term for the second institution, which is on the semester system. The text will be used in a class of 50 students at the first institution. After that class starts, students will be given the option to buy new texts on credit at a price of "between \$5.00 and \$5.50." The text will not be used the first week of the course, and the information about the number of students in the class who order the texts can be used to estimate how many will be sold and to determine what price to charge.

Assuming that the students at both institutions are alike in their decision to purchase new or used texts and that the class of 50 constitutes a sample from a Bernoulli process, what (n,c) decision rule should the authors use to interpret the sample (n, of course, is 50)?

6.3 Suppose you have been offered \$100 if you can pick a loaded pair of dice from among 2 pairs that appear identical. You know only that one pair is fair and that the other is loaded to come up showing a total of seven about 60% of the time. You examine each pair carefully but can detect absolutely no apparent difference between them.

(*a*) How much would you pay for the chance to try to select the loaded pair?

(*b*) How much would you pay to roll one pair (of your choosing) once before deciding which pair is loaded?

(*c*) How much would you pay to roll one pair *twice* before deciding?

(*d*) How much would you pay to roll one pair *four* times before deciding?

(*e*) What generalization can be drawn from your answers to (*b*) through (*d*)?

6.4 In the situation described in the previous problem, suppose one pair (call it pair A) of dice "looked" loaded to you. While you are not sure of your choice, you feel the odds are 4 to 1 that A is the loaded pair.

(*a*) How much would you pay for the chance to try to select the loaded pair?

(*b*) How much would you pay to roll the A pair once before making a decision?

(*c*) Compare your answers to part (*b*) of this problem to part (*b*) of the previous problem. What generalization is suggested?

(*d*) What is the $EVPI$ in this problem? How does it compare with $EVPI$ in the previous problem? Does this comparison relate to the comparison in (*c*)?

6.5 (*a*) Confirm the $EVSI$ data given in column 3 of Table 6.10 (for the product development problem) for $n = 10$, $n = 50$, and $n = 100$. To make this process somewhat shorter, assume that the optimum criterion numbers shown in column 2 are correct.

(*b*) Explain the meaning of the $EVSI$ for $n = 10$ in this problem.

6.6 Assume that a student has a part-time job in a city about 40 miles from the campus. He also has an old car that is badly in need of a minor repair costing \$37.50. Being a fair roadside mechanic, he can always fix the car so that it will get him to his job, but the repair is of a temporary nature, and the car is as likely to break down on the next trip as it ever was. If the car does break down while he is going to work, he will lose an hour's time, during which he could have made \$2.50. He figures that until he graduates, he will make 300 trips to work, after which he'll sell the car for junk.

Being a diligent statistics student, he decides to approach his decision problem—whether or not to repair the car—in a scholarly manner. On the basis of past experience he arrives at the following probability distribution for p, the proportion of times the car will break down.

p	$P(p)$
.01	.2
.05	.5
.10	.3

(*a*) Calculate the EOLs of the acts "repair" and "don't repair," and identify the optimal act. Assume that the breakdowns occur as a Bernoulli process.

(*b*) Being cautious as well as diligent, he decides to consider the history of the last 2 weeks (10 trips) as a sample before he makes a decision about a repair. Formulate the optimal decision rule for this sample of 10.

(*c*) If he had 1 breakdown in the sample of 10, what should he do?

(*d*) What is the $EVSI$ for the optimal decision rule found in part (*b*)?

6.7 For a given sample size, the $EVSI$ is equal to the $EVPI$ minus the EOL of the best decision rule for that sample size. Explain the process by which one obtains the $EVPI$ and the EOL of the best decision rule, and explain why it is logical to call the difference between them the $EVSI$.

6.8 Explain carefully the process through which one determines the optimal sample size for a particular decision problem.

6.9 A large computer manufacturer maintains an ongoing program to update its customer engineers. In the past they have sent all qualified engineers to a special school that lasts 10 weeks and costs the company $1000 per student. They are now contemplating a "two-track" program. They propose sending all students to a very intensive one-week program that costs $100 per student. Those students who pass this course will be sent to a supplementary school at a cost of $600 per student. Those who fail will be enrolled in the regular $1000 per student course. If the proportion of students who pass the intensive course is large enough, it will save money, whereas if the proportion is small, it will lose money. Having no previous experience, the manufacturer places the following probability distribution on the proportion of students who will pass. There are currently 500 engineers whom it would ordinarily enroll in the program.

p	$P(p)$
.15	.2
.20	.3
.25	.2
.30	.2
.35	.1

(*a*) If the company is to make an immediate decision without running a "pilot" sample, should it institute the special program or stay with the regular program?

(*b*) Because of the uncertainty with respect to the distribution of p prior to sampling, the company decides to check on the validity of its decision by taking a random sample of engineers and sending them through the first week of the special program to see how many will pass. The cost of this special school is $100 per student.

Determine the optimal (n,c) decision rule. (To make it more simple, assume that the optimal sample size will be one of the n's for which you have binomial tables in Appendix A.) Will it pay to sample? Why or why not?

6.10 In your plant you have an old machine which performs an operation on a part you are manufacturing. The cost of labor plus material for the work performed by this machine comes to $0.23 per piece. You have an order for 50,000 parts. Before you produce them, you want to consider the possibility of buying a new machine to replace the old one. The new machine costs $4253. You can get $300 scrap value for the old machine. Because of increased speed, the new machine can produce parts at a unit cost of $0.15. However, there is one drawback to the new machine. With the old machine the proportion of defectives is known to be .05. Since the defective rate is a function of both the operator and the machine, the manufacturer cannot specify the defective rate on the new machine. Based on his experience and yours, however, you arrive at the following probability distribution for the proportion defective.

p	$P(p)$
.05	.15
.07	.25
.09	.30
.11	.15
.13	.15

Assume that the defectives are generated by a Bernoulli process, and that the entire cost of the new machine can be allocated to the 50,000 parts.

Note: In the questions that follow you will have to calculate costs on the basis of *good* pieces, i.e., the cost for 50,000 *good* pieces on the old machine, for example, is

$$\$0.23\,\frac{50{,}000}{.95} = \$12{,}105$$

(*a*) If you must make a decision without sampling, what should that decision be, and what is the *EOL* of the optimal act?

The seller of the machine gives you the opportunity to sample to determine the proportion defective by having your operator run a sample on a new machine owned by another manufacturer in your city. The seller agrees to pay the other manufacturer for the time lost in production due to running your sample, but you have to pay the cost of sampling, which is \$10 + \$0.15(n).

(*b*) Should you sample? If so, how large a sample should you take, and what criterion number should you use? (In answering this question, consider only the sample sizes of 10, 20, 50, or 100.)

6.11 You have probably noted by now that for problems such as Prob. 6.10 you can easily calculate the optimal decision rule without sampling by simply finding the expected value of the random variable and comparing it with the break-even point. If this is the case, why is it necessary to calculate the *EOL* of the possible acts and compare them? Explain fully.

6.12 A distributor of Christmas tree lights is contemplating the purchase of the season's supply of 100,000 bulbs from a foreign manufacturer. This manufacturer claims that the new bulbs are "at least as good" as the domestically produced brand he has purchased in former years, which he knows from experience run about 2% defective. However, the distributor is doubtful concerning the quality of the foreign product, subjectively estimating the following probability distribution for fraction defective:

Fraction defective	*Probability*
0.01	.1
0.02	.4
0.05	.5

The cost of having to replace defective bulbs (including the cost of customer goodwill lost) is estimated at 50 cents per bulb. The foreign bulbs are 1 cent each cheaper to the distributor but can be sold at the same price as the domestic bulbs.

(*a*) Based on the information above, would you recommend purchase of the foreign-produced bulbs?

(*b*) Suppose an independent testing laboratory will obtain and test a random sample of 100 of the foreign bulbs for a fee of \$125. How could such a sample best be utilized?

(*c*) Would you recommend purchase of the sample information?

6.13 ABCO Controls purchases a certain machined part in lots of 4000 for use in a valve assembly it produces. Most of the time only about 1% of the purchased parts fail to meet specifications, but occasionally a bad shipment is received that may contain as many as 15% defective parts. Although only crude records are available, it appears that about 10% of the shipments received have been bad, as defined here.

Currently, incoming shipments are 100% inspected for defectives at a cost of $200 per lot. All defectives are found in this way and returned to the manufacturer, who replaces them at no cost. If the parts are not inspected, defectives would eventually be discovered in the assembly process. To remove and replace them at this point involves a cost of $3 per defective part.

ABCO is considering the establishment of a sampling procedure to replace the 100% inspection. To set up for the sampling procedure each time a lot is received would cost $35, and inspection of a random sample could then be accomplished at a cost of 10 cents per part included. Full (100%) inspection of the remaining parts would still cost about $200 after sampling.

(*a*) Should the sampling procedure be instituted? If so, how large a sample should be taken?

(*b*) What decision criterion should be used?

7
Combining Sample Data with Other Information

INTRODUCTION

The preceding chapter was concerned with the economic desirability of sampling, focusing on the question of how much (if any) sample information should be purchased *prior* to making a final decision. This analysis would, of course, be conducted before any sample was taken. In this chapter, we shall develop a means for incorporating sample information into our analysis of a decision problem *after* the sample has been taken and the results are known. We shall see that the procedures considered here duplicate some of the information obtained from the previous analysis. However, there may be situations where a sample was taken without the benefit of the analysis of the previous chapter. Clearly, the decision maker should include such sample information, once obtained, in his analysis, whether or not on an a priori basis it would have been desirable to obtain the sample information in the first place.

THE ANALYSIS OF SAMPLE DATA

To illustrate, let us return to the product development example of the previous chapter. In the circumstances of that example it is entirely reasonable that the decision maker, because of the high development costs involved, might have obtained additional information before making a final decision, even if no formal analysis were performed. For purposes of illustration, let us suppose that a sample of size 20 *had* been obtained at a cost of $10,000. It is quite clear that no analysis of the economics of sampling had been conducted prior to obtaining such a sample, for this analysis indicated to us in the last chapter that a sample of size 20 did not represent a desirable purchase of information, i.e., the cost of information obtained was greater than the resulting reduction in the cost of uncertainty.

Now just because this information is expected to be worth less than its cost, the decision maker can scarcely afford to ignore it. Suppose the sample of 20 customers that had been taken contained no customers who exhibited a desire to buy the product. Intuitively, we would feel less confident of the decision "to develop" that would have been made in the absence of sample information. Certainly a final decision at this point should give some weight to the sample results as well as the subjective business judgments on which the probability distribution of possible outcomes was originally based.

Of course, the analysis of the preceding chapter could always be carried out on an after-the-fact basis once the sample results were known. Recall that in the first part of that analysis we developed a method for determining sample size. For the product development example we found that for a sample of size 20 the optimal criterion number was $c = 1$. That is, if a sample of size 20 were to be taken prior to making a final decision, its results should be utilized in the following manner: If one or more of the 20 customers sampled expressed a desire to buy the product, then a decision should be made to develop the product. Only if none of the 20 customers expressed a favorable response to the product should its development be foregone.

Since the particular sample considered here actually contained no "buy" responses, we should therefore decide "don't develop," reversing the decision that would have been made without the benefit of the sample information. It would be perfectly proper to use this decision rule to interpret the sample results obtained and to make a final decision concerning product development. However, recall that the effort required to determine the optimal criterion number ($c = 1$) was considerable. It required a trial-and-error procedure, and each trial in itself involved a rather lengthy calculation.

As we shall see in this chapter, there is a somewhat more efficient means of incorporating sample results into the analysis once these results are known. Rather than considering all possible sample outcomes (as did the previous analysis), it requires consideration only of the specific sample outcome actually observed, after the fact. Incorporation of the known sample outcome into the analysis and ultimate selection of a decision alternative will be accomplished by *revising* the probability distribution of the various outcomes, or states of nature, which provided the weights for use in calculating the *EOL*s (or expected monetary values) of the decision alternatives. Once we have revised the *prior* probability distribution, we shall simply recompute the *EOL*s, using the same *COL*s as before, changing only the weighting system represented by the probability distribution.

REVISION OF PRIOR PROBABILITIES

To demonstrate the revision procedure, let us revise the subjective probability distribution of the product development example so that it includes the sample information ($n = 20$, $r = 0$). While it is obvious that the lack of favorable responses would make us less confident of the decision to develop, the revision in the original probability distribution (which favored development) might or might not be enough to swing our final decision the other way. Let us see by how much the original or prior probability distribution of the possible proportion of customers buying the product would be affected by this specific sample outcome.

Conditional probability of the observed sample outcome The first step in the revision procedure is to calculate the probability of obtaining the observed sample outcome, given various states of nature. In the problem at hand, this is represented by the probability of getting zero favorable responses in a sample of 20 customers for various possible levels of p, the proportion of customers actually buying the product. These values obtained are *conditional* probabilities, in that they depend on the value of p.

Although they may be assumed to be binomial probabilities, they cannot be read directly from a binomial table of the form given in this book because each probability is discrete, as opposed to the cumulative binomial probabilities of the form $P_b(r \geq R \mid n,p)$ contained in the table. If we look for a value of r equal to 0 in our binomial table, we find that such a value does not appear. This is, of course, because at least zero successes in a sample of any given size will *always* occur. The probability of *zero or more* successes is simply equal to 1. We are interested instead in the probability of *exactly* r successes out of n tries (in this case 0 out of 20), and this probability can be obtained only as the difference between the cumulative probabilities from the table. By subtracting the binomial probability that $r \geq 1$ from the binomial probability that $r \geq 0$ (which is 1.0000), we obtain the probability that r is *exactly* equal to 0.

Thus, given the condition that $p = .02$, the probability of zero successes will be $1.0000 - .3324$ (from the binomial table), or .6676.

Table 7.1 Revision of the prior probability distribution to incorporate the sample results ($n = 20$, $r = 0$)

(1)	(2)	(3)	(4)	(5)
(p)	$P(p)$ = prior	$P(r = 0 \mid p)$	$P(r = 0$ and $p)$	$P(p)$ = revised
.02	.1	.6676	.06676	.1985
.04	.3	.4420	.13260	.3943
.06	.3	.2901	.08703	.2588
.08	.2	.1887	.03774	.1122
.10	.1	.1216	.01216	.0362
			$P(r = 0)$ = .33629	1.0000

Similarly, other conditional probabilities where $p = .04, .06, \ldots$, can be obtained. They are shown in column 3 of Table 7.1.

Reversing the conditional probabilities: The use of Bayes' rule Note again that the numbers found in column 3 are *conditional* probabilities of $r = 0$, *given* p. We are ultimately interested in determining the probability of various levels of p, *given* the sample results ($r = 0$). Earlier in this book we encountered a method for reversing the direction of conditional probabilities, i.e., a method for determining $P(B \mid A)$ when $P(A \mid B)$ and certain other information was available. The technique involved the use of Bayes' rule. In one form, Bayes' rule simply states that

$$P(B \mid A) = \frac{P(A \text{ and } B)}{P(A)}$$
$$= \frac{P(A \mid B)P(B)}{P(A)}$$

Modifying these symbols for the problem at hand we have

$$P(p \mid r) = \frac{P(r \text{ and } p)}{P(r)}$$

The sample size n is of course fixed. Specifically, we want to know

$$P(p \mid r = 0) = \frac{P(r = 0 \text{ and } p)}{P(r = 0)}$$

where $n = 20$.

The joint probabilities of $r = 0$ *and* each level of p can be calculated by simply multiplying the numbers in column 2 (the marginal or prior probability of p) by the numbers in column 3 (the conditional probability of $r = 0$, given p), a straightforward application of the multiplication rule. The remaining need is to find the marginal probability of $r = 0$.

The marginal probability of any event can always be determined (if all else fails) by adding the joint probabilities of *all compound events* in which the event in question is involved. We *could* observe an actual sample outcome $r = 0$ in each of the cases, $p = .02$, $p = .04$, $p = .06$, $p = .08$, and $p = .10$. Adding these joint probabilities together, i.e., summing column 4, we obtain the marginal probability that $r = 0$. This number can also be interpreted as the likelihood of the particular sample $r = 0$ occurring, given only our prior probability information (or assumptions) regarding states of nature.

Completing our application of Bayes' rule, we may now determine the conditional probability, $P(p \mid r)$ by dividing each of the joint probabilities in column 4 by the marginal probability represented by the total of that column. Put another way, we are simply expressing the numbers in column 4 as a percentage of their total. These conditional probabilities of $(p \mid r)$ appear in column 5, representing the *revised* probability distribution.

USE OF THE REVISED DISTRIBUTION: RECOMPUTATION OF *EOLs*

Once these revised probabilities have been obtained, they may be employed in the same manner as the prior probabilities obtained earlier from subjective management judgments. We could use them, for example, to weight the conditional opportunity losses in the product development problem, as shown in Table 7.2. A comparison of the *EOLs* computed by using the revised probability distribution shows that the decision "don't develop," now having the lower *EOL*, represents the superior strategy. The "develop" decision, which was optimal without sampling (see Chap. 6) is changed as a consequence of incorporating the sample outcome ($n = 20$, $r = 0$) into our probability weights.

This result, of course, is consistent with the result obtained in the

Table 7.2 Computation of *EOLs* using revised probability distribution

		Develop		*Don't develop*	
(p)	$P(p)$ = *revised*	*Conditional loss*	*Weighted value*	*Conditional loss*	*Weighted value*
.02	.1985	$300,000	$59,550	$ 0	$ 0
.04	.3943	100,000	39,430	0	0
.06	.2588	0	0	100,000	25,880
.08	.1122	0	0	300,000	33,660
.10	.0362	0	0	500,000	18,100
		EOL =	$98,980	*EOL* =	$77,640

last chapter—that for a sample size of 20, the best criterion number is 1, indicating that the product should be developed only if one or more favorable responses are encountered in the sample. Since zero favorable responses have been encountered, the alternative decision "don't develop" would be made on the basis of an ($n = 20$, $c = 1$) decision rule. Thus, to this point, we have done nothing more with the revision of probabilities approach than could be done with the previous analysis of decision rules. The same selection between the decision alternatives would be made using either approach. Notice, however, that the effort involved in the revision is somewhat less. This is because the calculation is a once-through process, rather than the trial-and-error type required to select an optimal criterion number. In general, where sample results are already available, incorporating them into the analysis of the decision can be accomplished more easily by revising the probability distribution and recomputing the *EOL*s, as described in this chapter.

Some comment should be made about the magnitude of the *EOL* of the optimal act. Using the revised probability distribution, the *EOL* of the act "don't develop" is $77,640. On the other hand, we saw from Table 6.7 that the *EOL* involved in employing the decision rule ($n = 20$, $c = 1$) was $52,817. It is important to realize why these figures are different. The $52,817 obtained earlier represents a result *expected* from sampling and takes into consideration all possible sample outcomes. On the other hand the $77,640 figure is based on *one particular sample outcome*, $r = 0$, and its incorporation into the analysis.

The fact that the remaining cost of uncertainty *after* this particular sample outcome was higher than that expected *before* sampling (and indeed even higher than the $60,000 cost of uncertainty without sampling) is nothing more than bad luck. Other sample outcomes would most certainly have lowered the cost of uncertainty in this decision situation. In this particular instance the sample result ($n = 20$, $r = 0$) actually changed the best decision from "develop" to "don't develop." In changing our decision, the sample result also (unfortunately) made us somewhat less certain about what should be done. Although the decision maker's best alternative at this point is "don't develop," he is in a sense less sure of this decision than he was of the opposite decision which would have been made in the absence of sample information. This is because the sample results essentially contradicted or were (relatively speaking) inconsistent with the subjective prior probability distribution.

What has been accomplished here, and what is unique to the Bayesian type of analysis, is to merge subjective prior estimates of the probabilities of various states of nature or possible outcomes in a decision problem with observed sample outcomes. The classical approach, on the other hand, would generally consider *only* objective sample information in arriving at the decision. The Bayesian approach makes it possible to incorporate all available information into the analysis. Sample information can be combined with any sort of prior probability distribution, whether these prior probabilities are based on objective historical frequencies or purely subjective business judgments.

THE POSSIBILITY OF FURTHER SAMPLING

The revised probability distribution obtained in Table 7.1 and used as the set of weights in the calculations of Table 7.2 is in no sense final. It could in turn be employed as the *prior* probability distribution in another series of calculations to decide whether or not it would be profitable to sample still more. Whereas "don't develop" represents the superior decision alternative if a *final* decision is to be made after the first sample, it is not clear whether the decision should be made without still further information. Generally, the decision maker retains the alternative "purchase still more information before making a decision."

An analysis of the economics of further sampling could be undertaken by using procedures identical to those in the last chapter, except that the probability distribution of the various states of nature, $P(p)$, used would be given by the *revised* probabilities of Table 7.1. Except for the change in these probabilities, the rest of the analysis would be carried out exactly as before.

Thus a full and complete analysis of a decision problem would involve:

1. Deciding what size sample (if any) is desirable
2. Taking the sample in question and observing this sample outcome
3. Deciding on the basis of the sample outcome whether to:
   a. Choose strategy A
   b. Choose strategy B
   c. Decide that still further sampling is desirable

The important thing to remember here is that the appropriate set of probability weights at any point in the analysis is obtained from combining the original set of prior probabilities with *all* available sample information. This sample information can be incorporated in one step (by pooling all previous samples) or in a sequence of revisions made as additional information becomes available. If two successive samples are taken in the same problem, the revised probabilities after the first sample become the prior probabilities for the second sample. Notice that the only distinction between prior and revised probabilities is relative to some particular sample. Once the information in a sample has been incorporated into a revised probability distribution, the decision maker can essentially forget that that sample has been taken.

Earlier in this chapter, we assumed that a sample result ($n = 20$, $r = 0$) had been obtained in the product development problem (even though in the previous chapter a sample of size 20 was shown to be economically undesirable). Having used this result to obtain a revised probability distribution, we determined that the best final decision, considering all the information available, was "don't develop." However, the high cost of uncertainty associated with this decision ($77,640, from Table 7.2) suggests that an *additional* purchase of sample information be considered.

To determine whether further sampling is desirable, we must compute the *EVSI* and the net gain resulting from a second sample for various possible sample sizes. The net gain from sampling results, which can be confirmed by the student, are given in Table 7.3.

Note that the $10,000 cost already incurred from taking a sample of 20 plays no part in these calculations. It is in effect a sunk cost and has no relevance in considering whether to make an immediate final decision or to sample further. It is seen that the net gain from sampling is positive (and substantially so) for all sample sizes considered, even though once again 50 appears to be (roughly) the economically optimal size sample to take.

The fact that the prospective net gains from sampling are much higher than they were earlier might be somewhat puzzling. This occurs because the decision maker, after the first sample of 20 has been taken and the results interpreted, is much more uncertain about the proper decision to make. Recall that before any sampling was undertaken, the correct

Table 7.3 Net gain from further sampling, based on revised probability distribution of possible states of nature

(1) *Sample size,* n	(2) *Optimal criterion number* c	(3) *EVSI* [$77,640 − *EOL*$(n,c)$]	(4) *Sample costs,* $300n$[a]	(5) *Net gain from sampling* (3) − (4)
10	1	$18,659	$ 3,000	$15,659
20	2	25,010	6,000	19,010
50	3	39,823	15,000	24,823
100	6	49,871	30,000	19,871

[a] It is assumed that since one sample has already been taken, the $4000 "fixed" cost of sampling will not be incurred again. A different assumption could be made without changing the procedure or underlying reasoning.

decision would have been "to develop" the product and the associated *EOL* (cost of uncertainty) was $60,000.

The results of the first sample changed the proper decision to "don't develop" and also served to increase the cost of uncertainty to $77,640. Even though $10,000 has previously been spent for sampling, it is now more desirable than ever to purchase additional information. [Of course, if the first sample results had been different, say, ($n = 20$, $r = 4$), then the original decision "to develop" would have been confirmed and the cost of uncertainty would have been lowered. A final decision at that point might have been desirable.]

The calculations in Table 7.3 show that if it is possible in view of the time remaining to make a decision, an *additional* sample of roughly 50 items should be taken. As before, Table 7.3 gives us no assurance that exactly 50 represents the optimal sample size; we might wish to consider other sample sizes between $n = 20$ and $n = 100$ as possibilities.

It is interesting to note that the optimal criterion number for a sample size of 50 is no longer $c = 2$. Indeed, even though 50 again represents the best sample size for those considered, $c = 3$ is now the optimal criterion number. This change has occurred because the revised probability distribution was used in place of the prior probability distribution in the $EOL(n,c)$ computations. As indicated in Table 7.3, the optimal criterion number will change for other sample sizes as well.

When the results of a *new* sample of size 50 are obtained, any final decision should be based on the stated decision rule: If three or more of the 50 customers interviewed decide to buy the product, "develop"; if less than three buy, "don't develop." However, once the second sample has been taken and the results are known, we still have available the alternative of buying even more information before making a decision. The analysis summarized in Table 7.3 could be repeated by using a still further revision of the probability distribution. Ordinarily, of course, a large number of stages will not be required since one or two samplings may confirm the proper direction of a final decision, and the subsequent analysis of the economics of sampling will indicate that further sampling is not desirable.

SOME SUMMARY OBSERVATIONS

In this chapter, we have focused on an after-the-fact analysis that deals with a situation in which a sample has been taken and the outcome is known. The sample outcome is used to obtain a revised probability distribution, which is then used in the same way as any other probability distribution of possible states of nature in a decision problem. In the previous chapter, we dealt instead with a before-the-fact, or a priori, analysis designed to determine whether or not sampling was economically desirable.

As for making any final decision after sample results are obtained, the two approaches would result in exactly the same decision. That is, if we apply the optimal decision rule to use with a particular size of sample, determined by means of the analysis described in the previous chapter, it will direct us to the same decision that we should make by revising the original probability distribution of possible outcomes to incorporate the observed sample results, and applying the revised probability distribution as the weighting factors in computation of expected opportunity losses. One advantage of the revision procedure is that it is generally simpler. Perhaps more important, the revision procedure enables us to obtain a revised probability distribution which can form the basis for decisions about purchasing more information before making a decision. Although in many circumstances the two procedures may lead to the same result and the choice between them may be based solely on convenience, each has its place, and each belongs in the quantitative decision maker's tool kit.

It might be noted that a particular point of separation between classical and Bayesian analysis rests on the merging of sample information with a prior probability distribution that may have been subjectively derived. Classical statistical decision rules essentially assume that before the sample is taken, no prior probability distribution exists (or, more properly, that the prior probability distribution is rectangular, i.e., all possible states of nature are equally likely). The classical statistician would thus argue that statistical decision making must be based not on business judgment but entirely on sample results. The Bayesian, on the other hand, would argue that decision should be based on the *combined* impact of *all* information relevant to the decision problem, including both sample results and whatever prior information is available, whether the prior information is in the form of historical relative frequencies (objective information), businessmen's judgment (subjective information), or some combination.

If it is true, as it may be in many cases, that very little is known about the random variable which is the source of uncertainty in a decision problem, then the prior probability distribution of possible states of nature can properly be represented by a nearly rectangular distribution. In such a situation, it will be found that the revision procedure does result in giving the sample results prime importance, with very little weight being given to the prior distribution. What is important is that the state of the decision maker's prior knowledge (or lack of it) is made specific. In many business situations, it is tempting for the decision maker to say, "I have no idea what the demand will be" or "I have no idea what the fraction defective will be," etc. However, if pinned down, he will then admit that by saying "I have no idea," he does not really mean that all states of nature are *equally* likely. Forced to do so, he will attach a probability distribution to possible states of nature that is not necessarily rectangular, even though it may be rather broad and flat. It seems reasonable that whatever information the decision maker possesses should be incorporated into the analysis in an explicit way. Use of the Bayesian approach outlined in this chapter makes it possible to combine all information relevant to the decision problem.

PROBLEMS

7.1 A pinochle deck consists of 48 cards, a *double* run from the 9-spot up through the ace of each suit. There are two nines of clubs, two tens of clubs, two jacks of clubs, etc. Suppose you are asked to determine by intuition or sampling or both whether an ordinary looking package of new cards (with no markings on the package) is a pinochle deck or an ordinary 52-card deck. You are not allowed to count the cards in the package, but it looks a little thin to you. You therefore assign the following odds:

State of nature	*Probability*
Pinochle deck	.6
Ordinary deck	.4

Suppose you are allowed to draw two randomly selected cards from the deck. How would you revise the probability that it was a pinochle deck if the cards were:

(*a*) The king of hearts and the 10 of clubs
(*b*) The queen of spades and the 4 of spades
(*c*) Both jacks of diamonds

7.2 Criticize or explain the following statement: "The revision of probabilities using Bayes' rule provides a means for combining hunches with hard facts."

7.3 In the product development problem discussed throughout Chaps. 6 and 7, it was determined that a sample of size 50 should be taken before making a decision (see Table 6.10). Suppose that such a sample is taken and that 5 of the 50 customers indicate they will buy the product.

(*a*) Test the null hypothesis that the proportion of customers who will buy the product is less than .05 (the break-even value).

(*b*) If time pressures demand an immediate decision (following this sample), what should be done?

(*c*) Did you use your results from part (*a*) to answer (*b*)? Explain carefully why or why not.

(*d*) If additional time were available should additional information be collected?

7.4 You are a printer who specializes in photographic mail-order Christmas cards. You are considering a free high-quality enlargement of the picture on the card as an incentive for large-lot purchases. To process the enlargement, you will have to purchase additional photographic equipment, and you decide to check the market before embarking on the scheme by offering the opportunity to a random sample of customers. (You will then meet the commitment to them by contracting out the enlargement work.) Before taking the sample, your prior distribution on the proportion of customers who will accept the offer is:

p	$P(p)$
.05	.15
.10	.25
.15	.30
.20	.20
.25	.10

You take the sample of 100 and receive 12 special orders.

Revise the prior distribution to take into account the information provided by the sample.

7.5 Refer to Prob. 6.2. Assume that the sample of 50 is taken and that 37 students order the text.

(*a*) Revise the original prior distribution of the proportion of students ordering the text to take into account the information obtained from the sample.

(*b*) Use the revised distribution obtained in (*a*) above, to arrive at a new break-even price for the text. Fixed and variable printing costs remain the same as originally stated in Prob. 6.2.

7.6 Refer to the computer manufacturer training problem in Prob. 6.9. Assume that the company took a random sample class of 10 students, conducted the one-week session, and found that 5 of the students passed.

(*a*) Revise the prior distribution of Prob. 6.9 to take this information into account. Assume that the sampling was binomial.

(*b*) Having taken the first sample, would it pay to take a second sample? If so, what should the optimal decision rule be? If not, prove that it is better to make a final decision after the first sample.

7.7 For the machine purchase problem of Prob. 6.10, your answer to part (*b*) should indicate that sampling is desirable. Assume that you therefore sample with the optimal decision rule and that you observe six defectives in the sample.

(*a*) Revise the prior distribution of Prob. 6.10 to take this new information into account.

(*b*) Having taken the first sample, will it pay to take a second sample? If so, what should the optimal decision rule be? If not, prove that you are better off to make a final decision after having sampled only once.

7.8 After having performed the calculations for Probs. 6.10 and 7.7, your boss is quite impressed with your facility in decision theory problems. He is so impressed, in fact, that he asks you to write a concise but complete explanation of the reasoning process you have used so that he can present it to the executive committee at its next meeting. (He would like to do this himself, but he confesses that he really doesn't understand it.) Write such an explanation.

7.9 Refer to the Christmas light problem, 6.12. Suppose that the testing laboratory was retained to analyze the foreign-made bulbs and that their report showed 4 defectives out of 100.

(*a*) Revise management's subjective probabilities regarding these bulbs to reflect the sample information.

(*b*) Compute the *EOL* for the decision alternatives using the revised probability distribution.

(*c*) How much was this sample worth to the distributor (using hindsight)?

(*d*) Would you recommend that another sample of 100 be analyzed (at the same cost as before)?

7.10 Explain the statement, "The revised probability distribution for the random variable from the first sample becomes the prior probability distribution for use in deciding whether or not a second sample is desirable." How does this relate to the statement that the decision maker should make use of *all* the information available to him before making a decision?

7.11 Explain how a decision maker can tell when it is desirable to do no more sampling and to make a decision to act one way or another.

7.12 A large professional association is trying to estimate the percentage of its membership that will attend a convention. The executive committee assigns the following probabilities:

Percent attendance	*Probability*
0.05	.4
0.10	.3
0.15	.2
0.20	.1
	1.0

(*a*) In order to make better estimates for planning purposes, it is decided to poll a sample of the association membership by telephone. Ten members are called, and two of them state they will attend. Revise the probability distribution to account for this information.

(*b*) Based on the prior probabilities, how likely was it that this particular sample result would be obtained?

(*c*) Ten more members are called, with no favorable responses. Revise the revised distribution obtained as an answer to (*a*) to reflect this new information.

(*d*) Suppose the two samples of 10 each were pooled before the revision was made. Revise the *original* probability distribution for the result $n = 20$, $r = 2$.

(*e*) Compare your answers to (*c*) and (*d*). Can you generalize regarding successive revisions versus pooling sample information?

7.13 (*a*) Under what circumstances might sample information actually prove "worse than worthless" to a decision maker?

(*b*) Would such a situation indicate that the sample should not have been taken? Explain.

7.14 In Prob. 7.1, assume that you were allowed to draw four cards instead of two. Suppose that the cards drawn (in order) were:

(1) Queen of spades
(2) Four of spades
(3) King of hearts
(4) Ten of clubs

(*a*) What is your revised probability that the deck is a pinochle deck?
(*b*) Suppose the draws are costing you money, say, at the rate of $100 per card. Can you see any advantage to the use of sequential sampling procedure (i.e., drawing and observing the first card before deciding whether to draw the second, etc.)?
(*c*) Can you generalize your answer to (*b*) for all sampling situations?

7.15 Explain how you might determine in *advance* of taking the first sample in the product development problem what sample outcomes might lead you to make a final decision (at that point) and what outcomes would lead you to collect more information before making a decision. (This sort of analysis results in what is called a *sequential* sampling design.) You may wish to assume the availability of a computer to perform the necessary calculations.

8
Descriptive Statistics

MEASURED VARIABLES

In every sampling situation we have encountered up to this point, the random variable has involved counting. We have considered, for example, the number (or proportion) of customers who might buy a new product and the number of defective parts produced in a Bernoulli process. We have *counted* the number of "successes" in samples to estimate the proportion of items in populations that possess a certain attribute. The data have been discrete, as in all counting situations. Either 10 parts or 11 parts might be defective; we could not conceive of 10 1/2 defectives.

We will now turn our attention to measured variables in addition to counted variables. The distinction between the two types may be illustrated by comparing flash bulbs, which by the nature of their use can be regarded as "go" or "no-go," good or defective, with ordinary light bulbs. While a light bulb might be classed defective if it did not function at all, it is more useful and informative to *measure* its service life along a continuous time scale. Instead of being merely good or bad it has a life of X hours, where the X is a measurement.

Measured variables clearly can be fractional as well as whole numbers. Furthermore, given the capability of infinitely precise measurement, an infinite number of different measurements could conceivably be taken between any two previous measurements. The hand of a clock, for example, passes an infinite number of points between 3:00 and 3:30, 3:00 and 3:10, or 3:00 and 3:01, and one could conceive of an infinite number of measurements within any of these time spans.

Since any measuring technique is not in fact capable of infinite accuracy, measurements will always be discrete to one degree of accuracy or another. However, the notion of a theoretical continuous distribution of variables will prove extremely valuable as an approximation to many real-world discrete distributions.

USES OF DESCRIPTIVE MEASURES

The remainder of this chapter is devoted to an explanation of some statistical measures that are used to summarize or describe sets of numbers. Study of this area, often referred to as "descriptive statistics," is justified on two grounds. First, descriptive measures possess a usefulness of their own in providing the analyst or decision maker with a means for summarizing masses of unwieldy data. Second, and perhaps more important, we must know something of the measures used to describe probability distributions before we can extend the methods of statistical inference and decision making to problems involving measured variables and continuous distributions. This extension occupies the last four chapters of this book.

To simplify the explanation, we shall first consider problems involving small amounts of data (in the form of small samples). Methods of describing and summarizing large masses of data are reserved for the appendixes to this chapter.

MEASURES OF LOCATION

A measure of location is a single value that characterizes a particular *point* in an array of values. This point may be the "center of gravity," called the *arithmetic mean;* the "middle" value, called the *median;* or the point, for example, above which two-thirds of the values lie, called the .33 *fractile.* Each of these points may be important to a decision maker or to one whose fate rests on a decision. Witness the interest of a student in whether or not his grade on a test is above or below the .33 fractile if that point distinguishes a passing from a failing grade.

THE ARITHMETIC MEAN

The arithmetic mean is one of a number of "calculated averages" whose value depends on the value of every number in the group from which it is calculated. By common convention the word "mean" used without any qualifying adjective is understood to represent the arithmetic mean.[1]

The mean locates the center of gravity of a distribution of values. More precisely, the differences between the mean and each of the values from which it is calculated sum to 0. As you learned many years ago, the mean is calculated simply by adding the values and dividing by the number of values involved. Stating this formally, the mean of a set of measurements comprising a sample is obtained as:

$$\bar{X} = \frac{\Sigma_{i=1}^{n} X_i}{n} \tag{8.1}$$

where $\bar{X}$ is the mean of the sample, X_i represents a value of the variable, n is the number of items in the sample, and $\Sigma_{i=1}^{n}$ means the summation of the values of X_i from 1 through n. Throughout this text we shall always sum values through the entire group (rather than taking partial summations). Therefore we shall simplify the notation of (8.1) by using Σ without sub- or superscripts, thus

$$\bar{X} = \frac{\Sigma X}{n} \tag{8.2}$$

To illustrate the calculation and some characteristics of the mean, consider the sample of daily sales of a particular product in Table 8.1.

The sum of the values of this sample of size 10 is 15,000, and the mean is 1500. Column 3 demonstrates that the sum of the deviations from the mean is equal to 0.

An obvious and important characteristic of the mean is the fact that since $\bar{X} = \Sigma X/n$, then $n\bar{X} = \Sigma X$. This enables one to estimate a total based on knowledge of the mean. Another important but less obvious characteristic of the mean is that the sum of the *squares* of the deviations between the mean and each of the values is a minimum. Note that the sum of the squared deviations in column 4 of Table 8.1 is equal to 166,800. This is the smallest sum one could obtain by taking squared deviations between the original values and *any* number. If you're skeptical, try taking squared deviations about 1400 or any other value that appeals to you and see what happens. We shall refer to this characteristic of the mean later in the discussion of some other descriptive measures.

[1] Other calculated averages are the geometric, the harmonic, and the quadratic means. These will not be discussed specifically in this text, although an important measure of dispersion, the standard deviation, is really a quadratic mean.

Table 8.1 Sales of ABC Company

(1) *Day number*	(2) *Number of sales, X*	(3) $X - \bar{X}$[a]	(4) $(X - \bar{X})^2$
1	1,650	+150	22,500
2	1,450	−50	2,500
3	1,300	−200	40,000
4	1,560	+60	3,600
5	1,280	−220	48,400
6	1,500	0	0
7	1,620	+120	14,400
8	1,430	−70	4,900
9	1,540	+40	1,600
10	1,670	+170	28,900
	Σ = 15,000	0	166,800

[a] $\bar{X} = \frac{\Sigma X}{n} = \frac{15{,}000}{10} = 1{,}500$

THE MEAN OF A POPULATION

In the preceding example, the data used were assumed to represent a sample of daily sales figures. As we have seen in earlier chapters, the primary use of such sample information is to *estimate* salient characteristics, or *parameters*, of a population. Just as the sample proportion of "successes" was used as a point estimate of the population proportion, so will the sample mean $\bar{X}$ be used as an estimate of the population mean, denoted by μ_X (Greek lowercase mu).[2]

Of course, if data were available for an entire population, the population mean μ_X could be calculated. For a finite population of size N,

$$\mu_X = \frac{\Sigma X}{N} \tag{8.3}$$

FRACTILES

Unlike the arithmetic mean, a fractile is a measure of position, showing the value of a number that falls a given proportion of the way through an array. An array is simply a group of numbers arranged according to size. To find, for example, the 30th fractile for the sales values in Table 8.2,

[2] Technically, $\bar{X}$ has the desirable property of being an *unbiased* estimator of μ_X, which has the following meaning: While no particular sample estimate $\bar{X}$ is likely to equal the population mean μ_X, the mean of a large number of such $\bar{X}$ estimates *will* tend to equal μ_X. In other words, the mean of the sampling distribution of $\bar{X}$ is equal to μ_X. For further discussion of this point, see Chap. 9, pp. 160–162.

one would first arrange them in order of size:

1280
1300
1430
1450
1500
1540
1560
1620
1650
1670

The .30 or 30th fractile is the number such that 30% of the numbers in the distribution have a value equal to or less than it, while 70% of the numbers have a value equal to or greater than it. The third number in this array falls .30 of the way through the array ($10 \times .30 = 3.$) The third number has a value of 1430. Thus the .30 fractile could have any value between 1430 and 1450 (the value of the next number in the array, and the seventh from the largest number).

THE MEDIAN

The most frequently used fractile is the .50 fractile, called the *median.* For the distribution in question the median could be any value as large as the $10(.5) =$ fifth number and no larger than the sixth. The median, therefore, has a value between 1500 and 1540. Since a point estimate (one value rather than a range of possible values) is often desirable, it is customary to estimate the median for any even number of values by taking the mean of the two extreme possibilities, in this case $(1500 + 1540)/2 = 1520$.

For certain purposes the median is used as a typical value in preference to the mean. It is particularly useful in cases where a few extreme values would pull the mean away from what might be considered a typical or representative value. Note that the median of the sales data in Table 8.2 would remain the same, 1520, if the final number were 1670, 16,700, or even 167,000, while the mean would be altered considerably. Income distributions are frequently summarized by the median because such distributions often contain a few extremely high values which would distort the mean. A student might be interested in knowing the median score (and perhaps the values of other fractiles) on an exam so that he could estimate his rank in the class. An arithmetic mean for the class might give him a misleading picture of his standing because it would be influenced by a few very low scores.

THE MODE

Another commonly used positional descriptive measure is the mode. The *mode* is the value in a set of numbers that occurs most frequently. In the case of the sales values above there is no mode since no value occurs more than one time. Although particular sets of data may have no mode or more than one mode, they typically have but one, which occurs near the "middle" of the distribution. Like the median, the mode is unaffected by extremes.

MEASURES OF DISPERSION

All the measures described so far are measures of location. Another characteristic of sets of numbers that is often of interest is their uniformity or dispersion; that is, how close together or how far apart the values are from each other. Structural steel beams are expected not only to have a high average strength but also to be uniformly strong. You would not be likely to be impressed by the quality of a pair of shoes if the left one wore out in two weeks and the right lasted 10 years, even though the average length of life were high.

The *range*, defined as the difference between the values of the largest and the smallest number in a group, is the simplest measure of dispersion. However, its use in statistics is limited because it is (by definition) determined only by extreme values.

THE AVERAGE DEVIATION

A more general measure of dispersion can be developed by calculating the average difference between each of the numbers in the set and some central value such as the mean or the median. Recall that in Table 8.1 the $(X - \bar{X})$ column consisted of deviations from the mean. It was no accident that the sum of these deviations was 0. Since this will always be the case, no useful purpose could be served by averaging these deviations directly. A meaningful average could be obtained, however, by averaging the *absolute* values of the deviations. This measure is called the *average deviation* and is calculated by using one of the formulas below.

$$\text{Average deviation}_{\text{mean}} = \frac{\Sigma|X - \bar{X}|}{n} \tag{8.4}$$

or

$$\text{Average deviation}_{\text{median}} = \frac{\Sigma|X - \text{median}|}{n} \tag{8.5}$$

Referring again to Table 8.1, the sum of the *absolute* values in column 3 is 1080; the average deviation (based on the mean) is therefore 1080/10 or

108. Since the mean and the median do not have the same value in our example, the use of Eq. (8.5) would give a slightly different result.

The main use of the average deviation stems from the fact that the sum of the *absolute* deviations between a set of numbers and their median is a minimum. Thus, for example, if one wanted to locate a tool bin along an assembly line at a point that minimized travel from work stations to the bin, he would locate it at the median station, based on distances from the beginning of the line to each station. The average deviation calculated from the median would then measure the average distance of a one-way trip to the tool bin, and this distance would be the minimum possible.

THE VARIANCE

Another treatment of the $(X - \bar{X})$ deviation leads to the development of a measure that is extremely useful in all of statistics. If we square each $(X - \bar{X})$ deviation instead of taking its absolute value, the effect of the sign is also eliminated. The mean of these squared deviations is called the *variance*.

$$\text{Sample variance} = \frac{\Sigma(X - \bar{X})^2}{n} \tag{8.6}$$

Appropriate columns of Table 8.1 are shown in Table 8.2 to illustrate the calculation of the variance for the sample of sales.

The variance might seem to be a rather strange method for measur-

Table 8.2 Calculation of variance sales of ABC Company

X	$X - \bar{X}$	$(X - \bar{X})^2$
1650	+150	22,500
1450	−50	2,500
1300	−200	40,000
1560	+60	3,600
1280	−220	48,400
1500	0	0
1620	+120	14,400
1430	−70	4,900
1540	+40	1,600
1670	+170	28,900
		166,800

$$\text{Sample variance} = \frac{166{,}800}{10} = 16{,}680$$

ing dispersion since its units are in terms of squared errors. However, the variance is a most important measure of dispersion because it has a property that no other measure of dispersion has. The variance of a sum of independent variables is the sum of the variances of the individual variables. Thus, $\text{Var}(X + Y + Z) = \text{Var}(X) + \text{Var}(Y) + \text{Var}(Z)$, where X, Y, and Z are random variables that are independent. We shall make use of this unique property of the variance in Chaps. 11 and 12.

THE STANDARD DEVIATION

While the variance is widely used, an even more common measure of dispersion is the positive *square root of the variance* called the *standard deviation.* It has the advantage of being expressed in the same units as the data from which it was computed. Whereas the variance in the sales data example, 16,680, has the units "number of sales squared" (which makes interpretation difficult), the standard deviation is in the same units as the original data.

$$\text{Sample standard deviation} = \sqrt{\frac{\Sigma(X - \bar{X})^2}{n}} \tag{8.7}$$

For our example, the sample standard deviation equals $\sqrt{16{,}680}$, or 129. Note that 129 is typical of the $(X - \bar{X})$ deviations. To be sure, it is not their arithmetic mean, but is a different kind of average that possesses superior properties for the development of statistical theory. It has a variety of important practical applications in sampling problems, as we shall see presently.

VARIANCE AND STANDARD DEVIATION OF A POPULATION

If all the data for a population were available, the population variance ${\sigma_X}^2$ and the population standard deviation σ_X could be calculated based on the squared deviation from the population mean μ_X:

$${\sigma_X}^2 = \frac{\Sigma(X - \mu_X)^2}{N} \tag{8.8}$$

$$\sigma_X = \sqrt{{\sigma_X}^2} = \sqrt{\frac{\Sigma(X - \mu_X)^2}{N}} \tag{8.9}$$

where N is again the size of the population.

We shall be primarily interested in sampling problems in which the population variance and standard deviation are estimated from sample data instead of calculated directly. One might logically suppose that the sample variance, defined by Eq. (8.6), would be used to estimate ${\sigma_X}^2$. Such is not the case, however, since it has undesirable properties as an estimator, tending to underestimate population variance.[3] We can correct for this tendency by using $n - 1$ in the denominator of the formula in place of n.[4]

Denoting the sample estimate of population variance as s_X^2,

$$s_X^2 = \frac{\Sigma(X - \bar{X})^2}{n - 1} \tag{8.10}$$

Since our sole objective in using sample data is to estimate population characteristics, we shall use Eq. (8.10) throughout the remainder of the text, always dividing $(X - \bar{X})^2$ by $n - 1$ rather than n. (Notice that "sample variance" as it was defined in Eq. (8.6) was not even assigned a symbol.) Similarly, the population standard deviation s_X will be estimated by

$$s_X = \sqrt{\frac{\Sigma(X - \bar{X})^2}{n - 1}} \tag{8.11}$$

DESCRIPTIVE MEASURES FOR PROBABILITY DISTRIBUTIONS

The continuous probability distributions utilized in decision problems in subsequent chapters have the *mean* and *standard deviation* (or its square, the variance) as parameters which *determine* the distribution. This means that the probability that the (continuous) random variable will fall in any given interval can be obtained only if the value of the mean and variance are known.

[3] The trouble stems from the fact that we are trying to estimate $(X - \mu_X)^2$ terms for the sample using $(X - \bar{X})^2$ deviations around the *sample* mean, since the population mean is unknown. Since $\bar{X}$ is the calculated mean of the sample values, $\Sigma(X - \bar{X})^2$ will be smaller than the sum of squared deviations around any other value including the true population mean μ_X. Recall that this is a property of the mean of a set of numbers; see p. 125. Thus $\Sigma(X - \bar{X})^2$ will underestimate $\Sigma(X - \mu_X)^2$ for the same set of X values and $[\Sigma(X - \bar{X})^2]/n$ will underestimate the population variance. (It may help to note that any sample of one necessarily has a sample variance of 0, which is an underestimate of the population variance unless all the values are identical. Experimentation with hypothetical samples of two or three values should convince the student of the point being made here.)

[4] The term $n - 1$ is used because it represents the number of *degrees of freedom* involved in estimating the standard deviation. Of the total number of values in the sample, only $n - 1$ are "free" to vary. One degree of freedom is lost when the mean is used in the calculation of the squared errors, for if the mean of a group of values is specified, only $n - 1$ of those values can vary without changing the mean. For example, if you were asked to list five values whose mean was 10, you could assign any value to the first four numbers, but you would have no freedom concerning the fifth.

THE MEAN OF A PROBABILITY DISTRIBUTION

The mean of a probability distribution is equivalent to the expected value of the distribution (as defined in Chap. 3). Since a probability distribution, by definition, gives the probability of *all* possible values of a random variable, its mean is a population mean, to which we assign the symbol μ_X. Thus, for a probability distribution

$$\mu_X = E(X) = \Sigma XP(X) \tag{8.12}$$

THE VARIANCE AND STANDARD DEVIATION OF A PROBABILITY DISTRIBUTION

Similarly, the variance of a probability distribution is given the symbol $\sigma_X{}^2$. It is equal to the expected value of the squared deviations of the values of the random variable, X, from their mean:

$$\sigma_X{}^2 = E[(X - \mu_X)^2] = \Sigma(X - \mu_X)^2 P(X) \tag{8.13}$$

It follows that the standard deviation for a probability distribution is given by

$$\sigma_X = \sqrt{\Sigma(X - \mu_X)^2 P(X)} \tag{8.14}$$

COMPUTING DESCRIPTIVE MEASURES FOR A PROBABILITY DISTRIBUTION

Let us use a simple example to illustrate the concepts discussed above. Assume that four lots of a certain product were sold to a particular industrial user over a period of time to fulfill a contract. The four lots constitute the population—the entire number of lots sold under the contract. Recall that the size of a *population* is denoted by N; therefore in this problem $N = 4$. Now assume that each of these lots was examined for defectives, and it was found that two lots had no defectives, one lot had one defective, and one lot had three defectives. The defects per lot is considered here as a random variable.

The probability distribution of defectives per lot is summarized in the first two columns of Table 8.3. The remaining columns are used in the calculation of the population mean and standard deviation.

$$\mu_X = E(X) = \Sigma XP(X) = 1.00$$
$$\sigma_X = \sqrt{\Sigma(X - \mu_X)^2 P(X)} = \sqrt{1.50} \approx 1.22$$

Note that the population mean could also have been obtained by $\Sigma X/N$; $(0 + 0 + 1 + 3)/4 = 1.00$. The population standard deviation could have been calculated by using

$$\sqrt{\frac{\Sigma(X - \mu_X)^2}{N}} = \sqrt{\frac{(0 - 1)^2 + (0 - 1)^2 + (1 - 1)^2 + (1 - 3)^2}{4}}$$
$$\approx 1.22$$

Table 8.3 Probability distribution for defectives per lot

Number of defectives per lot, X	*Probability, P(X)*	$XP(X)$	$X - \mu_X$	$(X - \mu_X)^2$	$(X - \mu_X)^2P(X)$
0	.50	0	−1.0	1.0	.50
1	.25	.25	0	0	0
3	.25	.75	2.0	4.0	1.00
	1.00	1.00			1.50

The value of N rather than $N - 1$ is used in the denominator because we are finding the population standard deviation from the entire population; we are not estimating the population standard deviation from a sample. The method shown above would, of course, be exceedingly cumbersome for populations consisting of large numbers of values. Such problems are considered in Appendixes 8A and 8B.

Appendix 8A
Descriptive Measures for Frequency Distributions

SUMMARIZING DATA

Masses of raw data in themselves convey little information. While a business decision maker may be vitally interested in the kind of people who buy his product, a listing from a gigantic computer file containing each customer's income, age, family size, and a bewildering variety of information might be of little value. Without further analysis, the sheer volume of the data might simply overwhelm him. He would probably find himself in that familiar position of being unable to see the forest for the trees.

The fact is that data must be summarized in some way to provide for meaningful interpretation or use in the decision process. Questions concerning the income level of customers (which might be relevant for advertising decisions) would not be answered best by a complete listing of the incomes of each customer. Even if such data could be obtained, which is doubtful, it would be expensive. Besides, a lengthy list of exact dollar incomes is not what the decision maker is really looking for in his effort to zero in on this crucial variable in his problem. Actually faced with such a list, he would certainly attempt some means of summarizing the data, perhaps describing the entire list with one or two numbers that identify its salient characteristics. Here, we shall outline methods of classifying large quantities of data and computing those measures discussed in Chap. 8.

FREQUENCY DISTRIBUTIONS

When dealing with a large number of values, it is often convenient and more meaningful for presentation to group them, counting the number of values that fall within arbitrary limits or classes. Such a grouping is called a *frequency distribution.*

SELECTION OF CLASSES AND DEFINITION OF CLASS LIMITS

The selection of appropriate classes for a frequency distribution is an art. If we choose too few classes, the calculation of summary measures from the distribution will very likely be in error. If we choose too many classes, the pattern of distribution of the values is obscured and little time is saved in calculating summary measures. A satisfactory number of classes is usually between 8 and 20. Consider Table 8.4, which illustrates choices of class limits for a sample of 100 sales of gasoline at a service station.

One point should be noted with respect to the third of these distributions. Since these data were discrete to the nearest cent and the classes are nonoverlapping, the midvalues are $(.50 + 1.49)/2$, or \$.995, \$1.995, \$2.995, etc. This makes the midvalues very close to round dollar

Table 8.4 Sales of gasoline

Too few classes		*Too many classes*		*A reasonable number of classes*	
Class limits	*Frequency*	*Class limits*	*Frequency*	*Class limits*	*Frequency*
\$ 0–\$4.99	55	\$1.00–\$1.09	1	\$0.50–\$ 1.49	4
\$5.00–\$9.99	45	\$1.10–\$1.19	0	\$1.50–\$ 2.49	9
	100	\$1.20–\$1.29	1	\$2.50–\$ 3.49	17
		\$1.30–\$1.39	1	\$3.50–\$ 4.49	25
		\$1.40–\$1.49	1	\$4.50–\$ 5.49	19
		\$1.50–\$1.59	0	\$5.50–\$ 6.49	12
		\$1.60–\$1.69	2	\$6.50–\$ 7.49	7
		\$1.70–\$1.79	1	\$7.50–\$ 8.49	4
		.	.	\$8.50–\$ 9.49	2
		.	.	\$9.50–\$10.49	1
		.	.		100
			100		

figures of \$1, \$2, \$3, etc. This was done intentionally because of the tendency of people, such as underfed professors, to ask for even dollar amounts of gas rather than filling up the tank. If these even dollar points of concentration were placed, say, at the lower limits of the classes rather than at the midvalues, the midvalues would not be representative of the bulk of the values in a class. This would lead to a misleading representation of the actual data and inaccurate computations of descriptive measures since these measures will be calculated according to the assumption that the midpoint is typical of the values in that class. We must be careful, then, about both the number of classes we choose and the limits of these classes. If there are regular points of concentration in the values, these points should be made midvalues of the classes.

You will note that in each of the distributions above, the span of the classes, or the class interval, was kept constant. The first distribution had a class interval of \$5, the second one of \$0.10, and the third one of \$1. Unless there is some special reason for doing otherwise, frequency distributions should have a constant class interval.

THE ARITHMETIC MEAN: GROUPED DATA

Assume that through a questionnaire you obtained expenditures on transportation during the past academic year from a random sample of 2000 college freshmen. The results of the sample are summarized in the frequency distribution of Table 8.5.

In estimating the mean of the sample (and of the population from which the sample was drawn), we can assume that every value in a class corresponds to the class midvalue. That is, our computation will assume that the 25 students who spent between \$50 and \$149 each had an expenditure of \$99.50, and so on. Although this assumption is not likely to be

Table 8.5 Expenditures by freshmen for transportation

Expenditures	*Number of students*
\$ 50–\$149	25
\$150–\$249	130
\$250–\$349	720
\$350–\$449	530
\$450–\$549	365
\$550–\$649	135
\$650–\$749	75
\$750–\$849	20
	2000

Table 8.6 Calculation of the mean, transportation expenditures

Expenditures	*Midvalues, MV*	*Number of students, f*	*Sum of expenditures for any class, fMV*
\$ 50–\$149	\$ 99.50	25	\$ 2,487.50
\$150–\$249	199.50	130	25,935.00
\$250–\$349	299.50	720	215,640.00
\$350–\$449	399.50	530	211,735.00
\$450–\$549	499.50	365	182,317.50
\$550–\$649	599.50	135	80,932.50
\$650–\$749	699.50	75	52,462.50
\$750–\$849	799.50	20	15,990.00
		2000	\$787,500.00

$$\bar{X} = \frac{\Sigma fMV}{n} = \frac{787{,}500}{2000} = \$393.75 \text{ or } \$394\text{, rounding to the nearest dollar}$$

true for any class, if we use enough classes and choose the limits carefully, errors should average out over all the classes. We simply multiply each midvalue by the number of times it occurs and sum these products for all classes. The mean would be this sum divided by the total number of values in the distribution (the sum of the frequency column):

$$\bar{X} = \frac{\Sigma f(MV)}{n} \tag{8.15}$$

The mean is calculated in Table 8.6 for the transportation expenditures.

A short method that saves effort and time in calculating the mean for grouped data is shown in Appendix 8B.

THE STANDARD DEVIATION: GROUPED DATA

Knowing the arithmetic mean and again assuming that all the numbers in a class fall at the midvalue, the calculation of the standard deviation for grouped data is straightforward. The sum of the squared deviations for the entire distribution would then be $\Sigma f(MV - \bar{X})^2$, and the standard deviation of the population from which this sample was drawn would be estimated by

$$s_X = \sqrt{\frac{\Sigma f(MV - \bar{X})^2}{n - 1}} \tag{8.16}$$

Table 8.7 illustrates the calculation of the standard deviation for the transportation expenditures. Note that after the squared difference

Table 8.7 Calculation of the standard deviation, transportation expenditures

Expenditures	*Mid-value, MV*	*Number of students, f*	$MV - \bar{X}$	$(MV - \bar{X})^2$	$f(MV - \bar{X})^2$
\$ 50–\$149	\$ 99.50	25	\$−294.50	\$ 86,730.25	\$ 2,168,256.25
\$150–\$249	199.50	130	−194.50	37,830.25	4,917,932.50
\$250–\$349	299.50	720	−94.50	8,930.25	6,429,780.00
\$350–\$449	399.50	530	5.50	30.25	16,032.50
\$450–\$549	499.50	365	105.50	11,130.25	4,062,541.25
\$550–\$649	599.50	135	205.50	42,230.25	5,701,083.75
\$650–\$749	699.50	75	305.50	93,330.25	6,999,768.75
\$750–\$849	799.50	20	405.50	164,430.25	3,288,605.00
		2000			33,584,000.00

$$s_X = \sqrt{\frac{\Sigma f(MV - \bar{X})^2}{n-1}} = \sqrt{\frac{33{,}584{,}000}{1999}} = \sqrt{1680} = 129.6$$

or \$130, rounded to the nearest dollar

between the midvalue and the mean is obtained for each class, each of these squared values must be weighted by the frequency of its class before taking the sum. As might be expected, there is also a less time-consuming way of obtaining this result, as shown in Appendix 8B.

THE MEDIAN: GROUPED DATA

The median must be estimated when using a frequency distribution because the exact value of every number was lost in the process of summarizing the data. The median is estimated by finding the class that contains the middle value in the array and, if necessary, interpolating arithmetically within that class to estimate its value. The necessary calculations are shown in Table 8.8 for the transportation expenditures.

At first reading, the calculations are not likely to be obvious. Let us go through the process step by step. The median is the value of the number in the $(n + 1)/2$ position, in this case the $2001/2 = 1000.5$th position. Observing the cumulative frequencies, we note that the 1000.5th number is in the fourth class (there are 875 numbers below the fourth class, and 1405 below the fifth). Therefore the median must have a value somewhere within the limits of the fourth class, between \$350 and \$449. The 1000.5th number falls $(1000.5 - 875)/530$ of the distance through the class, assuming that the values in the class are spread out evenly throughout its range. The distance through the class is the class interval, in this case \$100. Therefore the median is assumed to have a

Table 8.8 Calculation of the median, transportation expenditures

Expenditures	*Number of students, f*	*Cumulative frequency*
\$ 50–\$149	25	25
\$150–\$249	130	155
\$250–\$349	720	875
\$350–\$449	530	1405
\$450–\$549	365	1770
\$550–\$649	135	1905
\$650–\$749	75	1980
\$750–\$849	20	2000
	2000	

$$\text{Median} = 350 + \frac{1000.5 - 875}{530} 100 = \$374$$

value of $350 + [(1000.5 - 875)/530]100 = \$374$. Formalizing this reasoning, we can define the median for grouped data as:

$$\text{Median} = L_{l,\text{median}} + p(i) \tag{8.17}$$

Where $L_{l,\text{median}}$ is the lower limit of the class containing the median value, p is the proportion of the way through that class to the point where the median number is located, and i is the class interval.

Other fractile values are estimated in a similar manner, by interpolating to find the value of the number at the desired fractile position.

THE MODE: GROUPED DATA

The mode can also be approximated for a frequency distribution. It is often assumed that the mode occurs at the midvalue of the class containing the greatest number of values. A more satisfactory estimate of the mode can be obtained by adjusting for the drop-off in frequency on either side of the modal class (the class containing the greatest number of values) by using Eq. (8.18).

$$\text{Mode} = L_{l,\text{modal}} + \frac{\Delta_1}{\Delta_1 + \Delta_2} i \tag{8.18}$$

Where $L_{l,\text{modal}}$ is the lower limit of the modal class; Δ_1 is the difference between the frequency of the modal class and the frequency of the class adjacent to the modal class having values smaller than those of the modal class; Δ_2 is the difference between the frequency of the modal class and the frequency of the class adjacent to the modal class having values larger than those of the modal class; and i is the class interval.

For the transportation expenditures, the mode is then

$$250 + \frac{(720 - 130)(100)}{(720 - 130) + (720 - 530)} = \$326$$

FREQUENCY POLYGONS, RELATIVE FREQUENCY DISTRIBUTIONS, AND HISTOGRAMS

FREQUENCY POLYGONS

It is often instructive to graph a particular frequency distribution to obtain a better understanding of its general characteristics. A frequency polygon is one such graph. To graph a frequency polygon, we plot the frequency of a class on the Y axis, and we plot the midvalue of the class on the X axis.

The frequency polygon for the transportation expenditures is shown in Fig. 8.1.

SKEWNESS

The mean, the median, and the mode as calculated earlier are shown in the frequency polygon of Fig. 8.1. Note that since the distribution tails off further on the right than on the left (i.e. there are more extreme values to the right than to the left), the mean is further to the right than the median and the mode. The mean will always be further toward the extremes of a distribution than the median or mode because every value

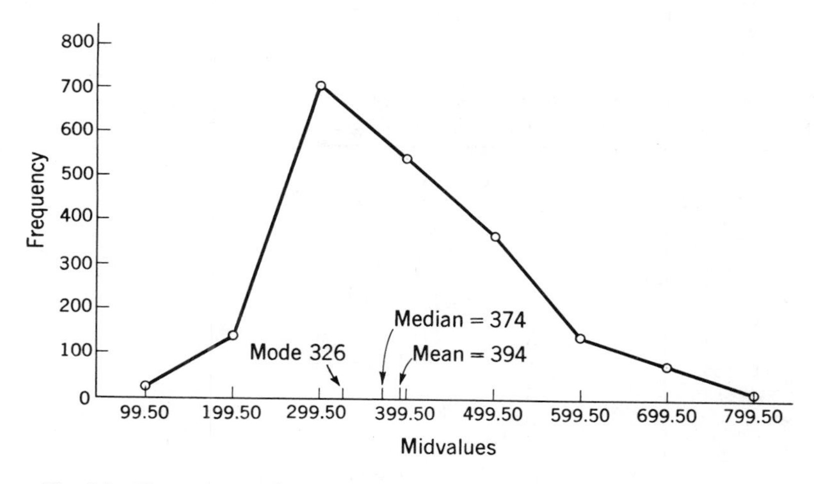

Fig. 8.1 Frequency polygon, transportation expenditures.

is used in its calculation, while the median and the mode are determined by considering the position rather than the value of every number.

Skewness, a statistical property describing lack of symmetry, can therefore be measured by comparing the arithmetic mean of a distribution with its median. A common formula for skewness is

$$\text{Skewness} = \frac{3(\bar{X} - \text{median})}{\text{standard deviation}} \tag{8.19}$$

The standard deviation is used as a denominator in order to make the measure relative (dimensionless) rather than absolute.

For the transportation expenditures, skewness measured by this formula is

$$\text{Skewness} = \frac{3(394 - 374)}{130} = +.462$$

If the distribution had extremes on the left rather than on the right, the mean would be smaller than the median and skewness would be negative. If the distribution were symmetrical, the mean and the median would be equal and the skewness would be 0.

There are other more precise methods of measuring skewness, but the one shown above is sufficient for a rough comparison of the symmetry of various distributions.

RELATIVE FREQUENCY DISTRIBUTIONS AND HISTOGRAMS

To form a relative frequency distribution, we merely express the frequency of each class as a ratio of the total frequency. This relationship is illustrated for the transportation expenditures in Table 8.9, where the

Table 8.9 Frequency distribution and relative frequency distribution, transportation expenditures

Expenditures	*Number of students, f*	*Relative frequency*
\$ 50–\$149	25	.0125
\$150–\$249	130	.0650
\$250–\$349	720	.3600
\$350–\$449	530	.2650
\$450–\$549	365	.1825
\$550–\$649	135	.0675
\$650–\$749	75	.0375
\$750–\$849	20	.0100
	2000	1.0000

first two columns constitute a frequency distribution and the first and third columns constitute a relative frequency distribution.

Mention was made in Chap. 3 of the fact that relative frequencies can be regarded as probabilities since the classes in a frequency distribution are mutually exclusive and the sum of the relative frequencies adds to 1. Therefore we should make equivalent statements by saying in reference to the third class of the transportation expenditure distribution that 36% of the students have expenditures between \$250 and \$349 or that the probability is .36 of selecting a student whose expenditures fall between \$250 and \$349.

Relative frequency distributions are portrayed graphically as histograms. In this form the probability of an occurance for a given class is made proportional to the area of a bar representing that class. Since the area of a rectangle is equal to its height times its width, the area is made proportional to the probability by converting the relative frequencies to relative frequencies per unit of width. In the case of the transportation expenditures, the relative frequencies from column 3 of Table 8.9 are divided by \$100, the class interval, and are plotted on the Y axis, while the class intervals are plotted on the X axis. Figure 8.2 shows this histogram.

To be sure that the maneuver just explained is clear, consider the class \$250–349. Since expenditures were rounded to the nearest dollar, the class starts at \$249.50 and ends at \$349.50. (An expenditure of, say, \$249.60 would be rounded up to \$250, while an expenditure of \$349.20 would be rounded down to \$349.) The relative frequency of .3600 is divided by the width of the class interval of \$100, and the value of .0036 is then the height of the bar between \$249.50 and \$349.50. Thus the area of the bar, its height times its width or .0036(100) = .36, is the proba-

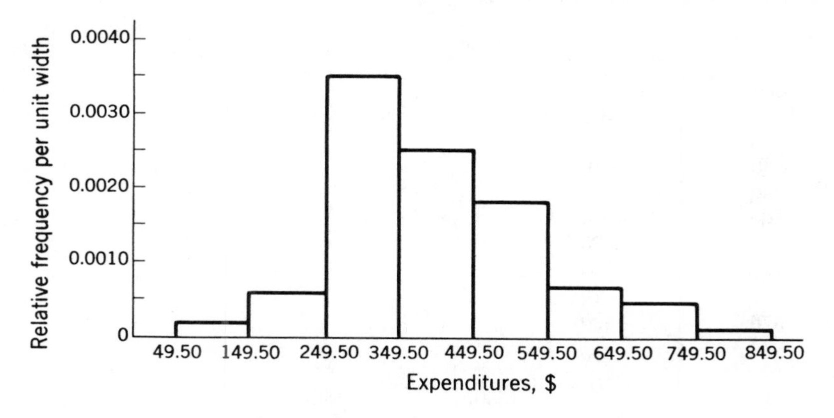

Fig. 8.2 Histogram for transportation expenditures.

bility of an expenditure falling within this class. The total area of all of the rectangles is, of course, equal to 1.

Appendix 8B
Short Method for Calculating the Arithmetic Mean and Standard Deviation

UNGROUPED DATA

MEAN

Since the sum of the deviations about the mean is equal to 0, we can obtain the mean by *estimating* its value and correcting the estimate by the average amount that the deviations about the estimate differ from 0. The formula for this calculation is

$$\bar{X} = EM + \frac{\Sigma(X - EM)}{n} \tag{8.20}$$

where EM is the estimated mean.

For the data from Table 8.1, let us assume that upon cursory inspection we guessed the mean to be 1550. The calculation of the mean based on this estimate is shown in Table 8.10. This answer is, of course, exactly the same as that obtained by adding the values and dividing by n.

Table 8.10 Calculation of the mean sales of ABC Company

Sales, X	$X - EM$
1650	+100
1450	−100
1300	−250
1560	+10
1280	−270
1500	−50
1620	+70
1430	−120
1540	−10
1670	+120
	−500

$$\bar{X} = EM + \frac{\Sigma(X - EM)}{n} = 1550 + \frac{-500}{10} = 1500$$

STANDARD DEVIATION

To arrive at a short-cut formula for the standard deviation for ungrouped data, we simplify the expression $\Sigma(X - \bar{X})^2$. This obviates the necessity of dealing with deviations from the mean which are often cumbersome.

$$\begin{aligned}\Sigma(X - \bar{X})^2 &= \Sigma(X^2 - 2\bar{X}X + \bar{X}^2) \\ &= \Sigma X^2 - 2\bar{X}\Sigma X + n\bar{X}^2 \\ &= \Sigma X^2 - 2\bar{X}\Sigma X + n\bar{X}\frac{\Sigma X}{n} \\ &= \Sigma X^2 - \bar{X}\Sigma X \\ &= \Sigma X^2 - \frac{(\Sigma X)^2}{n}\end{aligned}$$

Thus the formula

$$s_X = \sqrt{\frac{\Sigma(X - \bar{X})^2}{n - 1}}$$

reduces to

$$s_X = \sqrt{\frac{\Sigma X^2 - (\Sigma X)^2/n}{n - 1}} \qquad (8.21)$$

While this formula looks more complicated than the original one, it often simplifies computations since it involves only the sum of the original values and the sum of their squares.

GROUPED DATA

The short formulas for grouped data are derived from those for ungrouped data. They make use of deviations from an assumed mean, where the deviations are expressed in units of class intervals.

Let us assume for the moment that after having looked at the transportation expenditure data of Table 8.5, we estimated the arithmetic mean as $399.50 (it is most convenient to use some midvalue as the assumed mean) and coded the differences between this assumed mean and the other midvalues by expressing them in terms of *class interval* units. The data needed for the calculation of the mean and the standard deviation are shown in Table 8.11.

If the estimated mean were in fact the mean of the sample, the sum of the $f(d)$ column would be 0. Therefore the mean is found by adjusting the estimated mean by the average of the weighted deviations fd times the class interval i using the formula

$$\bar{X} = EM + \frac{\Sigma fd}{n}(i) \qquad (8.22)$$

Table 8.11 Calculation of the mean and standard deviation, transportation expenditures

Expenditures	*Midvalue, MV*	*Coded midvalue, d*	*Number of students, f*	*f(d)*	*f(d²)*
\$ 50–\$149	\$ 99.50	−3	25	−75	225
\$150–\$249	199.50	−2	130	−260	520
\$250–\$349	299.50	−1	720	−720	720
\$350–\$449	399.50	0	530	0	0
\$450–\$549	499.50	+1	365	365	365
\$550–\$649	599.50	+2	135	270	540
\$650–\$749	699.50	+3	75	225	675
\$750–\$849	799.50	+4	20	80	320
			2000	−115	3365

Substituting the appropriate values from Table 8.11,

$$\bar{X} = EM + \frac{\Sigma fd}{n}(i) = 399.50 - \frac{115}{2000}(100) = \$393.75$$
$$= \$394, \text{ rounded to the nearest dollar}$$

In coding the midvalues for Table 8.11, we subtracted the assumed mean from the midvalues and used class interval units. Subtracting a constant from a group of numbers will not change their dispersion, so we can apply Eq. (8.21) except that we have to weight the deviations and their squares by their frequencies and multiply the answer by the class interval i. Thus the formula

$$s_X = \sqrt{\frac{\Sigma X^2 - (\Sigma X)^2/n}{n-1}}$$

is expressed as

$$s_X = i\sqrt{\frac{\Sigma f(d^2) - (\Sigma fd)^2/n}{n-1}} \qquad (8.23)$$

For the data of Table 8.11 the standard deviation of the population is then estimated as

$$s_X = 100\sqrt{\frac{3365 - (-115^2)/2000}{1999}} \approx \$129$$

It is easy to see that this computation is much simpler than the "long method" shown below Table 8.7. The only difference is rounding error (and the short formula contains less rounding error than the long one).

PROBLEMS

8.1 There are many silly stories about statistics—like the one about the nonswimming statistician who drowned wading across a stream that had an average depth of 3 feet, or about the new convoy commander during World War II who ordered his ships to proceed at the median of the maximum speeds of the ships in the convoy, or the golfer who always hooked or sliced and therefore whose average drive was straight down the fairway. What important point do these stories all illustrate?

8.2 A sample of five college professors, drawn at random from a list maintained by a national professional association, had total annual incomes last year as follows:

A	$ 8,700
B	12,300
C	14,600
D	11,800
E	87,100

(*a*) Compute the mean income from this sample.
(*b*) What is the median income for these values?
(*c*) Explain the reason for the sizable difference between $\bar{X}$ and the median. Which is more "typical" of the data?
(*d*) Compute s_X and s_X^2 for these data.

8.3 (*a*) Find the mean and the variance of a population consisting of the five numbers 10, 12, 14, 16, and 18.
(*b*) Subtract 4 from each of the values given in (*a*) above, and find the mean and variance of the population.
(*c*) Divide each of the original five values in (*a*) by 2 and find the mean and variance of the population.
(*d*) Can you make any generalization based on your experience in completing parts (*a*), (*b*), and (*c*)?

8.4 (*a*) If the two values 144 and 152 are added to a sample of size 98, the mean of all 100 values is 50. What was the mean of the original 98 values?
(*b*) What simple but important characteristic of the mean is illustrated by the computation in part (*a*)?

8.5 One of the best ways of making sure you understand something is to have to explain it to someone else.
(*a*) Explain step by step, in the language of a person who knows no statistics, exactly how to calculate the standard deviation of a set of numbers.
(*b*) Make up a demonstration problem involving five numbers in which the mean and standard deviation both come out whole numbers (integers).

8.6 Refer to Prob. 2.8. Compute the arithmetic mean and standard deviation of last year's sales.

8.7 Refer to Prob. 2.9. Compute the arithmetic mean and standard deviation of demand.

8.8 Which exhibits greater variability, lemonade sales (Prob. 8.6) or the demand for shoes (Prob. 8.7)? Do the units involved give you any difficulty here? How does one lemonade translate into a dozen pair of shoes? (*Hint:* to compare the variability of these two distributions, try dividing each σ_X by the μ_X for the distribution. This *relative* measure of dispersion is called the *coefficient of variation.*)

8.9 (*a*) Show that the variance of a population, $\sigma_X{}^2$, can be calculated by an alternative formula that does not involve deviations around the mean. Specifically, prove

$$\sigma_X{}^2 = \frac{\Sigma(X - \mu)^2}{N} = \frac{\Sigma X^2}{N} - \left(\frac{\Sigma X}{N}\right)^2$$

(*b*) Under what circumstances would this alternative formula prove more convenient to use?

8.10 Explain why the sample variance $\Sigma\,(X - \bar{X})^2/n$ tends to underestimate the population variance σ_X. Unless you are equipped to do this job mathematically, you may want to use data such as that in Prob. 8.2, to show that squared deviations around the sample mean total less than squared deviations around any other value. (Suppose, for example, that the population mean μ_X for the data in Prob. 8.2 were \$12,500.)

8.11 If you were to make a frequency distribution of the heights (or weights) of all college students in the United States, you would probably obtain a bimodal distribution. On the other hand, if you were to make a frequency distribution of IQs of all college students, you could expect to obtain a distribution with a single mode.

(*a*) How do you explain the difference between these two distributions?

(*b*) How might you want to modify the distribution of heights so that it made more sense?

8.12 Files of a life insurance company show the following data on mortgages owned:

Mortgage balance outstanding	*Number of mortgages*
\$ 0–\$ 3,999	2
\$ 4,000–\$ 7,999	14
\$ 8,000–\$11,999	17
\$12,000–\$15,999	29
\$16,000–\$19,999	50
\$20,000–\$23,999	41
\$24,000–\$27,999	20
\$28,000–\$31,999	7
\$32,000–\$35,999	2
\$36,000–\$39,999	0
\$40,000–\$43,999	0
\$44,000–\$47,999	1

(*a*) Compute the arithmetic mean mortgage balance outstanding.

(*b*) Estimate the median balance.

(*c*) Twenty-five percent of the mortgages are less than ________.

(*d*) What is the probability that a mortgage selected at random will have a balance greater than \$30,000?

(*e*) Estimate the mode of this distribution.

(*f*) Compute the standard deviation of this distribution.

(*g*) Compute the skewness of this distribution.

8.13 Assume that you are an accountant with a high-quality mail-order firm. You are asked to make an investigation of errors in billing. After laboriously going over a large number of orders, you arrive at the following distribution of errors:

Size of error	*Number of errors*
\$ 0–\$ 3.99	36
\$ 4.00–\$ 7.99	14
\$ 8.00–\$11.99	6
\$12.00–\$15.99	3
\$16.00–\$19.99	1
	60

(*a*) Calculate the arithmetic mean size of error.
(*b*) Calculate the median size of error.
(*c*) For this problem, do you think the mean or the median represents the best measure of location? Explain.
(*d*) Calculate the standard deviation of the distribution.
(*e*) Calculate a measure of skewness for the distribution.

8.14 A children's photographer cannot be sure as to the number of pictures or the dollar sales of pictures that each sitting will produce. From 60 appointments during one week's operation, the following dollar sales resulted:

\$ 6.00	\$19.00	\$ 0	\$16.00
16.00	12.00	9.00	12.50
0	64.00	13.00	6.00
0	10.00	19.00	6.00
10.00	26.00	6.00	15.00
26.00	32.50	25.00	8.00
50.00	16.00	22.00	16.00
0	0	20.00	22.00
42.00	26.00	0	20.00
16.00	15.00	72.00	16.00
16.00	13.00	70.00	17.50
44.00	39.00	18.00	0
0	22.00	0	23.00
6.00	27.00	76.00	11.00
10.00	5.00	10.00	14.00

(*a*) Calculate the arithmetic mean sale per sitting, using the ungrouped data.
(*b*) Obtain the median, using ungrouped data.
(*c*) Obtain the mode, using ungrouped data.
(*d*) Calculate the variance, using ungrouped data.
(*e*) Calculate the standard deviation, using ungrouped data.
(*f*) Group these data into a frequency distribution, using at least six class intervals.
(*g*) Repeat parts (*a*) through (*e*) for the grouped data.
(*h*) Explain why each answer in (*g*) differs from its counterpart in (*a*) through (*e*).

(*i*) You may have calculated the arithmetic mean and standard deviation of the grouped data using the short method explained in Appendix 8B. Would the answers obtained differ from those obtained using the longer method?

(*j*) Confirm your answer to (*i*) by actually performing the calculations by the alternative method.

8.15 You operate a small retail store and have tabulated the amounts of credit sales for a typical day. These sales are as follows:

$27.42	$21.04	$18.93	$27.80	$15.23	$ 5.23
44.08	38.92	29.37	15.82	24.16	26.12
14.73	11.32	7.60	20.17	34.28	29.26
45.45	18.70	41.82	36.03	8.30	47.46
17.38	28.76	23.75	27.18	21.32	13.46
29.00	3.20	24.82	48.92	40.37	41.26
25.14	16.47	12.13	30.00	31.26	21.63
22.45	31.82	42.60	32.04	10.27	22.04
35.27	21.24	26.50	19.90	27.13	25.92
24.95	24.87	34.08	37.26	22.34	25.25

For the numbers, ungrouped, calculate:

(*a*) The arithmetic mean
(*b*) The median
(*c*) The mode
(*d*) The standard deviation

Group the data in five classes, from 0 to 9.99, 10.00 to 19.99, etc. From the grouped data calculate:

(*e*) The arithmetic mean by the long method
(*f*) The arithmetic mean by the short method (coding from an assumed mean)
(*g*) The median
(*h*) The mode
(*i*) The standard deviation by the long method
(*j*) The standard deviation by the short method

8.16 The following distribution shows the width of slots that have been cut in pieces of aluminum that are used in a precise assembly.

Width of slot, inches		
From	*Up to but not including*	*Number of pieces*
0.1100	0.1110	40
0.1110	0.1120	65
0.1120	0.1130	122
0.1130	0.1140	183
0.1140	0.1150	165
0.1150	0.1160	142
0.1160	0.1170	57
0.1170	0.1180	26
		800

(*a*) Find the arithmetic mean of the distribution.
(*b*) Find the median.
(*c*) Find the standard deviation.
(*d*) Plot a histogram of the distribution.
(*e*) What percent of the pieces would be rejected if tolerance limits were set by accepting any piece that was within ± 2 standard deviations from the mean?

8.17 The New York Stock Exchange Index represents the average price of a share traded on the Exchange. Suppose the computer that normally takes care of this sort of thing breaks down, and you are asked to compute the index based on today's closing prices. Without even an adding machine the problem appears almost insurmountable.

(*a*) How might you compute the index?
(*b*) If you decide to use a frequency distribution, how wide should the class intervals be? On what does your answer depend?
(*c*) How would you select class limits? Will it make any difference in your computation of the average?
(*d*) Try your approach on those stocks beginning with the letter A for a recent day's prices. (Don't be alarmed if your answer is not the same as that calculated by the computer and published in the financial press. Because you have used only part of the prices, there is a problem in statistical inference here.)

8.18 (*a*) Why are so many distributions of importance in business positively skewed?
(*b*) Give an example drawn from a business context of a distribution you would expect to be negatively skewed.

9

The Normal Distribution and Problems of Estimation for Continuous Distributions

THE NORMAL DISTRIBUTION

We now undertake a study of the *normal probability distribution*, doubtlessly the most important distribution in statistics. Its importance derives from three sources. First, it provides a useful means of approximating the binomial distribution, which was seen to be useful in business problems but somewhat cumbersome in certain applications. Second, many real-world variables and processes are accurately described by the normal distribution. That is, many variables are themselves "normally distributed." Third, and most important by far, is the use of the normal distribution in sampling theory. As we shall see, a variety of useful *sampling distributions* conform to the normal, making it a cornerstone in the study of statistical inference.

THE NORMAL DISTRIBUTION AS AN APPROXIMATION TO THE BINOMIAL DISTRIBUTION

You have had enough experience with the binomial distribution to remember that its calculation becomes rather tedious as n becomes

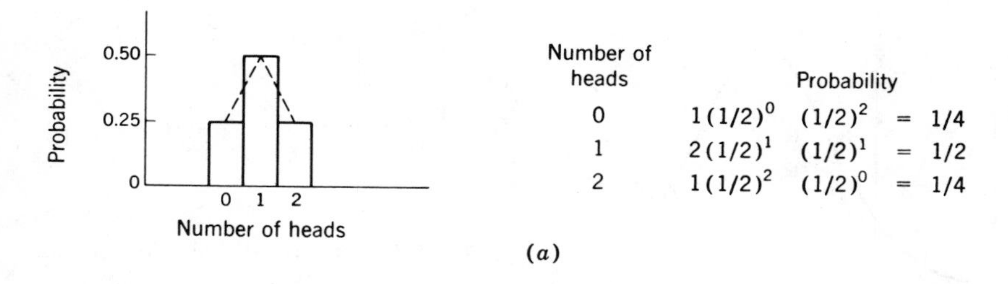

Number of heads	Probability			
0	$1(1/2)^0$	$(1/2)^2$	=	1/4
1	$2(1/2)^1$	$(1/2)^1$	=	1/2
2	$1(1/2)^2$	$(1/2)^0$	=	1/4

(*a*)

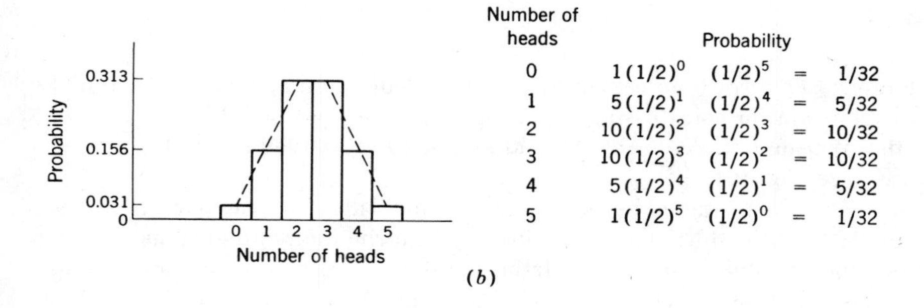

Number of heads	Probability			
0	$1(1/2)^0$	$(1/2)^5$	=	1/32
1	$5(1/2)^1$	$(1/2)^4$	=	5/32
2	$10(1/2)^2$	$(1/2)^3$	=	10/32
3	$10(1/2)^3$	$(1/2)^2$	=	10/32
4	$5(1/2)^4$	$(1/2)^1$	=	5/32
5	$1(1/2)^5$	$(1/2)^0$	=	1/32

(*b*)

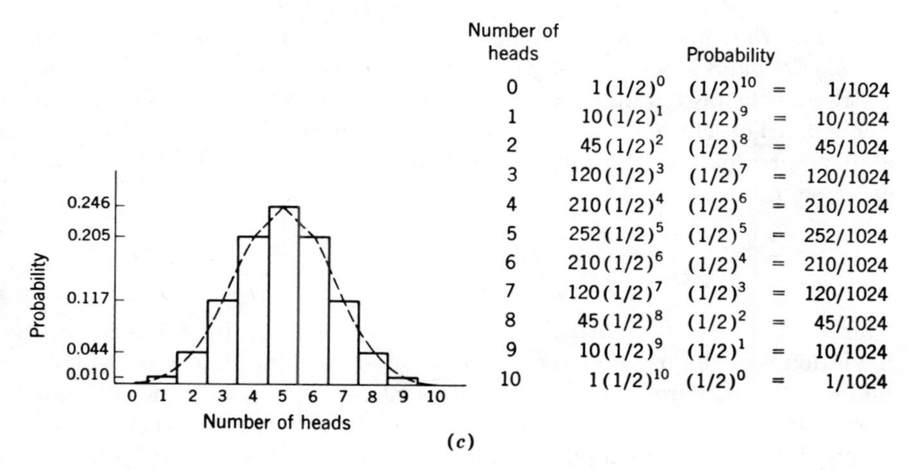

Number of heads	Probability			
0	$1(1/2)^0$	$(1/2)^{10}$	=	1/1024
1	$10(1/2)^1$	$(1/2)^9$	=	10/1024
2	$45(1/2)^2$	$(1/2)^8$	=	45/1024
3	$120(1/2)^3$	$(1/2)^7$	=	120/1024
4	$210(1/2)^4$	$(1/2)^6$	=	210/1024
5	$252(1/2)^5$	$(1/2)^5$	=	252/1024
6	$210(1/2)^6$	$(1/2)^4$	=	210/1024
7	$120(1/2)^7$	$(1/2)^3$	=	120/1024
8	$45(1/2)^8$	$(1/2)^2$	=	45/1024
9	$10(1/2)^9$	$(1/2)^1$	=	10/1024
10	$1(1/2)^{10}$	$(1/2)^0$	=	1/1024

(*c*)

Fig. 9.1 Binomial distributions for $p = .5$, $n = 2$, 5, and 10. (*a*) Binomial distribution, $p = .5$, $n = 2$; (*b*) binomial distribution, $p = .5$, $n = 5$; (*c*) binomial distribution, $p = .5$, $n = 10$.

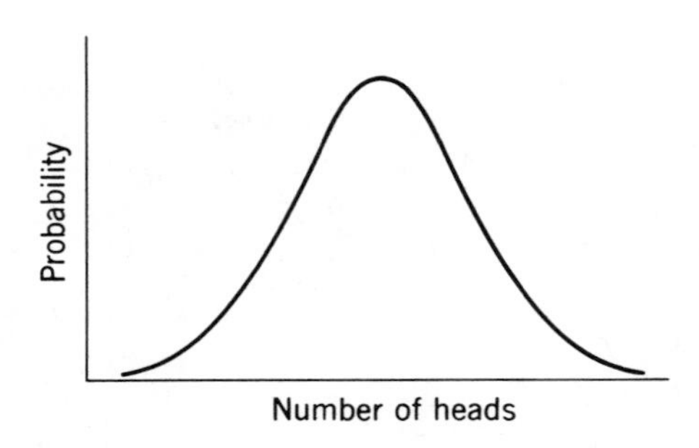

Fig. 9.2 Binomial distribution where n = infinity—the normal distribution.

larger. To refresh your memory, let us calculate and graph the binomial distribution for coin-tossing experiments where $p = .5$ and $n = 2, 5$, and 10. We shall also connect the midpoints of successive bars with a dotted line (see Fig. 9.1).

Obviously, as n becomes larger, the width of the bars becomes smaller and the dotted straight line between the midpoints begins to look like one continuous curve. Furthermore, the area under the dotted line comes very close to equaling the sum of the areas of the bars.

If this process were repeated with larger and larger n's, we should find that the distinction between the bars and the dotted line would become less and less obvious. If n were infinite, the bars would have no width and the dotted lines would become a continuous curve, as shown in Fig. 9.2. This curve is known as the *gaussian* or *normal curve*. The probability corresponding to any given value X can be found by using the expression

$$P_N = \frac{1}{\sigma_X \sqrt{2\pi}} e^{-(X-\mu_X)^2/2\sigma_X{}^2}$$

where P_N stands for normal probability, σ_X and μ_X are the standard deviation and the mean of the distribution of X values and $\pi = 3.14159$ and $e = 2.71828$ are constants. A little investigation will show that this curve tails off to plus and minus infinity and that its highest value occurs where $X = \mu_X$, at which point P_N becomes equal to $1/\sigma_X \sqrt{2\pi}$. Further investigation would prove that the two points of inflection on the curve occur at distances of $-\sigma_X$ and $+\sigma_X$ from μ_X.

Carl Friedrich Gauss, a nineteenth-century astronomer, didn't arrive at this formula by tossing an infinite number of coins. His problem was one of measurement. He was trying to find the exact orbit of a planet, but successive measurements all had different values. His theory was that there was a "normal" curve of error distributed around the true value, and he used the formula above to represent this distribution of error.[1] While his normal curve is by no means universally applicable, it does prove extremely useful in all sorts of problems involving measurement. We shall illustrate some of these situations as we develop further capabilities in using the normal curve in the discussion which follows.

USE OF NORMAL PROBABILITIES: STANDARDIZED NORMAL DEVIATES

The area under the normal curve between any two limits is equal to the probability that a variable chosen from the distribution at random will fall within these limits. To find such an area, we should have to substitute the values of the mean and the standard deviation in the formula for the normal curve and integrate between the limits in question. This would be a good exercise in mathematics for most of us (and an impossibility for some). Moreover, if we had another problem involving a normal distribution with a different mean and standard deviation and different limits, we should have to repeat the same difficult process again. The necessity of repeated integrations to find specific areas for particular normal distributions is obviated by the use of a standardized normal distribution having a mean of 0 and a standard deviation of 1. The areas under various portions of the standardized normal distribution are available in tables such as Appendix B at the end of this book.

To illustrate the use of such a distribution, suppose that a test had been administered to a very large population and it was found that the distribution of raw scores was normal, with a mean of 100 and a standard deviation of 20. What is the probability that a person chosen at random would have a score of 140 or more? The desired area is shown as the dark shaded area in Fig. 9.3.

The standardized normal deviate z is found by expressing the distance between the mean and the limit in terms of standard deviations. Thus

$$z = \frac{140 - 100}{20} = +2.00$$

[1] The normal distribution was discovered by Abraham De Moivre in 1773 but was first applied by Gauss.

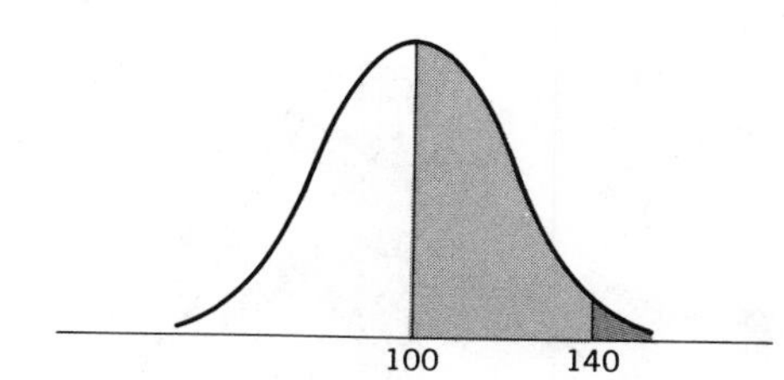

Fig. 9.3.

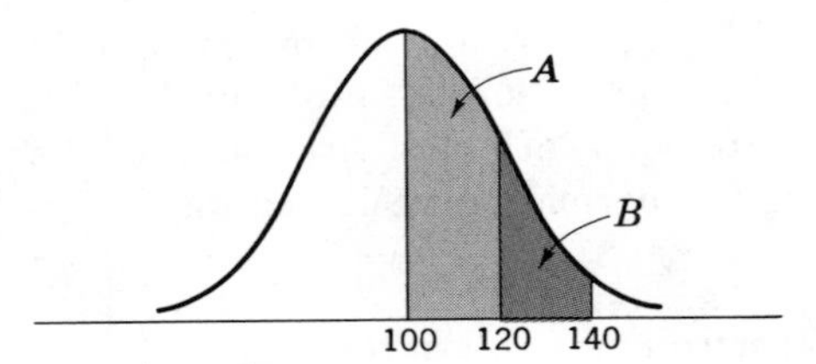

Fig. 9.4.

Looking up a value of 2.00 in the $(X - \mu_X)/\sigma_X$ column of the area table in Appendix B, we find that .4772 of the total area under the curve falls between the mean and +2.00 standard deviations or, in terms of this problem, between 100 and 140 (the light shaded area in the diagram). Therefore .4772 is the probability that a person selected at random would have a score between 100 and 140. Since the normal distribution is symmetrical, 50% of the area falls above the mean. Therefore the probability that a person would have a score of 140 or more is equal to .5000 − .4772, or .0228.

In using the normal table to find probabilities, we must always be sure that the standardized value we are using is related to the mean of the distribution. Only areas adjacent to the mean of the distribution can be found directly in the table. Other areas must be calculated by adding or subtracting areas that are adjacent to the mean. Consider the problem of finding the probability that a person would have a score between 120 and 140, area B in Fig. 9.4. Area B can only be found from the standardized table by subtracting area A from area (A and B) since any area in the table must have the mean as one of the limits. The solution is shown below.

$$z_{140} = \frac{140 - 100}{20} = +2.00 \rightarrow .4772 = \text{area } A + B$$

$$z_{120} = \frac{120 - 100}{20} = +1.00 \rightarrow \frac{.3413 = \text{area } A}{.1359 = \text{area } B}$$

In the expressions above, z_{140} refers to the standardized normal deviate corresponding to a score of 140, and the arrow can be read "which leads to an area (or probability) of."

Similarly, to find area $(A + C)$ in Fig. 9.5, we must add area A to

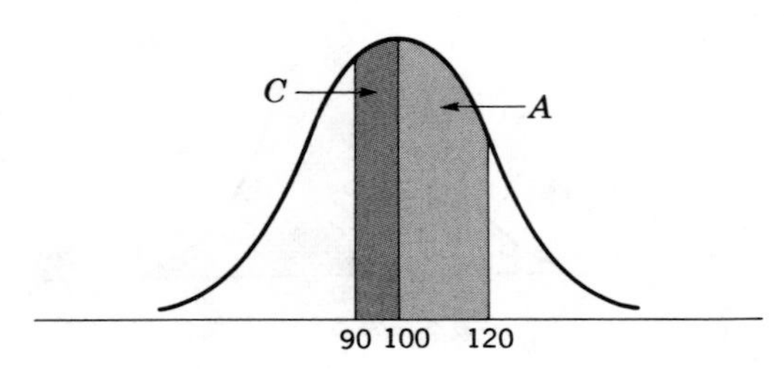

Fig. 9.5.

area C.

$$z_{90} = \frac{90 - 100}{20} = -.50 \rightarrow \quad .1915 = \text{area } C$$

$$z_{120} = \frac{120 - 100}{20} = +1.00 \rightarrow \frac{.3413 = \text{area } A}{.5328 = \text{area } A + C}$$

In the problems above we found an area or probability between two limits, given the mean, the standard deviation, and the limits in question. Other types of problems arise in which the probability is known, and the unknown is either the limit, the mean, or the standard deviation. We shall give one example of each of these problems.

Example 1: Suppose that we wanted to establish limits for letter grades for the same distribution of test scores used above, which had a mean of 100 and a standard deviation of 20. Further, suppose that we wanted to give 10% A's, 25% B's, 40% C's, 15% D's, and 10% F's. What test scores represent the limits to such a grade distribution? The problem could be sketched as in Fig. 9.6. Starting with the right tail, we can determine that $(A - 100)/20 = z_{.40}$, where A refers to the lower limit of the grade A, since 40% of the scores are between the mean and the lower limit of 10% A's. Since $z_{.40} = 1.28$ from the area table (looking for the z value corresponding to the area closest to .40),

$$\frac{A - 100}{20} = 1.28$$

and

$$A = 1.28(20) + 100 = 125.6 \text{ or } 126$$

Similarly, $(B - 100)/20 = z_{.15}$ since 15% of the scores must be between the mean and the lower limit of the B's if there are to be 25% B's and 10% A's. Thus

$$z_{.15} = .39$$

and

$$\frac{B - 100}{20} = .39$$

$$B = .39(20) + 100 = 107.8 \text{ or } 108$$

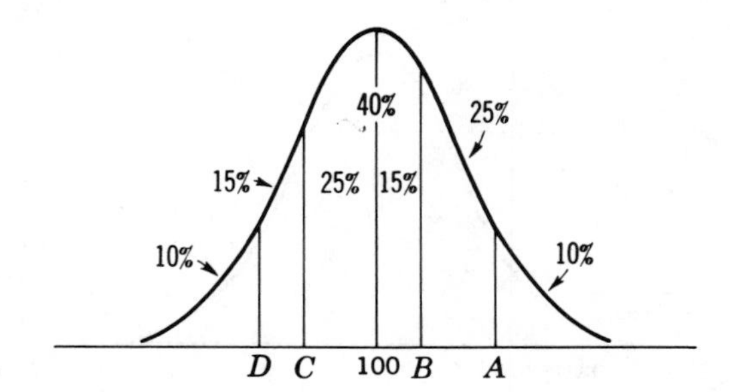

Fig. 9.6.

Therefore the lower limit of the B's would be 108 and the upper limit 125.

It is left to the student to prove that by using the same logic, the C's would fall between 87 and 107, the D's between 74 and 86, and the F's below 74.

Example 2: Suppose that you own an Alaskan cannery which packs king crab meat in cans that say "6 oz., drained weight" on the label. Further, suppose that the machine that packs the meat cannot pack every can with exactly the same weight, the weights being normally distributed with a standard deviation of .04 ounce. (The standard deviation is a function of the accuracy of the machine. While the mean can be adjusted up or down by setting the machine, the standard deviation is fixed in the short run. It will increase only gradually as the machine wears out and can be decreased only by repairing the machine. We shall assume that the standard deviation of .04 oz. will hold throughout this season's pack.)

It would be unrealistic for any regulatory authority to expect that every single can would have a drained weight of 6 ounces or more. This is true because such a rule could be enforced only by opening every can and weighing it, which would leave none to sell. Actually, regulations would be set up in terms of permitting some small percentage of cans to fall below the 6-ounce limit. This would enable the regulatory authorities to test cans on a sampling basis, using methods which will be developed in the next chapter. Now suppose that these specifications say that no more than 0.3% of the cans can have a drained weight of less than 6 ounces. The question for management then is at what level to set the mean to be assured that it will meet specifications and at the same time put no more meat in the cans than is necessary. Stated in this way, the problem is simply solved.

$$\frac{\text{Limit} - \mu_X}{\sigma_X} = z_{.003}$$

$$\frac{6.00 - \mu_X}{.04} = -2.75$$

$$\mu_X = 6.110$$

Therefore the mean would be set at 6.110 ounces.

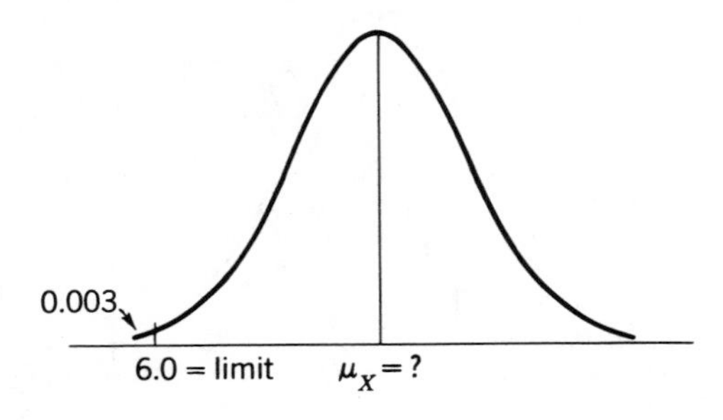

Fig. 9.7.

Example 3: For the situation described in Example 2, assume that the manufacturer of the packing machine claims that he can repair your machine at a cost of $2000 and reduce its standard deviation to .03 ounce. You now want to determine whether or not this is a good deal for you. The crab meat costs you 15 cents per ounce. The season's pack is 400,000 cans.

While the manufacturer's representative is still on the phone, you whip out your slide rule and a normal table, and perform the following calculations:

If σ_X were .03, the mean could be set at $6.000 + 2.75(.03) = 6.0825$
Savings per can would be $6.1100 - 6.0825 = 0.0275$ ounce
Savings per 400,000 cans $= 400{,}000(.0275) = 11{,}000$ ounces
11,000 ounces at 15 cents per ounce = $1650 = net savings for a reduction in standard deviation from .04 to .03 (or for any reduction in the standard deviation of .01).

Your response is that $2000 is too much to pay for the repair if the guarantee is for a standard deviation of .03. However, you *would* take the deal if they would guarantee a σ_X of .02 ounce (in fact, a guarantee of .02 ounce would be worth $1650(2) = $3300, well over the $2000 cost).

Now that we have learned how to use the normal table to solve some simple but practical problems where the variables involved were normally distributed, let us return to the use of the normal table as an approximation to the binomial and its use in making statistical inferences about a population proportion.

NORMAL APPROXIMATION TO AN INTERVAL ESTIMATE FOR A POPULATION PROPORTION: INFINITE POPULATION, LARGE SAMPLE

In Chap. 4 we found how to make an interval estimate for a population proportion using the binomial tables. The specific example, you will remember, involved observing 7 defective flash bulbs in a sample of 100 bulbs taken at random from a production process that could be viewed as infinite.

Now if we knew the *true* proportion of defective bulbs in the population, we could derive the entire sampling distribution for the number of defective bulbs in the sample by using binomial tables. That is, we could specify all the possible outcomes of sampling 100 bulbs, together with the probability of each. Since there are 101 possible outcomes (from 0 defectives to 100 defectives inclusive), such a listing would be very time-consuming. For illustrative purposes, we list a few of the possible outcomes together with their probabilities below:

Table 9.1

Possible outcome (proportion defective)	*Probability*
0	$P_b(r = 0 \mid n = 100, p)$
.01	$P_b(r = 1 \mid n = 100, p)$
.02	$P_b(r = 2 \mid n = 100, p)$
.03	$P_b(r = 3 \mid n = 100, p)$
.	.
.	.
.	.
.	.
1.0	$P_b(r = 100 \mid n = 100, p)$

Having made the entire distribution, we could find its mean and its standard deviation, using the techniques described in Chap. 8. If we did so, we should find that the mean of the distribution of sample proportions would be equal to the true proportion of successes in the population p and that the standard deviation of the distribution of sample proportions, denoted by $\sigma_{\bar{p}}$, would be equal to $\sqrt{p(1-p)}/\sqrt{n}$. These results are extremely important to the discussion that follows and should be kept firmly in mind. Formal proofs that the sample proportions, for which we use the symbol $\bar{p}$, have a mean of p and that $\sigma_{\bar{p}} = \sqrt{p(1-p)}/\sqrt{n}$ are more appropriate for a course in mathematical statistics than business decision theory and will not be given here. However, the exercises at the end of this chapter will give the student ample opportunity to prove them on an inductive basis.

Since the true proportion is not known, we shall have to estimate it by using the proportion that we observed in the sample, $\bar{p} = .07$. Thus our point estimate of p is .07, and our best estimate of $\sigma_{\bar{p}}$ is $s_{\bar{p}}$, the estimate of the standard deviation of the distribution of sample proportions based on sample information, which is equal to

$$s_{\bar{p}} = \frac{\sqrt{\bar{p}(1-\bar{p})}}{\sqrt{n-1}} = \sqrt{\frac{(.07)(.93)}{99}} = .0255$$

Note that we use $n - 1$ rather than n in the denominator when calculating $s_{\bar{p}}$ since we are estimating a population standard deviation from sample information.

Now the process for making an interval estimate for p becomes much simpler than it was when we used the binomial table. The interval estimate of p is $\bar{p} \pm z(s_{\bar{p}})$. If we choose to use a 95% confidence coefficient, as we did earlier in Chap. 4, we look up the z value corresponding to a tail area of .025, obtaining a z value of 1.96. Then the interval estimate for $p = .07 \pm 1.96(.0255) = .07 \pm .05$, or .02 to .12. Note that these values correspond closely to those of .02 and .14 obtained for the same problem in Chap. 4 by using the more tedious procedure involving the binomial table.

The normal approximation shown here gives an adequate approximation of binomial probabilities when np and $n(1 - p)$ are both equal to or greater than 5 and where $n \geq 30$. In other cases (involving small samples or small p or both) the approximation to true binomial probabilities becomes very rough.

NORMAL APPROXIMATION TO AN INTERVAL ESTIMATE FOR A POPULATION PROPORTION: FINITE POPULATION, LARGE SAMPLE

Populations can be assumed to be infinite when the sample is taken from an ongoing process or when the sampling is done with replacement. If the population size is finite and sampling is done without replacement, the assumption of independence essential to a Bernoulli process is violated and the general law of multiplication must be used rather than the special law in determining the number of possible combinations of a given outcome. In these cases the appropriate distribution is the hypergeometric rather than the binomial.

The mean of a hypergeometric sampling distribution is equal to the population proportion, as it was for the binomial. However, the standard deviation of the hypergeometric sampling distribution differs from that of the binomial by a fraction called the *finite correction factor*, which takes into account the relationship between the size of the population and that of the sample. Thus for the hypergeometric distribution, $s_{\bar{p}} = \sqrt{(N - n)/(N - 1)}\sqrt{[\bar{p}(1 - \bar{p})]/(n - 1)}$ where $\sqrt{(N - n)/(N - 1)}$ is called the finite correction factor. Inspection of the terms in the finite correction factor shows the relationship between the binomial and the hypergeometric distribution. As the size of the sample becomes smaller in relation to the size of the population, the finite correction factor approaches a value of 1, and the hypergeometric approaches the binomial distribution.

Let us change the flash bulb example slightly to illustrate the use of the normal approximation for the hypergeometric distribution. Assume that instead of having the manufacturer sample from a process, the sampling is done by a large distributor of flash bulbs, who tests a random sample of 100 bulbs from a shipment of 1000 and finds that 7 are defective. (Since the cost of sampling is very expensive for a destructive process, it would be unusual to take a sample this large in actual practice.)

In this case $\bar{p} = .07$ is used as a point estimate of p, and $\sigma_{\bar{p}}$, the standard deviation of the sampling distribution of the proportion defective, is estimated by

$$s_{\bar{p}} = \sqrt{\frac{N-n}{N-1}}\sqrt{\frac{\bar{p}(1-\bar{p})}{n-1}}$$

For the problem in question, then,

$$s_{\bar{p}} = \sqrt{\frac{1000-100}{999}}\sqrt{\frac{(.07)(.93)}{99}} = .024$$

and the interval estimate for p using a 95% confidence coefficient is

$$.07 \pm 1.96(.024) = .07 \pm .047, \text{ or } .023 \text{ to } .117$$

This answer is close to that provided by the binomial distribution since the finite correction factor was .95. In cases where the sample size is a large fraction of the population the difference would be more pronounced.

THE SAMPLING DISTRIBUTION OF THE MEAN

A sampling distribution can be generated for any sample statistic whether it is based on a count, as in the case of the proportion defective, or measurement. The most common statistic that is used to summarize measurements is the simple average, or mean. The sampling distribution of the mean is a listing of all the possible sample means that could be obtained from random samples of a given size taken from the population in question, together with the probability associated with each sample mean. Let us see if we can develop an intuitive feeling for the meaning of the expression "sampling distribution of the mean" by using the following example.

Suppose that there are 25,000 men stationed at a large army base. Furthermore, suppose that you know the weight of each man. From these data you calculate a mean weight, μ_X, of 170 pounds and a standard deviation, σ_X, of 20 pounds. The distribution of these weights is not normal since there are more people who are greatly overweight than greatly underweight. The men are housed in barracks that contain 100 men each. We shall assume that the assignment of a man to a barrack is at random with respect to his weight. If this is the case, each barrack can be considered a random sample of 100 men. You could now find the arithmetic mean of the weights of men in each barrack and would have 250 different sample means.

Now conceptualize an experiment in which every *possible* combination of 100 individual weights (rather than just the 250 described above) were calculated. If the mean of each possible random sample of size 100 were calculated and summarized in a probability distribution by determining the relative frequency associated with each mean, the result would be called the *sampling distribution of the mean.* What characteristics do you think this distribution would have?

The first observation you might make is that the mean of all the sample means would be the same as the mean of the population. This observation is correct and can be generalized. The mean of the distribution of sample means will *always* be equal to the overall mean of the population.

Although this concept is simple enough and the result intuitively obvious, notice that the language is already somewhat confusing. In the discussion which follows the student should keep firmly in mind the distinction between (1) the distribution of items (weights of individuals) within a particular sample (one barrack) and (2) the distribution of sample means (the set of average weights for every barrack) around the overall mean for the population (all the men on the base).

Your second observation would probably be that the standard deviation of this distribution of sample means should be considerably smaller than the standard deviation of the population from which the samples were drawn. After all, you reason, the smallest average weight for any group of 100 men couldn't be as low as the weight of the lightest man on the base, nor could the highest average weight for a barrack be as high as the weight of the heaviest man. If pressed further about the problem of the dispersion of the distribution of mean weights, you just might see that the standard deviation of this distribution would have to be a function of (1) the standard deviation of the *population*, and (2) the size of the *sample.* If the men all weighed the same, the standard deviation of the population would be 0 and the sample means would also show no variation. Furthermore, the smaller the sample size, the greater the variation you would expect in the distribution of sample means. If each man lived in his own one-man tent rather than a barrack of 100 men and were therefore considered a sample of one, the standard deviation of the sample means would be the same as the standard deviation of the population. As more and more men were grouped in a sample, we should expect less and less variation in the means of these samples from the mean of the population.

These observations can be generalized in the statement that the standard deviation of the sampling distribution of the mean is directly related to the standard deviation of the population and inversely related to the size of the sample. To be exact $\sigma_{\bar{X}}$, used to represent the standard deviation of the sampling distribution of the mean, is equal to $\sigma_X/\sqrt{n}$, the standard deviation of the population divided by the *square root* of the size of the sample.[2] To avoid some of the confusing language used here, $\sigma_{\bar{X}}$ is often referred to as the *standard error of the mean.*

Your third observation—if you had any strength left after the second and if you were really a mathematician at heart—might be that the distribution of sample means would be likely to resemble a normal distribution more closely than did the original population. This observation has been generalized by statisticians as the *central limit theorem,* which states that for a wide variety of sample statistics (including the sample mean) the *sampling distribution* of the statistic approaches normality as the size of the sample is increased. This fact is one of the prime reasons for the wide use of the normal distribution in statistics and decision theory.

The discussion above can be illustrated by the three diagrams in Fig. 9.8. The first of these illustrates the population. It is asymmetrical and has a mean of 170 pounds and a standard deviation of 20 pounds. The second illustrates the distribution of weights we might find in one barrack. The mean in this case is, say, 175 pounds, and the standard deviation is 18 pounds. Other barracks, of course, would have other means and standard deviations. The third curve represents the distribution of all the sample means. It is normal, its mean is 170 pounds and its standard deviation is $20/\sqrt{100} = 2$ pounds. Note that in the first two cases values of X, or individual weights, are graphed on the X axis about their means. In the third case, sample means ($\bar{X}$'s) are graphed on the X axis.

Let us summarize what we have tried to show intuitively in the example above.

1. The mean of the sampling distribution of the mean is equal to the mean of the population.
2. The standard deviation of the sampling distribution of the mean is equal to the standard deviation of the population divided by the square root of the size of the sample, for an infinite population.
3. The sampling distribution of the mean approaches normality as the sample size is increased.

The student should note the similarity between these statements about the sampling distribution of the mean and those in previous sections regarding the sampling distribution of a proportion.

[2] This is strictly true only if the population is infinite or if the sampling is done with replacement. In this illustration we should use the finite correction factor $\sqrt{(N - n)/(N - 1)}$ as we did earlier in making interval estimates for a population proportion for a finite population. However, the finite correction factor in this case is $\sqrt{24{,}900/24{,}999} = .998$ and is rounded to 1.

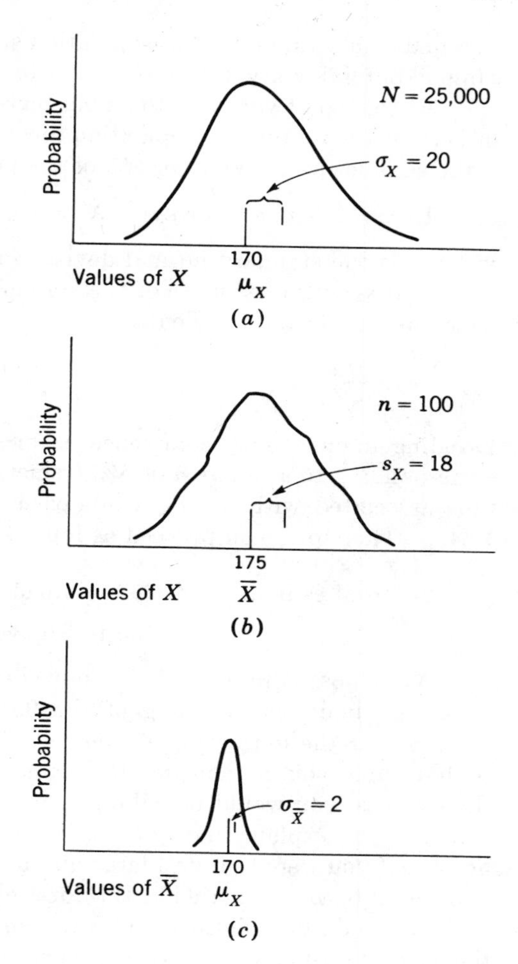

Fig. 9.8 (*a*) Population values; (*b*) values from one sample; (*c*) all sample means.

INTERVAL ESTIMATE FOR THE POPULATION MEAN: INFINITE POPULATION, LARGE SAMPLE

Suppose that you work in a district office of a life insurance company. The general agent in charge of the office asks you to take a sample of records from your files to determine the average size of policy held by individuals. You remember that way back in your college days some professor kept insisting that if you were to make estimates of population parameters based on sample statistics you should take a random sample. That being about all you remember, you proceed to take a random sample of 25 policies and find from them that the sample mean $\bar{X}$ is \$9200. You also make an estimate of the population standard deviation based on the sample, obtaining a value of s_X of \$5000.

At this point you refer to an old text and find that you can make an interval estimate for the population mean through the following process if the sample size is less than 5% of the population:[3]

$$\text{Interval estimate for } \mu_X = \bar{X} \pm z s_{\bar{X}}$$

where z is the standard normal deviate for the desired confidence coefficient and $s_{\bar{X}}$ is the estimate of the standard error of the mean $\sigma_{\bar{X}}$ that is based on sample data. That is,

$$s_{\bar{X}} = \frac{s_X}{\sqrt{n}}$$

Deciding upon a 90% confidence coefficient, you look up the z value corresponding to a tail area of 5% (remembering that there are two such tails associated with a 90% confidence coefficient) and find that it is 1.645. Therefore, you proceed as follows:

$$\begin{aligned}\text{Interval estimate} &= \$9200 \pm 1.645 \frac{\$5000}{5} = \$9200 \pm 1645 \\ &= \$7555 \text{ to } \$10{,}845\end{aligned}$$

Your boss is impressed by your adeptness at statistics but is a bit confused about the meaning of the 90% confidence coefficient. You explain that the most simple interpretation of the confidence coefficient is that while you cannot guarantee that the true mean will lie between these limits, you would be willing to bet with odds of 9 to 1 that it does. Further, you explain that you feel confident that these are proper odds because if you were to take a large number of sample means of size 25 and make an interval estimate like this for each sample, you would get different means, standard deviations and intervals, but you know from statistical theory that 9 times out of every 10 (on the average) the interval described would include the true mean. You even make a sketch showing how successive estimates might look (Fig. 9.9).

He says that this is fine, but what if the estimate you just gave him is that shown in Fig. 9.9 for sample 4, the one that did *not* include the true mean. Your response is that in that case you simply would have made an error due to random variation in your sample. You hasten to explain that if he is not willing to take a 1 in 10 chance of making this kind of error, you can recalculate the estimate using whatever confidence coefficient he feels is desirable.

[3] If the sample were more than 5% of the population, the finite correction factor should be taken into account. This is explained in the next section.

He says that a 9 in 10 chance seems about right to him, but the thing that does bother him is the spread of the interval—it is too large to be of a great deal of use. In fact, he would feel much better if you could produce an interval that would have a spread of about $1000 and still retain the 90% confidence coefficient. At this point you remember something else that your professor said—that you should have asked your boss to tell you the confidence coefficient and the approximate size of the interval that would be meaningful to him *before* you determined the sample size.

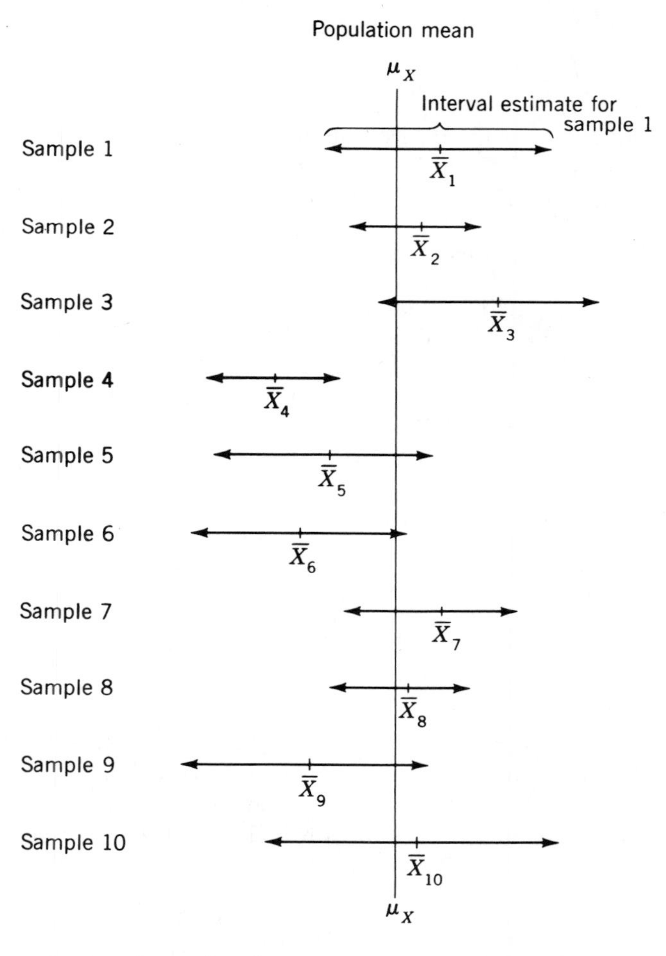

Fig. 9.9 Interval estimates of true population mean for 10 successive samples.

DETERMINATION OF SAMPLE SIZE FOR AN INTERVAL ESTIMATE OF THE POPULATION MEAN

To cope with the problem above, you reason as follows: To have an interval estimate that spans \$1000 means that the interval would spread ±\$500 from the sample mean. Therefore the upper limit L_u could be determined using the following expression

$$L_u = \bar{X} + z \frac{s_X}{\sqrt{n}}$$

Therefore

$$L_u - \bar{X} = z \frac{s_X}{\sqrt{n}}$$

Substituting the desired quantities in the expression above and using the estimate of the population standard deviation derived from your first sample, you could solve for n.

$$500 = 1.645 \frac{5000}{\sqrt{n}}$$

$$\sqrt{n} = \frac{1.645(5000)}{500} = 16.45$$

$$n = 271$$

The same result could be achieved by using the lower limit since

$$L_1 = \bar{X} - z \frac{s_X}{\sqrt{n}}$$

$$L_1 - \bar{X} = -z \frac{s_X}{\sqrt{n}}$$

$$-500 = -1.645 \frac{5000}{\sqrt{n}}$$

$$n = 271$$

To satisfy your boss, you therefore take a random sample of 271. Let us assume that this size of sample is still not an appreciable part of the population and that you obtained a sample mean of \$9300 and a standard deviation of \$4700. The interval estimate for the population mean would then be

$$\bar{X} \pm z \frac{s_X}{\sqrt{n}} = 9300 \pm 1.645 \frac{4700}{\sqrt{271}}$$

$$= 9300 \pm 469$$

$$= \$8831 \text{ to } \$9769$$

This estimate meets the criteria asked by your boss. The confidence coefficient is 90%, and the interval is $938. The interval is not exactly $1000 because the standard deviation estimated from the sample of 271 turned out to be a little smaller than that estimated from the sample of 25. Note that it was necessary to have an estimate of the standard deviation of the population in order to determine the necessary sample size. If such an estimate were not available from past experience, it would have to be obtained from a small "pilot" sample.

INTERVAL ESTIMATE FOR THE POPULATION MEAN: FINITE POPULATION, LARGE SAMPLE

In the illustration used above, we have assumed that the population was so large that it could for practical purposes be considered infinite. In situations where the population is finite *and* the sample size is an appreciable proportion of the population, the finite correction factor would have to be applied, just as it was for interval estimates made for the population proportion earlier in the chapter. To be sure that the mechanics of this process are understood, we shall recalculate the interval estimate made for the insurance example above, assuming now that the population size was 600.

The proper sample size would be found as follows (assuming a confidence coefficient of 90%, a desired interval of $1000, and an approximate standard deviation of $5000):

$$L_u - \bar{X} = +z\sqrt{\frac{N-n}{N-1}}\frac{s_X}{\sqrt{n}}$$

Since n appears in the expression two times, it is a bit more difficult to solve.

$$500 = 1.645\sqrt{\frac{600-n}{599}}\frac{5000}{\sqrt{n}}$$

$$500 = \frac{1.645(5000)}{\sqrt{599}}\sqrt{\frac{600-n}{n}}$$

$$500 = 335.7\sqrt{\frac{600-n}{n}}$$

$$\left(\frac{500}{335.7}\right)^2 = \frac{600-n}{n}$$

$$2.218 = \frac{600}{n} - 1$$

$$n = \frac{600}{3.218} = 187$$

Note that when we assumed an infinite population, the sample size necessary for an interval estimate spanning \$1000 was 271. The calculations above show that if the population size is 600 rather than infinite, the same accuracy could be attained with a smaller sample size. This is as we might expect since the larger the sample is in relation to the population, the more closely it should reflect the characteristics of the population. Therefore, for the same accuracy, we could use a smaller sample size if that sample were an appreciable part of the population. Remember, however, that if the sample is not an appreciable portion of the population—say, more than 5%—it is the absolute size of the sample, rather than its size relative to the population that determines the accuracy of the estimate.

Assume that a sample of size 187 were taken and that $\bar{X}$ was found to be \$9250 with s_X equal to \$4800. The standard deviation of the sampling distribution of the mean, $s_{\bar{X}}$, would then be

$$\sqrt{\frac{N-n}{N-1}}\frac{s_X}{\sqrt{n}} = \sqrt{\frac{600-187}{599}}\frac{4800}{\sqrt{187}} = \$291$$

The interval estimate for μ_X would be calculated as before. With a 90% confidence coefficient,

$$\mu_X = \bar{X} \pm z_{.90}s_{\bar{X}} = 9250 \pm 1.645(291) = \$8771 \text{ to } \$9729$$

Again, the interval estimate is not exactly \$1000 as planned because the approximate standard deviation used to plan the sample size did not turn out to be the same as the standard deviation estimated from the sample.

INTERVAL ESTIMATE FOR THE DIFFERENCE BETWEEN TWO POPULATION MEANS: LARGE SAMPLES

There are many situations in business in which one wants to make a judgment relative to the similarity or dissimilarity between two population means. One such example could be that of a tire company that has developed a new process which it hopes will increase the mean length of life of tires (as measured by tread wear). In order to find out whether the new process really does produce tires with a greater mean life than those from the old process, the company proposes sampling tires from each process and comparing their mean life. (Both the populations of new and old tires can be considered infinite since they are results of processes.)

The problem now becomes one of deciding whether or not the *population* means are different on the basis of an observed difference between *sample* means. Even if there were no difference whatsoever between the mean length of life produced by the two processes, we should

Table 9.2 Example of differences between sample means for two processes

Sample pair	(1) *Mean, new process, miles*	(2) *Mean, old process, miles*	(3) *Difference, miles* (1) − (2)
1	19,780	19,600	+180
2	17,960	18,250	−290
3	19,320	19,230	+90
4	18,480	18,520	−40
n	18,465	18,440	+25

still expect random variation among samples. For example, we might obtain the pairs of sample means shown in Table 9.2.

If a very large number of differences between paired sample means such as those in Table 9.2 were observed, we could construct a distribution of *differences* between sample means. The theoretical distribution corresponding to this experimentally derived distribution is called the sampling distribution of the *difference between sample means*. It would look like the distribution sketched in Fig. 9.10. Upon investigating the properties of this sampling distribution we should discover three important characteristics. First, the distribution would approach normality as the size of the sample was increased. (The sampling distribution of the difference between sample means is one of the distributions that approaches normality under the central limit theorem.) Second, the mean of the sampling distribution would be 0. This is intuitively appealing since if the population means were identical, we should expect that the sum of the differences between paired sample means for the new and the old processes would average 0. Third, the standard deviation of the sampling distribution, estimated from the standard deviation of the samples, would be

$$s_{\bar{X}_1-\bar{X}_2} = \sqrt{s_{\bar{X}_1}{}^2 + s_{\bar{X}_2}{}^2}$$

This equation expresses the standard deviation of the sampling distribu-

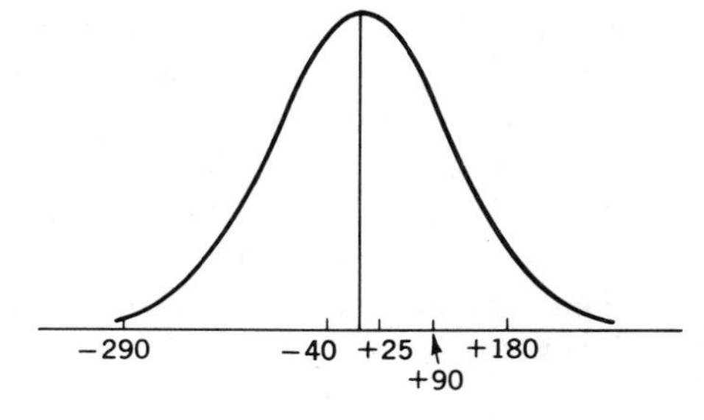

Fig. 9.10 Distribution of differences between sample means (mean, old − mean, new).

tion of the difference between sample means as a function of the estimates of the standard error of the mean obtained from each of the two samples.

Fortunately for practitioners, we do not have to derive the complete sampling distribution in order to make an interval estimate for the difference between the population means. We simply need to take one set of paired sample means and use the following relationship:

$$\text{Interval estimate, } \mu_{X_1} - \mu_{X_2} = (\bar{X}_1 - \bar{X}_2) \pm z(s_{\bar{X}_1 - \bar{X}_2})$$

where $\bar{X}_1 - \bar{X}_2$ is the observed difference between the sample means, z is the standardized normal deviate corresponding to the desired confidence coefficient, and

$$s_{\bar{X}_1 - \bar{X}_2} = \sqrt{s_{\bar{X}_1}{}^2 + s_{\bar{X}_2}{}^2}$$

For the tire problem, let us assume that we took random samples of size 60 from both the old and the new process, obtaining a sample mean for the new tires of 19,780 miles, with an estimate of the standard deviation of 3000 miles, and a sample mean for the old tires of 19,600, with an estimate of the standard deviation of 2900 miles. Then, with a 90% confidence coefficient, the interval estimate would be

$$\begin{aligned}\mu_{\text{new}} - \mu_{\text{old}} &= (19{,}780 - 19{,}600) \pm 1.645 \sqrt{\left(\frac{3000}{\sqrt{60}}\right)^2 + \left(\frac{2900}{\sqrt{60}}\right)^2} \\ &= +120 \pm 1.645\,(539) \\ &= -767 \text{ to } +1007\end{aligned}$$

This result is interpreted by saying that we are 90% sure that the difference between the population means for the new and the old processes will not be more than −767 to +1007 miles. The negative sign before the 767 is very important since it indicates that the population mean for the new process might well be as much as 767 miles *less* than that for the old. Obviously the manufacturer's hopes for producing a tire with a higher average life are not substantiated by the results of the sampling. One would not be convinced that the new process was better until the entire range of the interval estimate was positive.

The formula that was used above to make the interval estimate is strictly valid only under the circumstances listed below:

1. The samples must be equal in size.
2. The samples must have been taken independently of one another.
3. The variances $(s_X)^2$ estimated from the two samples must be nearly the same.

If one or another of these conditions is not met, techniques must be used which are beyond the scope of this text.

INTERVAL ESTIMATE FOR THE DIFFERENCE BETWEEN TWO POPULATION PROPORTIONS: LARGE SAMPLES

It was shown earlier in the chapter that techniques for making interval estimates are similar for means and proportions. The method for making an interval estimate for differences between population *proportions* is indeed perfectly analogous to that used for differences between population *means*. It is shown by:

$$\text{Interval estimate, } p_1 - p_2 = (\bar{p}_1 - \bar{p}_2) \pm z s_{\bar{p}_1 - \bar{p}_2}$$

where $p_1 - p_2$ is the difference between two population proportions; $\bar{p}_1 - \bar{p}_2$ is the observed difference between two sample proportions; z is the standardized normal deviate for the desired confidence coefficient; and

$$s_{\bar{p}_1 - \bar{p}_2} = \sqrt{s_{\bar{p}_1}{}^2 + s_{\bar{p}_2}{}^2} = \sqrt{\frac{\bar{p}_1(1 - \bar{p}_1)}{n_1 - 1} + \frac{\bar{p}_2(1 - \bar{p}_2)}{n_2 - 1}}$$

Practice involving the use of this formula can be obtained in the exercises at the end of this chapter.

SMALL SAMPLES: THE t DISTRIBUTION

The astute student will have noticed by now that every time we have used the normal distribution to make an interval estimate, we have stated that the sample size must be reasonably large, meaning at least 30. The reason for this proviso is that whenever the standard deviation of the population is *estimated from a sample* (as it usually will be), the normal distribution is only an approximation to the correct sampling distribution. The accuracy of that approximation is good only if the sample size is large.

The distribution that theoretically should be used whenever the standard deviation of the population is estimated from a sample is called the *t distribution* (also known as student's distribution—not in honor of all struggling statistics students, but because "student" was the pseudonym used by W. S. Gosset, who formulated it in 1908).[4] Actually, there is not just one standardized t distribution, but an entire family of them, one for each "degree of freedom." In the estimation of a population standard deviation from a sample, the number of degrees of freedom is always

[4] Actually, the t distribution is theoretically applicable only when the *parent* population from which the sample is drawn is normal. As a practical matter, however, it works reasonably well for problems involving a variety of nonnormal parent distributions where the departure from normality is not too severe.

$n - 1$, the size of the sample minus 1.[5] The t distribution rapidly approaches the normal distribution as the number of degrees of freedom increases. In Fig. 9.11 the t distributions for 2, 5, and 20 degrees of freedom are compared with the normal distribution.

From Fig. 9.11 it is obvious that appreciable errors, especially in the calculation of tail areas, could result if the normal distribution were used to approximate the t distribution for small samples. Since a separate table similar to the normal area table is necessary for each degree of freedom, tables for the t distribution are usually condensed, showing only the standardized deviates corresponding to a limited number of two-tail areas for a number of degrees of freedom. Such an abbreviated t table is found in Appendix C.

In order to make clear the difference between interval estimates made with the t distribution and the approximation made using the normal distribution, we shall redo the interval estimate for the insurance policy example that appeared earlier in the chapter and then show the more accurate calculations using the t distribution for sample sizes of 25 and 10.

Note that in our solution to the problem using the normal approximation and a sample size of 25, we *underestimated* the width of the interval by \$1711 − \$1645 = \$66 or approximately 4%. If we had used the normal approximation with the sample size of 10, we should have obtained an interval estimate of \$9200 ± \$2602 rather than the correct value of \$9200 ± \$2900. This error of \$2900 − \$2602 = \$298 is greater than 10% and would be unacceptable for most problems. The magnitude of the error, then, becomes larger in both absolute and relative terms as the sample size is decreased. This is the reason that the normal distribution is used only for "large" samples, those greater than or equal to 30.

In summary, the t distribution should always be used in making interval estimates when the true standard deviation of the population is unknown and is estimated using s_X, the standard deviation estimated from the sample. The magnitude of the error involved in using the

[5] See footnote on p. 131, Chap. 8.

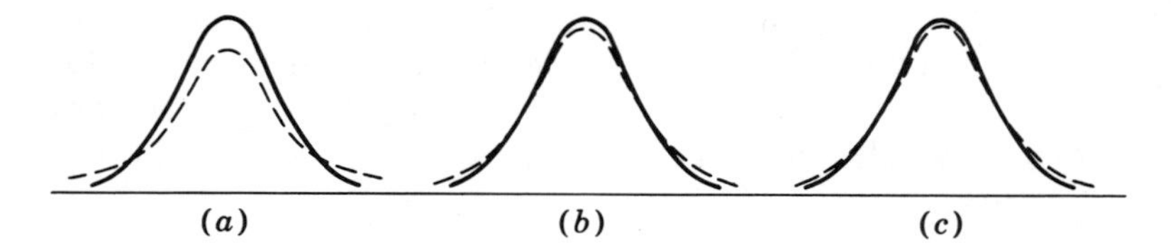

Fig. 9.11 Comparison of normal (solid line) and t (dashed line) distributions for (*a*) 2 degrees of freedom, (*b*) 5 degrees of freedom, and (*c*) 20 degrees of freedom.

Table 9.3 Insurance example, interval estimate for the population mean—infinite population

	Normal approximation	*t distribution*	*Normal approximation*	*t distribution*
Sample size	25	25	10	10
$\bar{X}$	\$9200	\$9200	\$9200	\$9200
s_X	5000	5000	5000	5000
$s_{\bar{X}} = \dfrac{s_X}{\sqrt{n}}$	1000	1000	$\dfrac{5000}{3.16} = 1582$	$\dfrac{5000}{3.16} = 1582$
Standardized deviate for 90% confidence coefficient	$z = 1.645$[a]	$t = 1.7111$[b]	$z = 1.645$[a]	$t = 1.833$[c]
Interval estimate	$\bar{X} \pm z(s_{\bar{X}})$ \$9200 ± \$1645	$\bar{X} \pm t(s_{\bar{X}})$ \$9200 ± \$1711	$\bar{X} \pm z(s_{\bar{X}})$ \$9200 ± \$2602	$\bar{X} \pm t(s_{\bar{X}})$ \$9200 ± \$2900

[a] From normal table

[b] From t table for 24 degrees of freedom and a two-tail probability of .10

[c] From t table for 9 degrees of freedom and a two-tail probability of .10

normal approximation rather than t varies with the size of the sample, becoming smaller as the sample size is increased. In most cases the error becomes negligible if the sample size is greater than or equal to 30.

PROBLEMS

9.1 The discussion of Example 1 in this chapter concludes with the sentence: "It is left to the student to prove that by using the same logic, the C's would fall between 87 and 107, the D's between 74 and 86, and the F's below 74." Prove that the limits specified in this sentence are correct.

9.2 A men's sportswear manufacturer is coming out with a new line of golf shirts. Because of the nature of the shirt, a customer's required size can be determined from his weight, as follows:

Weight, pounds	*Shirt size*
Under 140	Small
140–170	Medium
170–200	Large
Over 200	Extra large

If men's weights are (approximately) normally distributed with a mean of 165 pounds and a standard deviation of 20 pounds, how many of each size should a lot of 1000 shirts contain?

9.3 The Neversell Co. pays its salesmen a fixed bonus if they produce over $100,000 in business in any calendar month. Analysis of monthly sales records of three of their crack salesmen yields the following results.

Salesman	*Mean monthly sales*	*Standard deviation of monthly sales*
Xavier	$90,000	$ 5,000
Young	80,000	10,000
Zimmer	75,000	20,000

(*a*) How often does each salesman receive a bonus?
(*b*) Is the bonus plan a good one from the company's point of view? Discuss.

9.4 One of the lathes in your auto parts manufacturing company bores the inside diameter of piston rings to their finished dimension. The rings are usable if their inside diameter is between 1.980 and 2.020 inches; however, in order to use them, they must be sorted by size. If the machine is set to produce a mean diameter of 2.000 inches, the standard deviation of the machine is 0.0085 inch, and the distribution of diameters is normal, what proportion of the rings will
(*a*) Fall below the lower limit?
(*b*) Fall between 1.980 and 1.990 inches?
(*c*) Fall between 1.990 and 2.010 inches?
(*d*) Fall between 2.010 and 2.020 inches?
(*e*) Fall above the upper limit?

9.5 If the rings in Prob. 9.4 are made with too large an inside diameter (greater than 2.020), they must be scrapped at a cost of 27 cents per ring. If they are made with too small an inside diameter, they can be rerun at a cost of 3 cents per ring. The setting of 2.000 used in Prob. 9.4, equalizes the number of scrap and rework pieces. (You realize that the best setting for the mean will be one that would equalize the *cost* of scrap and rework pieces.) At what mean should you set the machine in order to minimize the cost of scrap and rework? (*Hint:* cost is a function of the cost per unit times the proportion too large or too small. Use successive approximations to find the mean that will make the proportion reworked equal 9 times the proportion of scrap. Assume that a 5 standard deviation spread covers the range of all possible values. Also assume that the mean can be set to 1/10,000 inch.)

9.6 Assume that a population consists of the dollar value of purchases made in a supermarket on successive Thursdays in September by a typical housewife and that these purchases were $3, $12, $9, $22, and $6.

(*a*) Find the mean and the standard deviation of this population. Now assume that we take samples of size 2 at random from this population.

(*b*) Calculate the mean and standard deviation of the sampling distribution of the mean. Do this by listing all the possible combinations obtainable for samples of size 2 taken from the population without replacement. After you have listed all the combinations, summarize them, and calculate the sample mean for each combination, together with the relative frequency of each. Then find the mean and standard deviation of the resulting sampling distribution. For example, some of the combinations are 3 and 12, 3 and 9, 3 and 22, 3 and 6, 12 and 9, 12 and 22, etc. There are 10 such combinations.

(*c*) You should observe from (*a*) and (*b*) that: (1) The mean of the sampling distribution is equal to the mean of the population; (2) the standard deviation of the sampling distribution is equal to the standard deviation of the population divided by the square root of the size of the sample times the finite correction factor. That is $\sigma_{\bar{X}} = (\sigma_X/\sqrt{n})\sqrt{(N-n)/(N-1)}$. Perform these calculations and prove the relationships stated.

9.7 Assume that the sampling in Prob. 9.6 was done *with* replacement. Answer questions (*b*) and (*c*) of Prob. 9.6, assuming replacement.

Note: Your calculations for part (*b*) will be different from those of Prob. 9.6 because combinations such as 3 and 3 are now possible. There will be 25 different combinations. Your calculations for part (*c*) should show that the mean of the sampling distribution is still equal to the mean of the population but that $\sigma_{\bar{X}}$ is now equal to $\sigma_X/\sqrt{n}$. (The finite correction factor becomes equal to 1 because the population size is now in effect infinite.)

9.8 Explain the differences and relationships among:

(*a*) The standard deviation of a sample
(*b*) The standard deviation of a distribution of sample means
(*c*) The standard deviation of a population

9.9 The Plushtone Carpet Company selected a sample of 101 rolls of carpet from its production process in order to estimate the mean number of defects per roll. Careful examination of the rolls yielded the following data:

Number of defects found in roll	*Number of rolls*
0	50
1	21
2	15
3	10
4	5
Total	101

(*a*) Make a point estimate of the mean and standard deviation of number of defects per roll for this process.

(*b*) Make an interval estimate of the mean number of defects per roll, using a 98% confidence interval.

(*c*) Is the variable "number of defects per roll" normally distributed? How does this affect your answer to (*a*) and (*b*)?

9.10 As general agent for a life insurance company you are interested in the average size of policy sold under a special program for graduating seniors. You have your secretary take a simple random sample of 100 of this year's sales, and she presents you with the following distribution:

Policy size, in thousands of dollars	*Number of sales*
0–5	20
5–10	40
10–15	25
15–20	10
20–25	5

(*a*) Estimate the standard deviation of the population.
(*b*) Make an interval estimate for the population mean, using a 90% confidence coefficient.

9.11 The following data are collected by an alumni office, showing the annual income (in thousands of dollars) of a random sample of 101 business school graduates four years after graduation. Assume that the size of the population is 10,000.

Income, in thousands of dollars	*Number*
6–8	31
8–10	44
10–12	18
12–14	7
14–16	1
	101

(*a*) Make a point estimate of the population mean.
(*b*) Make a point estimate of the population standard deviation.
(*c*) Make an interval estimate of the population mean, with a 90% confidence coefficient.

9.12 A company that manufactures light bulbs wishes to estimate the mean life of the bulbs produced. A sample of 20 bulbs is tested, giving a mean life of 186.6 hours and a standard deviation of 24.2 hours. Construct a 95% confidence interval estimate of the process mean life.

9.13 Demonstrate the effect of sample size in an interval estimate for a population mean by assuming that you take random samples of the sizes indicated below and that in *each* case you obtain an $\bar{X} = 26.0$ and an $s_{\bar{X}} = 3.5$. Make an interval estimate for μ_X for:

(*a*) $n = 2$
(*b*) $n = 5$
(*c*) $n = 10$
(*d*) $n = 15$
(*e*) $n = 20$
(*f*) $n = 30$
(*g*) $n = \infty$

9.14 Using the normal approximation of the binomial distribution, compute the probability that in 100 tosses of a fair coin you will obtain

(*a*) exactly 50 heads.

Hint: Since you are using a continuous distribution to represent one that is actually discrete, you must "break up" the continuous distribution into discrete chunks. Here, for example, obtain the normal probability that the sample proportion of heads is between .495 and .505, given $p = .50$ and $\sigma_{\bar{p}} = \sqrt{[p(1-p)]/n}$.

(*b*) at least 50 heads.

(*c*) less than 40 heads.

Compare your answers with results obtained from the binomial tables. What explains any differences?

9.15 Assume that a manufacturer of inexpensive bicycle tires produces tires with a proportion of defectives of .01. You buy two of these tires (presumably selected at random from the process).

(*a*) Derive the sampling distribution for p, the proportion of defectives.

(*b*) Find the mean and the standard deviation of the sampling distribution.

(*c*) Find the mean and the standard deviation of the *population*.

Hint: The population is specified in the following table, where an occurrence has a value of 1 and a nonoccurrence a value of 0.

Occurrences (defectives)	*Probability of occurrence*
1	.01
0	.99

(*d*) Show that the mean of the sampling distribution is equal to the mean of the population, which is equal to p, and that the standard deviation of the sampling distribution, $\sigma_{\bar{p}}$, is equal to the standard deviation of the population divided by the square root of the size of the sample, $\sigma_p/\sqrt{n}$, where $\sigma_p = \sqrt{pq}$.

9.16 Assume that you bought two bicycle tires in a small store that carried a stock of 10 tires, two of which were defective. Assume also that you chose the tires by a random process.

(*a*) Derive the sampling distribution for p, the proportion of defectives.

(*b*) Find the mean and the standard deviation of the sampling distribution.

(*c*) Find the mean and standard deviation of the population.

Hint: This is the same as the distribution in Prob. 9.15 except for the values of probability p.

(*d*) Show that the mean of the sampling distribution is equal to the mean of the population, which is equal to p, and that the standard deviation of the sampling distribution is equal to the standard deviation of the population, $\sqrt{pq}$, divided by the square root of the sample size, times the finite correction factor

$$\sqrt{(N-n)/(N-1)}$$

That is,

$$\sigma_{\bar{p}} = \frac{\sigma_p}{\sqrt{n}} \sqrt{\frac{N-n}{N-1}}$$

$$= \sqrt{\frac{pq}{n}} \sqrt{\frac{N-n}{N-1}}$$

9.17 (*a*) For the distribution of sample proportions in Prob. 4.1, compute the mean of the sample proportions and the standard deviation of the sample proportions. Use the frontal approach, i.e., use the formulas of Chap. 8 to compute these descriptive measures for this sampling distribution.

(*b*) Obtain the mean and standard deviation of the sampling distribution by use of the theoretical relationships given in this chapter.

(*c*) Are the results in (*a*) and (*b*) the same? Will they always be the same?

9.18 How large a sample would be needed to determine the proportion of voters favoring the Republican candidate in a hotly contested election to within .01?

9.19 A company wishes to estimate the effects of a training program that is provided for some of its first-year salesmen. A random sample of 100 salesmen is selected for observation. Fifty of the sample salesmen were exposed to the training program, and fifty were not. First-year commissions earned by the two groups were as follows:

	With training program	*Without training program*
Average commissions	\$10,100	\$9,950
Standard deviation, s_X	1,800	2,100

(*a*) Make a point estimate of the net effect of the training program.

(*b*) Make an interval estimate of the effect, using a 98% confidence coefficient.

(*c*) What would you recommend to management regarding continuation of the program? Explain.

9.20 A large department store chain in studying its credit sales took random samples of size 65 in each of two stores, one located on the East Coast and one in the Midwest. They found that .56 of the customers in the East used charge accounts, while .67 of the customers in the Midwest did. Make an interval estimate for the difference between population proportions for the two areas using a 95% confidence coefficient.

Do you think that the difference between the two sample proportions indicates a real difference in the proportion of customers using charge accounts? Why?

9.21 (*a*) Under what circumstances does the precision of a sample estimate depend only on the absolute size of the sample?

(*b*) Under what circumstances does it depend on the relative size of the sample, i.e., the size of the sample as a percentage of the population?

(*c*) Give some illustrations of cases in which you think nonstatisticians are overly concerned about *relative* sample size when they should not be.

10
Statistical Decision Rules and Tests of Hypotheses for Continuous Distributions

This chapter will be concerned with the reinforcement of certain concepts of classical inference. In particular, it will extend the study of the various continuous distributions (for which interval estimates were made in the previous chapter) to the areas of hypothesis testing and formulation of decision rules. In one sense, there is little that is new here. Although the specific methods applicable to continuous distribution problems and the examples used to illustrate them will be different, the basic concepts involved have all been explored earlier. The fundamental notions of statistical inference, hypothesis tests, decision rules, error characteristics, etc., have been explained at length in Chaps. 4 and 5.

DECISION RULES AND TESTS OF HYPOTHESES ABOUT A POPULATION MEAN

Assume that you are a large contractor working on the interstate highway system in a midwestern state. In a particular area you need a great deal of dirt for fill that is not available from the right-of-way. You contract with a local gravel-pit operator to deliver 200,000 tons of dirt to be delivered over-the-road in 20-ton trucks. You have reason to believe that the pit operator might short-weight you if he had the opportunity. At the same time, you can hardly afford to check each truck. You therefore set up a system for spot-checking the trucks by weighing a random sample of 64 trucks. If you are willing to take no more than a 1% chance of making a type I error (in this case concluding that you are being shorted when in fact you are not), what should your decision rule be? We shall assume that from past experience you know that the net weight of dirt carried will vary from truck to truck and that this variation can be described by a standard deviation of about 1 ton, $\sigma_X = 1$.

We know from Chap. 5 that the maximum risk of a type I error, which is 1% for this problem, occurs at the point where the pit operator is just barely meeting the standard of a mean weight of 20 tons per truck. If μ_X were 20 tons and you concluded that you were being short-weighted, you would be making a type I error. If the true mean weight per truck were less than 20 tons, you would *in fact* be short-weighted, and such a conclusion would be a correct decision rather than an error.

We could then find the action limit for the decision rule by assuming that μ_X is exactly 20 and by locating the limit so that the lower tail probability is 1%. This provides a 1% chance of the sample mean $\bar{X}$ falling below the action limit when the standard is just being met. The limit is determined as follows:

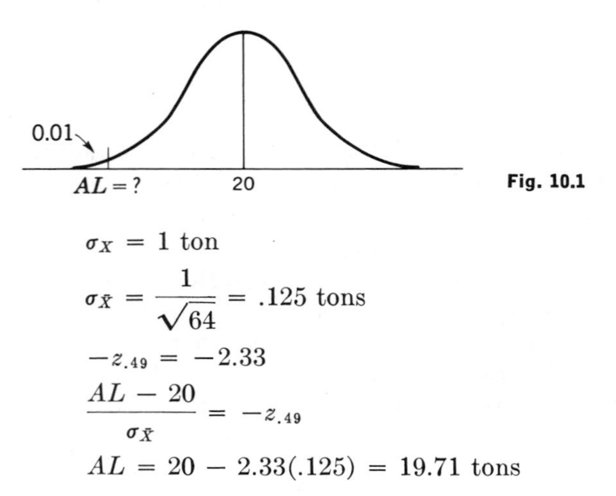

Fig. 10.1

$$\sigma_X = 1 \text{ ton}$$

$$\sigma_{\bar{X}} = \frac{1}{\sqrt{64}} = .125 \text{ tons}$$

$$-z_{.49} = -2.33$$

$$\frac{AL - 20}{\sigma_{\bar{X}}} = -z_{.49}$$

$$AL = 20 - 2.33(.125) = 19.71 \text{ tons}$$

Thus the decision rule is: Take a simple random sample of size 64, and observe $\bar{X}$, the sample mean. If $\bar{X} \geq 19.71$ tons, conclude that the true mean weight per truck is 20 tons or more and that the total tonnage meets requirements. If $\bar{X} < 19.71$, conclude that the true mean weight per truck is less than 20 tons and that the total tonnage requirement is not being met.

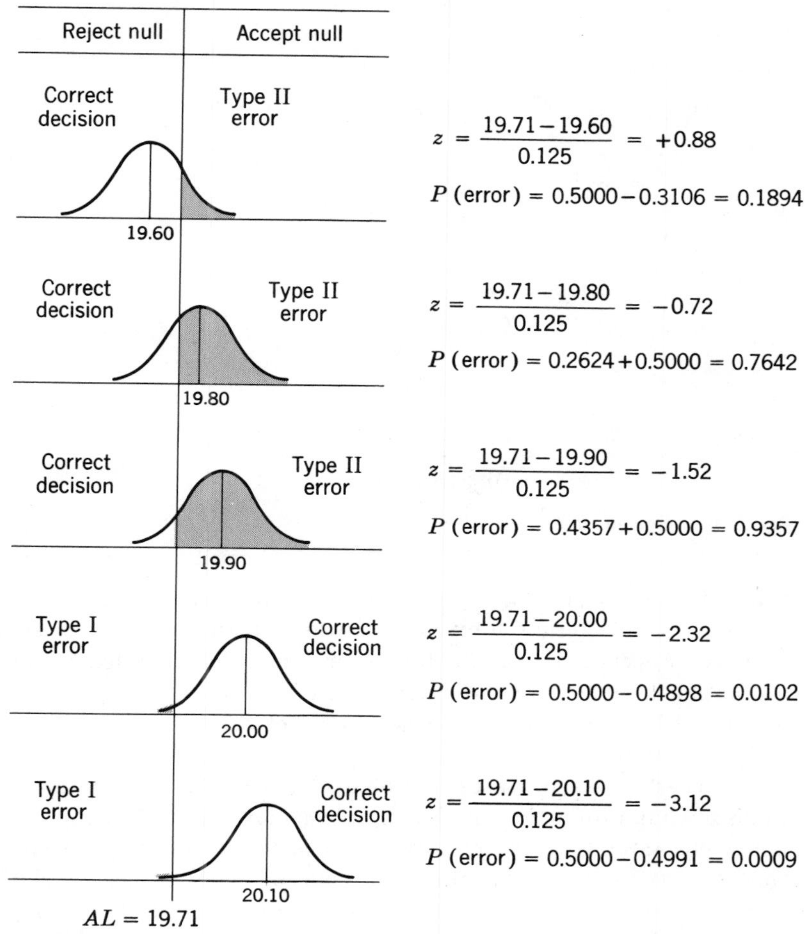

Fig. 10.2 Determination of probabilities of error, dirt fill problem.

The ordinates for the error curve for this decision rule can be determined easily by sketching the sampling distribution of the mean for various possible values of μ_X and finding the areas that represent the probability of an error (see Fig. 10.2).

The error curve is obtained by plotting probabilities of error against various possible values for μ_X (see Fig. 10.3).

TWO WAYS OF TESTING HYPOTHESES

In the analysis of the preceding section we tested a null hypothesis by formulating an appropriate decision rule and then sampling. To be precise, we first found the appropriate action limit for the decision rule by

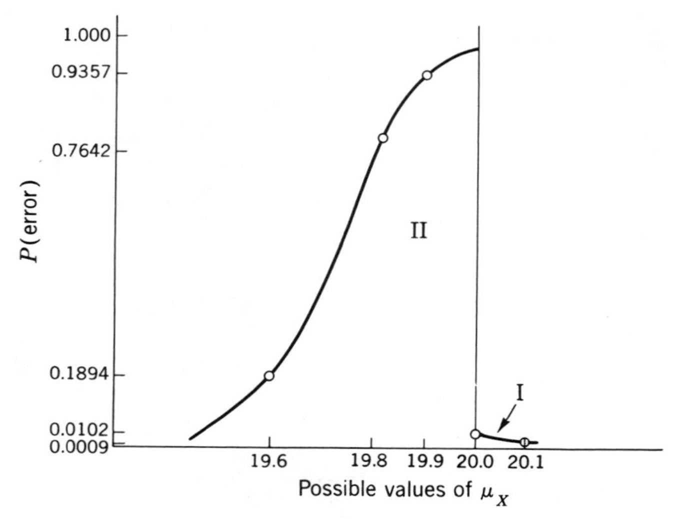

Fig. 10.3 Error curve for dirt fill problem.

using the desired level of significance, and then we compared the sample mean with the action limit to see whether the hypothesis should be rejected or accepted. In the dirt-fill problem, for example, we found that the action limit corresponding to an α of .01 was 19.71. If our sample mean had been, say, 19.65, we should reject the null hypothesis that the weight was acceptable.

Exactly the same test could be made, after the sample was taken, by finding what proportion of the sample means could be expected to fall below the sample mean actually obtained if the true mean were 20. If that proportion were less than the level of significance, we should not attribute the difference between the sample mean and the population mean to chance, and therefore we should reject the null hypothesis. Thus, for the sample mean of 19.65 we should find the left tail area to be less than .01, as in Fig. 10.4. We should therefore reject the null hypothesis and conclude that the population from which the sample was drawn could not have a mean greater than or equal to 20.

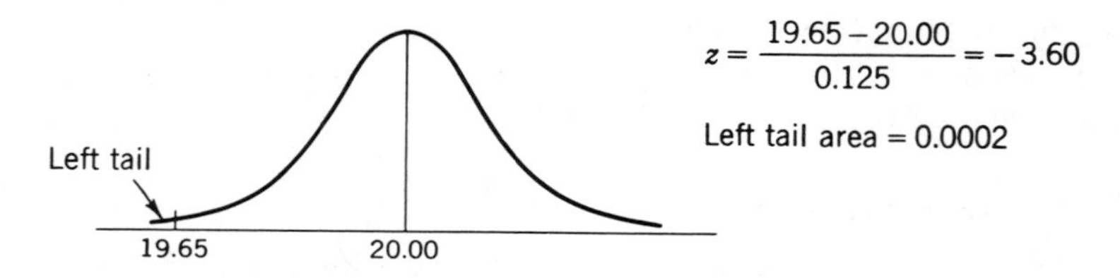

Fig. 10.4

EFFECT OF A CHANGE IN THE ACTION LIMIT

The effect of a change in the action limit is easy to see for a continuous distribution. For a lower tail test such as the dirt-fill example, the action limit would be lowered if we wanted to reduce the level of significance (the maximum risk of a type I error) and raised if we wanted to increase the level of significance. To make this point more clear, let us chart the sampling distributions for various possible values of the true mean and identify the action limits appropriate for: (*a*) an α level of .01, (*b*) an α level of .05, and (*c*) an α level of .25 (see Fig. 10.5). We shall also graph the error characteristics for each action limit (see Fig. 10.6). We are

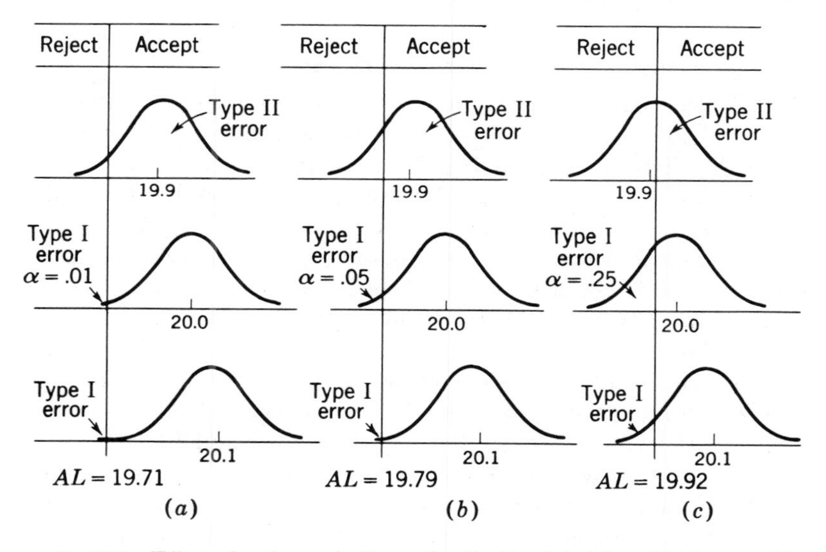

Fig. 10.5 Effect of a change in the action limit. (*a*) $AL = 19.71$, $\alpha = .01$; (*b*) $AL = 19.79$, $\alpha = .05$; (*c*) $AL = 19.92$, $\alpha = .25$.

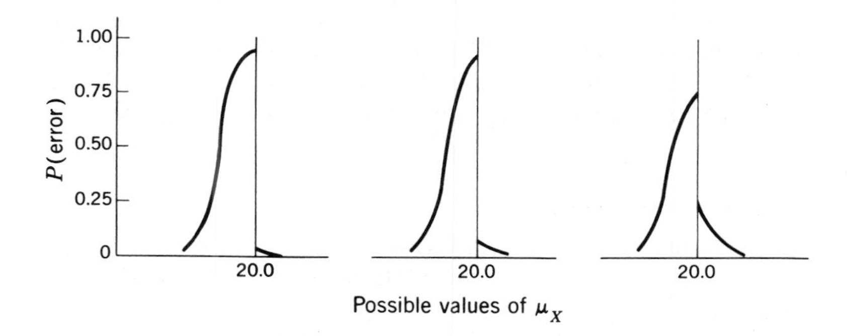

Fig. 10.6 Error curves corresponding to (*a*), (*b*), and (*c*) in Fig. 10.5.

assuming, as before, that the true standard deviation of the weights of trucks is 1 ton and that the sample size is 64, so that $\sigma_{\bar{X}} = 1/\sqrt{64} = .125$.

Note that the action limit is found in every case from the knowledge that α occurs when the value for the true mean is the lowest *acceptable* value, in this case 20 tons. If the level of significance is .01, the action limit is low and the risks of type II errors are very large. As the level of significance is raised, the action limit also goes up. This increases the risk of a type I error wherever $\mu_X \geq 20$ but decreases the risk of a type II error wherever $\mu_X < 20$. It is important to note that *for a given sample size* we can only trade off the risks of type I errors for their type II counterparts; there is no way to reduce both risks simultaneously.

EFFECT OF A CHANGE IN THE SIZE OF THE SAMPLE

We know that the dispersion of the distribution of sample means is reduced as the sample size is increased, as measured by $\sigma_{\bar{X}} = \sigma_X/\sqrt{n}$. For the dirt-fill problem the standard deviation of the weights of the trucks was 1 ton. Therefore for a sample size of 64 the standard deviation of the sampling distribution of the mean $\sigma_{\bar{X}}$ was $1/\sqrt{64} = 1/8 = .125$. If we wanted to *double* the accuracy of our tests, we should need to cut $\sigma_{\bar{X}}$ in half. This could be accomplished by *quadrupling* the sample size to 256, since $1/\sqrt{256} = 1/16 = .0625$. Calculation of the size of errors for various values of μ_X and the error curve for the decision rule with an action limit of 19.71 are shown in Figs. 10.7 and 10.8 for sample sizes of 64 (solid line) and 256 (dotted line). The curves for $n = 64$ are, of course, exactly the same as those shown in Figs. 10.2 and 10.3.

Note that where the value of μ_X is between the action limit (19.71) and the standard (20.0), the risk of a type II error is increased with an increase in the sample size but that both type I and type II errors are decreased with an increased sample size for all other possible values of μ_X.

It might be worthwhile to note specifically what is meant by "doubling the accuracy" by quadrupling the sample size. With a sample size of 64 it was necessary to set the action limit at 19.71 to achieve a level of significance α of .01. With $\sigma_{\bar{X}}$ only half as large for a sample of 256, it would be necessary only to go half as far from the minimum acceptable value of 20 to achieve this same accuracy, as the calculations in Fig. 10.9 show.

DETERMINATION OF SAMPLE SIZE

In problems where the relative costs of type I and type II errors cannot be quantified or where there is not time to engage in such a process, the decision with respect to the appropriate sample size is often made by considering the maximum permissible risk of a type I error, α, and a desir-

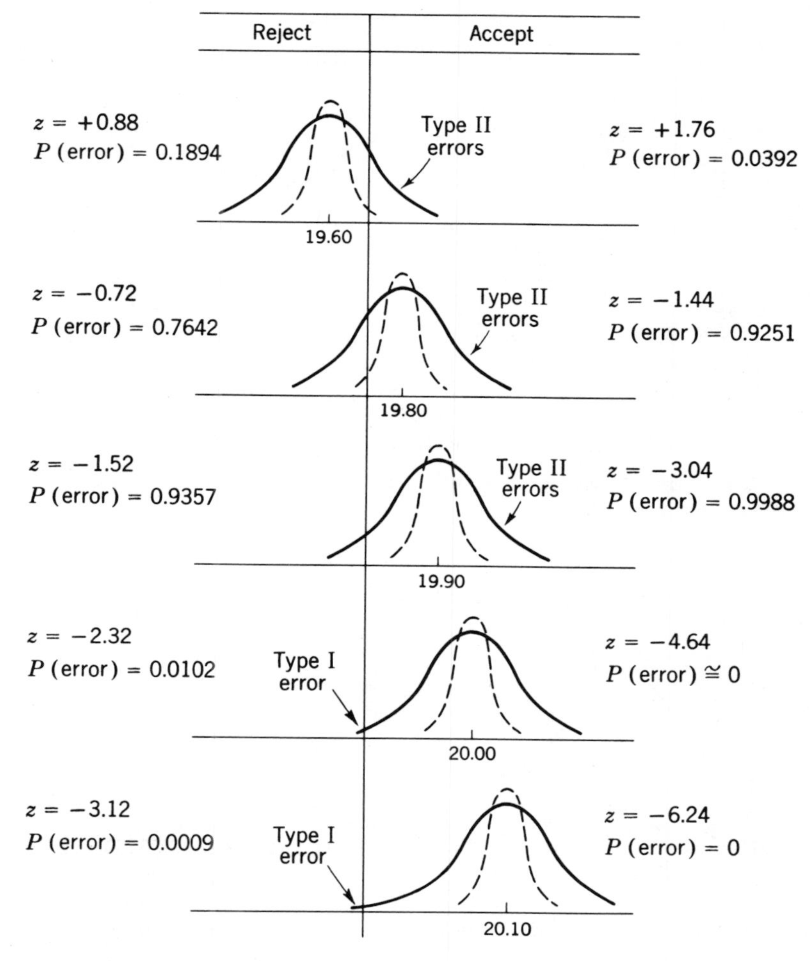

Fig. 10.7 Effect of a change in the sample size. Solid line: $n = 64$; dashed line: $n = 256$.

able level of risk of a type II error, β. For the dirt-fill problem the α risk, as noted previously, will occur when $\mu_X = 20$, but the β risk must be defined relative to some *particular value of* μ_X. For example, suppose that prior to sampling in the dirt-fill problem, we decided that we should be satisfied with no more than a 5% chance of making a type I error and no more than a 10% chance of making a type II error *if* the true mean were actually 19.5 tons. We shall assume that from previous studies we were sure that the standard deviation of the population was very close to 1 ton. The problem could be sketched as in Fig. 10.10.

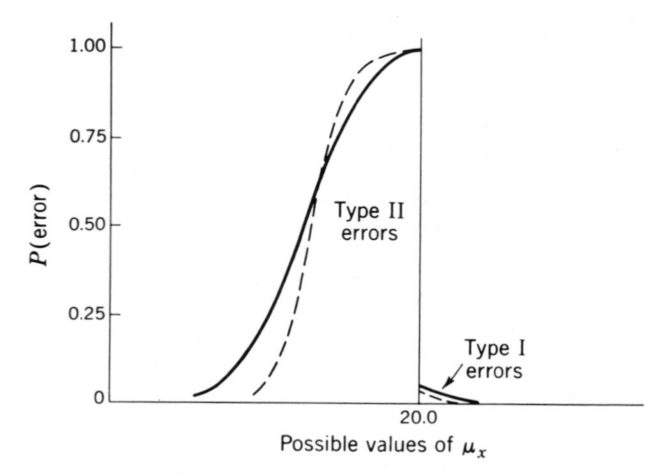

Fig. 10.8 Error curves for Fig. 10.7. Solid line: $n = 64$; dashed line: $n = 256$.

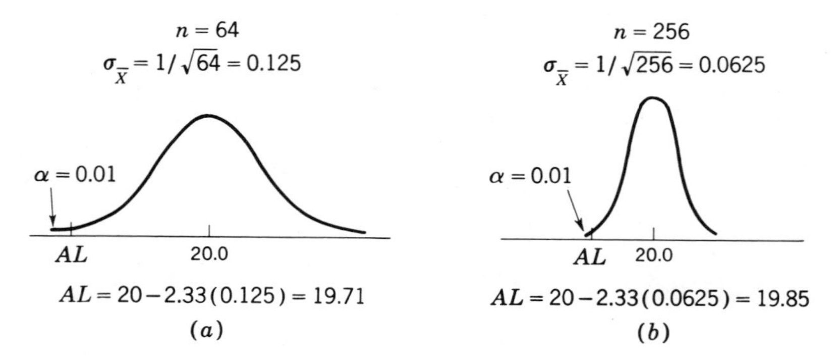

Fig. 10.9 Calculation of action limit for $\alpha = .01$, where $\sigma_X = 1.00$.

Remember that if the true mean is in fact 19.5, we are being short-weighted. We want to take no more than a 10% chance of concluding that the tonnage is acceptable if in fact the true mean is 19.5. On the other hand, we are willing to take at most a 5% chance of concluding that the tonnage is short when it really is not. This α risk will always occur at the *smallest* acceptable mean, namely, 20 tons. We find that we can develop two equations to find the action limit:

$$AL = 19.5 + z_{.40}\sigma_{\bar{X}}$$

and

$$AL = 20.0 - z_{.45}\sigma_{\bar{X}}$$

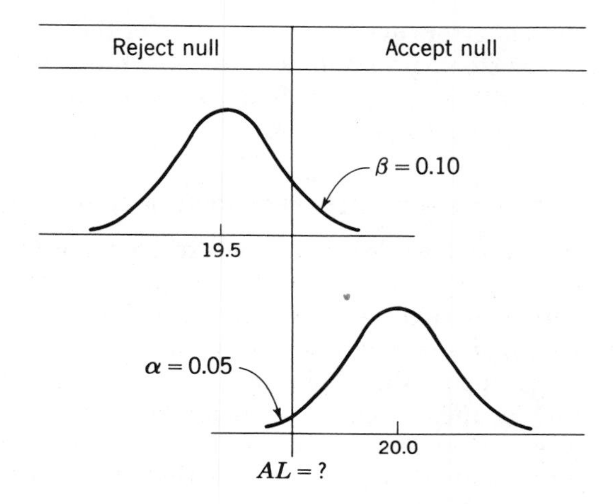

Fig. 10.10

Since there is but one action limit and we know $z_{.40}$, $z_{.45}$, and σ_X, we can set the two expressions on the right of the equations equal to each other. When we do so, we find that the only unknown is n, the necessary sample size.

$$19.5 + 1.28 \frac{1}{\sqrt{n}} = 20.0 - 1.645 \frac{1}{\sqrt{n}}$$

Solving for n,

$$\sqrt{n} = \frac{2.925}{.5}$$

and

$$n = 35$$

(The value of n is 34.22 to the nearest hundredth. In order to achieve at least the accuracy we desire, we must round *up* to the nearest whole number of 35.)

Having found the sample size, we can substitute its value in either of the original equations to determine the appropriate action limit.

$$AL = 19.5 + 1.28 \frac{1}{\sqrt{35}} = 19.72$$

Thus the decision rule is stated as follows: Take a simple random sample of size 35 and obtain $\bar{X}$, the sample mean. If the sample mean is greater than or equal to 19.72, conclude the tonnage is acceptable. If the sample mean is less than 19.72, conclude that we are being short-weighted.

It must be emphasized that this technique should be used *only* in cases where it is not possible to obtain the functions which show the cost of both types of errors over the *entire range* of the decision problem. Techniques for developing such functions have already been discussed in Chap. 6. They will be applied again in Chaps. 11 and 12 in conjunction with the use of continuous distributions.

TEST OF A HYPOTHESIS REGARDING A POPULATION PROPORTION

In Chap. 9 we learned to make an interval estimate for a population proportion by using the normal approximation to the binomial. In this section we shall use the same normal approximation to test a hypothesis regarding a population proportion.

Suppose that a pharmaceutical company had developed a shot to be used for the prevention of Asian flu. This new treatment was both more expensive and more painful than the previous treatment, and the company wanted to be very sure that its results were better than the old treatment before introducing it. With the old treatment, the proportion of persons exposed who got the flu after having had the shot was .5. The company tested 144 exposed persons by giving them the new shots and .55 of them did not get the flu. They now want to test the hypothesis that the true proportion of "successes" is higher than .5. Since the consequences of making a type I error (concluding that the new treatment is better than the old when in fact it is not) are serious, they decide to test at an α level of .02. The action limit for an appropriate decision rule would be found as follows:

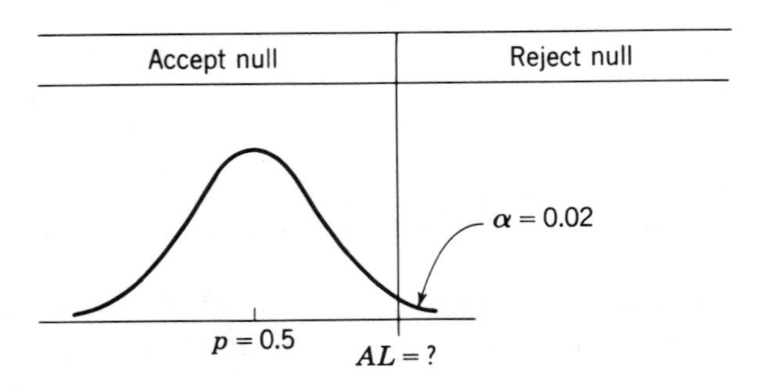

Fig. 10.11

$$\frac{AL - p}{\sigma_{\bar{p}}} = z_{.48}$$

$$AL = p + z_{.48}\sigma_{\bar{p}} = .5 + 2.05\sqrt{\frac{(.5)(.5)}{144}}$$

$$= .5 + 2.05\ (.0417)$$

$$= .5855 \text{ or } .59 \quad \text{rounding to the nearest hundredth}$$

Therefore, the decision rule would be stated as follows: Take a simple random sample of size 144, and observe the proportion of "successes." If that proportion is .59 or more, conclude that the new treatment is better than the old. If the proportion in the sample is less than .59, conclude that the new treatment is no better than the old.

On the basis of this decision rule, the new treatment would not be considered better since the observed sample proportion was .55.

Since the sample had already been taken before the decision rule was formulated, an alternative procedure is available to test the same hypothesis. We could merely find the area of the upper tail beyond .55, assuming that the true p was .5, and then compare this probability with the level of significance α. The z value is $(.55 - .5)/.0417 = 1.20$, and the probability equals $.5000 - .3849 = .1151$. Since this area is *larger* than the level of significance, we should conclude that the observed difference occurred by chance and that the true population proportion was not greater than .5.

Since this decision rule involves an upper-tail test (the region of rejection of the null hypothesis is the upper tail) it may be instructive to calculate a few points on the error curve and graph them as in Figs. 10.12 and 10.13. Notice that type I errors can occur only if the true proportion has a value *equal to or less than* .5. If $p \leq .5$, then the null hypothesis should be accepted and a type I error would be to reject the null falsely. This type of error would be made if the sample proportion happened by chance to fall *above* the action limit when $p \leq .5$. Similarly, type II errors can occur only if the true proportion has a value greater than .5. If $p > .5$, the null hypothesis *should* be rejected. An error would be to accept the null falsely. This type of error would be made if the sample proportion happened by chance to fall *below* the action limit when $p > .5$.

Comparing this error curve with any of those for the dirt-fill example, you should note that the regions identifying type I and type II errors are reversed. This, of course, is caused by the fact that the dirt-fill problem involved a lower-tail test (type I errors occurred in the lower tail of the sampling distribution), while this problem involved an upper-tail test (type I errors occurred in the upper tail of the sampling distribution).

DECISION RULES INVOLVING THE DIFFERENCE BETWEEN POPULATION MEANS

We shall illustrate the formulation of decision rules for the difference between population means using a problem very similar to the tire-testing problem of Chap. 9. Suppose that you decided to test two samples of tires, one from an established process and one from a new process, to see whether or not you would be justified in concluding that the tires from the new process produced a higher mean length of life. You

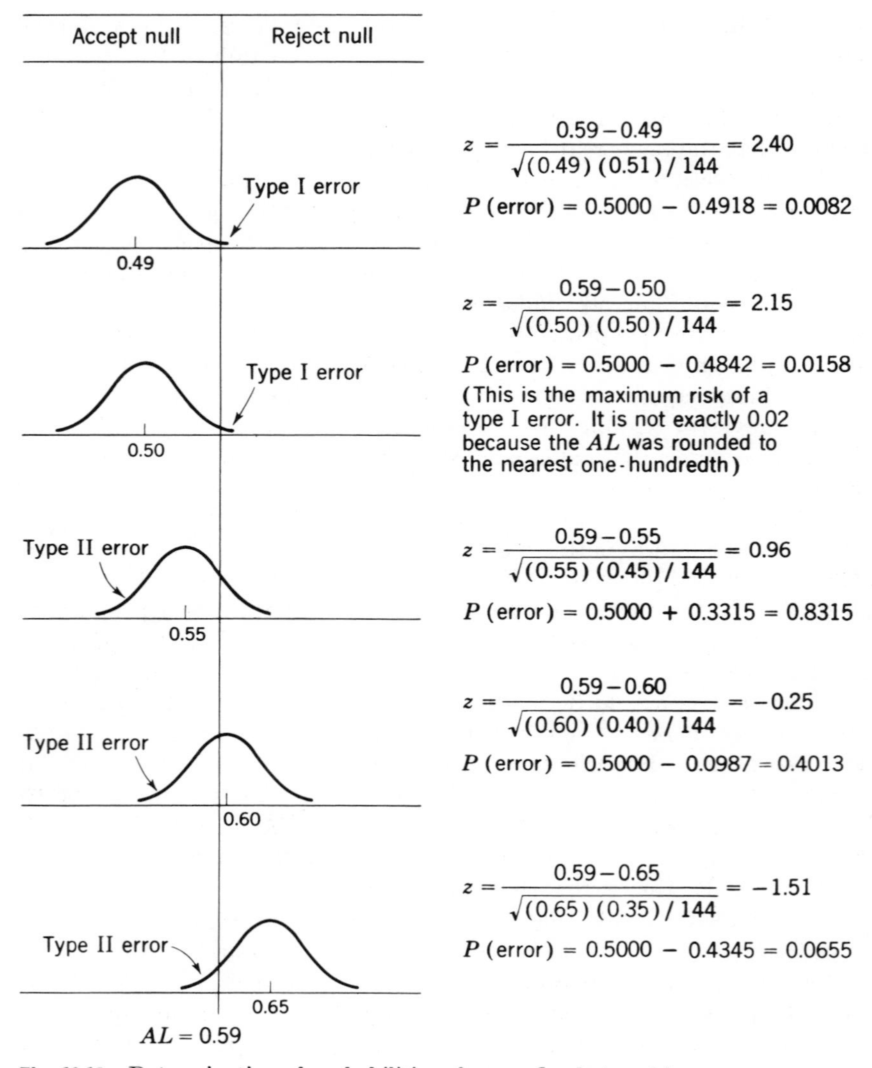

Fig. 10.12 Determination of probabilities of error, flu shot problem.

decide to take a maximum risk of no more than .10 of concluding that the new tires are better if in fact they are not. At the same time, you are willing to take at most a .20 risk of concluding that the new tires are not superior, if in fact the difference between the population means is as much as +1000 miles, where the plus sign indicates superiority of the new tires over the old. We shall assume that from past experience we can estimate

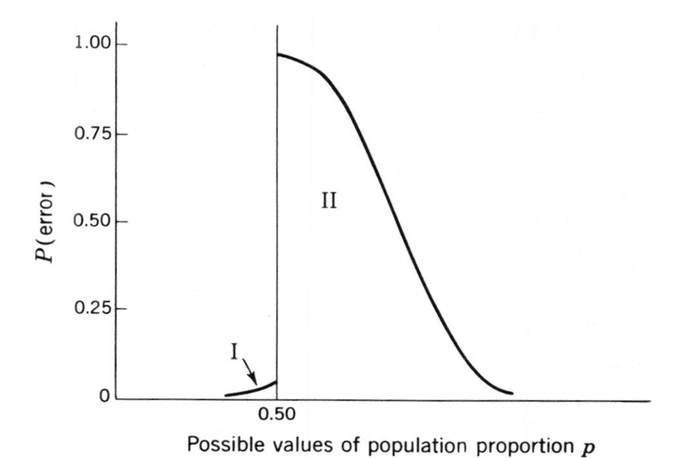

Fig. 10.13 Error curve for flu shot problem.

that the standard deviation of each of the two processes is 3000 miles. We want to find the size of samples appropriate for this test, with $n_1 = n_2$, and to find the appropriate decision rule.[1]

The sampling distribution and the relevant information are illustrated in Fig. 10.14.

[1] The assumptions of independence, equal sample size, and comparable variances mentioned in Chap. 9 relative to the use of the formula for $\sigma_{\bar{X}_1-\bar{X}_2}$ also apply here.

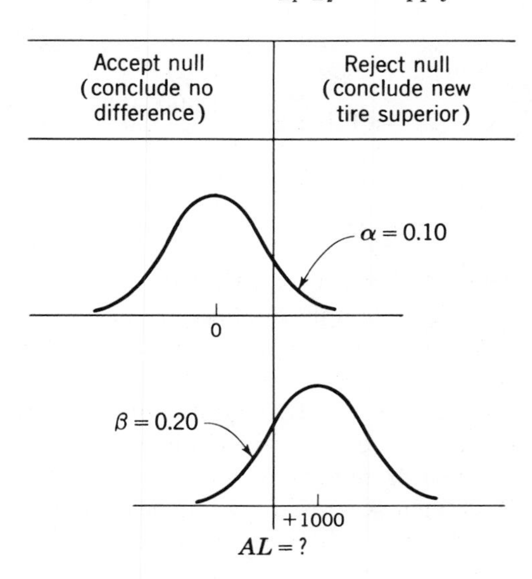

Fig. 10.14

The appropriate sample size is found as follows:

$$AL = 0 + z_{.40}\sigma_{\bar{X}_1-\bar{X}_2}$$
$$AL = 1000 - z_{.30}\sigma_{\bar{X}_1-\bar{X}_2}$$
$$0 + 1.28\sigma_{\bar{X}_1-\bar{X}_2} = 1000 - .84\sigma_{\bar{X}_1-\bar{X}_2}$$
$$2.12\sigma_{\bar{X}_1-\bar{X}_2} = 1000$$
$$\sigma_{\bar{X}_1-\bar{X}_2} = \frac{1000}{2.12} = 472$$

but

$$\sigma_{\bar{X}_1-\bar{X}_2} = \sqrt{\sigma_{\bar{X}_1}{}^2 + \sigma_{\bar{X}_2}{}^2} = \sqrt{\frac{\sigma_{X_1}{}^2}{n_1} + \frac{\sigma_{X_2}{}^2}{n_2}}$$

since

$$\sigma_{X_1} = \sigma_{X_2} = 3000$$

and

$$n_1 = n_2$$
$$\sigma_{\bar{X}_1-\bar{X}_2} = \sqrt{\frac{(3000)^2}{n} + \frac{(3000)^2}{n}} = \sqrt{\frac{18{,}000{,}000}{n}}$$

Therefore

$$\sqrt{\frac{18{,}000{,}000}{n}} = 472$$
$$\frac{18{,}000{,}000}{n} = (472)^2 = 222{,}784$$

and

$$n = \frac{18{,}000{,}000}{222{,}784} = 81$$

Having determined the sample size, the action limit is determined by solving

$$AL = 0 + 1.28\sqrt{\frac{18{,}000{,}000}{81}}$$
$$= 0 + 1.28\,\frac{4243}{9}$$
$$= 604$$

The decision rule can then be stated as follows:

Take simple random samples of 81 old tires and 81 new tires, and observe the difference between the sample means. If the difference is equal to or less than +604, conclude that there is no difference in the process means. If the difference is greater than +604, conclude that the mean for the new tires is higher than for the old.

After having formulated this rule, we should test the hypothesis that the new tires had a higher mean life than the old simply by obtaining the difference between the sample means and comparing it with +604.

For example, if $\bar{X}_{\text{old}} = 19{,}450$ and $\bar{X}_{\text{new}} = 20{,}095$, we should observe that the difference of $+645$ was greater than $+604$ and should therefore conclude that the new tires in fact had a higher population mean. This test was made, of course, at a .10 level of significance.

If the standard deviation calculated from the samples diverged from the estimate of 3000 used to calculate n, the level of significance would be altered, becoming larger if 3000 were an underestimate of the population standard deviation and smaller if it were an overestimate.

Calculation of the ordinates for the error curve for this decision rule will be left to the student as an exercise at the end of this chapter.

TEST OF A HYPOTHESIS INVOLVING THE DIFFERENCE BETWEEN POPULATION PROPORTIONS

It should come as no surprise to the student at this point that the process for formulating decision rules about differences between population proportions is analogous to that just described for differences between population means. In order to illustrate the process without excessive repetition, we shall develop an example in which the sample size is small but an appreciable part of the population and in which the samples are independent. This will necessitate the use of the finite correction factor and the t distribution.

Assume that we need to produce 200 complex parts using a turret lathe. Two operators are assigned to the job. If each produces the same proportion of defectives, as we originally hypothesize, we should prefer to let each operator produce 100 parts in order to cut production time by one-half. However, after each man has produced 26 parts, we find that operator A has produced 8 defectives and that operator B has produced 11. The question now is whether our original hypothesis that operators A and B are equally good is still valid and S the difference in their defective rate is caused by chance or whether operator A is really better than operator B. If we conclude the latter, we shall assign the remaining parts entirely to operator A in order to cut down the defective rate (even though the production time would be increased). Therefore, we decide to test the hypothesis that the difference between the population proportion defective produced by operators A and B is 0, using a level of significance of .05.

We would proceed as follows:

$$\text{Operator } A\text{'s proportion of defects} = \frac{8}{26} = .308 = \bar{p}_A$$

$$\text{Operator } B\text{'s proportion of defects} = \frac{11}{26} = .423 = \bar{p}_B$$

We want to compare the probability that a difference between sample proportions as great as .423 − .308, or +.115, could happen by chance if the true difference between population proportions were 0 with the level of significance of .05. This can be done by determining t from the expression

$$\frac{(\bar{p}_A - \bar{p}_B) - 0}{s_{\bar{p}_A - \bar{p}_B}} = t$$

and using the t table.

However, we must first find the value of $s_{\bar{p}_A - \bar{p}_B}$, the estimate of the standard deviation of the sampling distribution of the difference between population proportions. Since the size of the sample is an appreciable part of the population, we must incorporate the finite correction factor in the formula for $s_{\bar{p}_A - \bar{p}_B}$.

$$\begin{aligned} s_{\bar{p}_A - \bar{p}_B} &= \sqrt{s_{\bar{p}_A}{}^2 + s_{\bar{p}_B}{}^2} \\ &= \sqrt{\frac{\bar{p}_A(1 - \bar{p}_A)}{n_A - 1}\frac{N - n_A}{N - 1} + \frac{\bar{p}_B(1 - \bar{p}_B)}{n_B - 1}\frac{N - n_B}{N - 1}} \\ &= \sqrt{\frac{.308(.692)}{25}\frac{74}{99} + \frac{.423(.577)}{25}\frac{74}{99}} = .117 \end{aligned}$$

Therefore

$$t = \frac{(\bar{p}_A - \bar{p}_B) - 0}{s_{\bar{p}_A - \bar{p}_B}} = \frac{.115}{.117} = .983$$

For 50 degrees of freedom $(n_1 + n_2 - 2)$, the value of t corresponding to a one-tail level of significance of .05 is approximately 1.680 (interpolating between 30 and ∞ for a two-tail area of .10). Therefore, the one-tail probability for $t = .983$ would be considerably *greater* than .05, and the hypothesis that there is no difference between the population proportions is substantiated. We therefore conclude that the two operator's population proportion of defects is the same, and we should proceed with the production run using *both* operators.

INCORPORATION OF COSTS OF ERRORS INTO THE DECISION MATRIX

In this chapter we have assumed that the specific costs of type I and type II errors for various values of the population parameter were either impossible to determine or that their determination was prohibitively expensive. If it is possible to determine these costs, they should be incorporated into the process of formulating decision rules. The method of accomplishing this for continuous distributions is the subject of Chaps. 11 and 12.

PROBLEMS

10.1 An airline company for which you work decides to check the mean weight of luggage checked by passengers since weight restrictions were lifted. They know that when weight regulations were in force, the mean weight per piece of luggage in December was 20.5 pounds, with a standard deviation of 6 pounds. They ask you to set up a simple sampling plan to check on the current December mean. You ask the management within what tolerance they want to measure the true mean, and what degree of confidence they want. They say that they want to estimate the true mean weight within ± 1 pound, with 96% confidence.

What size random sample will you take to meet their specifications?

10.2 For Prob. 10-1, you should have determined that the required simple random sample size was 151. You set up a sampling plan using a table of random numbers and arrive at the following distribution of weights.

Weight, pounds	*f*
<10	0
10–14	24
15–19	40
20–24	33
25–29	30
30–34	16
35–39	5
40–44	3
>44	0

(*a*) What is the best point estimate you can make for the population mean?

(*b*) What is the best point estimate you can make for the population standard deviation?

(*c*) Assuming that the true standard deviation is the value you obtained in part (*b*), test the hypothesis that the true mean is still equal to or less than 20.5 pounds, using a .01 level of significance.

10.3 Professors at a certain institution have developed an extensive set of programmed learning materials for their introductory business statistics course. In order to determine whether the materials help the students, a large statistics class of 130 students is divided into halves, using a random process. One-half of the students are given the usual instructional materials and problems in the statistics lab. The other half are given the programmed learning material. The students attend the same lecture and are given the same tests. At the end of the semester the students' grades are analyzed with the following results:

	Regular	*PL*
n	65	65
Mean grade	62	68
Standard deviation of grades	18	19

(*a*) Do you think that the PL labs enable the students to earn better grades? Use a 2%, one-tail level of significance.

(*b*) What are the two kinds of errors one might make in interpreting these data? Which type of error is more likely for this problem?

(*c*) What is the probability of concluding in error that PL does not enable the students to earn better grades *if* the average gain of students using the PL lab over the regular lab is really 5 grade points?

10.4 A manufacturer of TV color tubes was disturbed by reports from the field that a new, "improved" tube being manufactured had a shorter service life than the tubes made formerly. It found that its research division was already testing a random sample of 20 TV sets for component failures by plugging them in and letting them run continuously until failures occurred. The manufacturer ordered that records be kept on tube life and that the sets be operated until tube failure. It was known from past experience that the mean length of life for "old process" tubes was 9000 hours. After considerable time the test was completed, with the following results:

$n = 20$
mean life = 8700 hours
standard deviation = 1200 hours

Test the hypothesis that the new tubes have a true mean length of life equal to or greater than 9000 hours. Use a 10% level of significance.

10.5 A company is concerned about the amount of time required for clerical personnel to file a certain kind of record. A sample of 225 observations of the filing operation gives the following results:

$\bar{X} = 58.2$ seconds
$s_x = 18$ seconds

Test the hypothesis that the true mean time required is 60 seconds or more. Use a level of significance of 5%.

10.6 Suppose the company in Prob. 10.5 is also concerned that the proportion of records filed incorrectly is greater than the 1% level considered satisfactory. A check of the sample observations in the previous problem shows that 5 of the records were incorrectly filed.

(*a*) Could this error rate be considered satisfactory?

(*b*) Suppose all the filings were performed by one employee. Could her performance be considered satisfactory? What would you recommend with respect to this employee?

(*c*) Discuss any differences in the way you answered parts (*a*) and (*b*).

10.7 Refer to the Plushtone Carpet Company problem (9.9). These data can be used in the construction of a statistical decision rule that will tell the company when its process is out of control, i.e. producing more defects per roll than considered tolerable. Assume that the company considers one defect per roll tolerable. Because a costly shutdown and inspection is made when the process is judged to be out of control, the company wishes to take only one chance in 20 of concluding it is out of control when in fact it is operating satisfactorily.

(*a*) What is the appropriate decision rule for a sample of 50 rolls?

(*b*) Plot a power curve for this decision rule.

(*c*) Plot an error curve for this decision rule, identifying the regions of type I and type II errors.

10.8 Redo parts (*a*) and (*b*) of Prob. 5.2 using the normal approximation of the binomial distribution.

10.9 The standard set for the proportion of defective items involving a complicated assembly in a production process is .20. The company has an order for 500 items. Upon testing the first 100 items, they find 25 defective assemblies. Test the hypothesis that the true proportion of defectives for the lot is less than or equal to .20. Use the normal approximation, with a level of significance of .05.

10.10 In an effort to improve its brand image, the Perkup Coffee Company has retained a marketing research consultant specializing in motivational research. Among the consultant's first recommendations is one that the company change from its traditional blue coffee can to a bright red one with a different design. To substantiate this recommendation, the consultant conducts an interview study in which he examines the purchasing motivation of 80 consumers. His findings are that 46 of the 80, or 57.5% prefer the red can.

What action do you believe management should take in this situation? Why?

10.11 (*a*) In order to calculate the ordinates of a power curve (or *OC* or error curve) for a statistical decision rule involving a sample mean, you must have an estimate of σ_X, the population standard deviation. Why?

(*b*) How would the estimate of σ_X usually be obtained?

(*c*) To calculate the points for a power curve for a statistical decision rule involving a sample proportion (using the normal approximation), what parameter must be estimated?

(*d*) Why are the *calculations* referred to in (*c*) somewhat more cumbersome than those referred to in (*a*)?

10.12 Does the specification of the maximum risk of type I error determine the sample size to be used in statistical decision procedure? Explain.

10.13 For the tire example in the text concerning the difference between population means,

(*a*) Calculate the ordinates for the error curve for $(\bar{X}_1 - \bar{X}_2) - 0$ values of -500, -200, 0, $+200$, $+500$, and $+1{,}000$ for the following decision rule: Take a simple random sample of 81 old tires and 81 new tires and observe the sample means. If the difference between the sample means is less than or equal to $+604$, conclude that there is no difference in the process means. If the difference is greater than $+604$, conclude that the mean for the new tires is higher than for the old.

(*b*) Assume that when you took the samples of 81 of each kind of tire, you found that your preliminary estimate of 3000 miles for the standard deviation of tire life for each type of tire was evidently in error since you got an $s_X = 2500$ from both of the samples. Calculate the level of significance for the decision rule in (*a*), using 2500 as the estimate of the population standard deviation for each type of tire.

10.14 You have doubtless noticed by now that regardless of the parameter under consideration, the formulation of a decision rule always involves the same relationship between z or t value corresponding to the level of significance, the action limit (which is one particular value of the sample statistic making up the sampling distribution), the mean of the sampling distribution, and the standard deviation of the sampling distribution. This relation can be expressed as

$$z \text{ or } t_{\text{level of significance}} = \frac{\begin{pmatrix}\text{sample statistic} \\ \text{that is the action limit}\end{pmatrix} - \begin{pmatrix}\text{mean of sam-} \\ \text{pling distribution}\end{pmatrix}}{\begin{pmatrix}\text{standard deviation of} \\ \text{the sampling distribution}\end{pmatrix}}$$

For example, assuming an infinite population and a large sample size, when formulating decision rules about a *population mean* we use the expression

$$z_{\text{level of significance}} = \frac{\bar{X}_{AL} - \mu_X}{s_{\bar{X}}} = \frac{\bar{X}_{AL} - \mu_X}{s_X/\sqrt{n}}$$

Using the appropriate symbols and still assuming an infinite population and a large sample size, specify the same relationship for decision rules concerning:

(*a*) The difference between population means
(*b*) The population proportion
(*c*) The difference between population proportions

11
Continuous Prior Distributions and Their Revision

In an earlier section of this book (Chaps. 6 and 7), we saw how sample evidence could be combined with prior information in solving a decision problem. There, the sampling was binomial, and the prior information took the form of a discrete probability distribution. We now wish to extend the concepts developed earlier to situations where the sampling and prior distributions are continuous. We shall first consider the use of the normal distribution to summarize prior information.

NORMAL PRIOR PROBABILITIES

The normal distribution has characteristics which are representative of a typical decision maker's prior beliefs in many kinds of decision problems. It works especially well when these beliefs are subjective, i.e., informed business judgments, rather than objectively based on historical relative frequencies or other "hard" facts. You learned in Chap. 9, for example, that the normal distribution is symmetrical and bell-shaped, implying that the values of a normally distributed variable are equally likely to fall a given distance from either side of the mean and that small deviations from the mean are more likely than large ones. Using the normal as a prior estimating distribution then implies: (1) that the decision maker's best guess is as likely to be in error by a given amount in one direction as another, and (2) that while various sizes of estimating error are possible, small errors are more likely than large ones. Certainly such statements will not describe the prior distribution in *all* decision situations, but they do seem to describe the nature of most subjective estimates of the random variables that provide the source of uncertainty in decision problems. Generally we *do* feel that our best guess is as apt to be high as low and, however unsure we may be, that it is more apt to be near the true value than far away.

Of course, the use of a normal prior distribution actually involves some much more specific assumptions than these. Given the mean μ_o and the standard deviation σ_o of the normal prior distribution, we can state, according to our knowledge of the normal distribution, that the decision maker believes there are about two chances out of three the true mean μ of the random variable is within 1 σ_o of his estimate, i. e., that the true μ lies within the range $\mu_o \pm \sigma_o$. Or we could say that he is about 95% sure that μ is within $2\sigma_o$ of his estimate, etc.

But where do we obtain the standard deviation σ_o for a prior estimating distribution? A decision maker may willingly give you his best guess (the mean, μ_o) of the prior distribution but may plead that he is quite unable to provide the σ_o (especially if he has not spent the hours you have spent poring over a decision theory text). Actually, if he is able to provide any sort of statement regarding the betting odds or probabilities of estimating errors of a certain size, then the assumption of a normal prior distribution enables you to compute σ_o. Suppose, for example, that he is willing to bet even money that his estimate of the true mean of some variable is correct to within 10 units. This means he is assigning a probability of .5 to the event that μ is within the range $\mu_o \pm 10$. Now recall from our earlier discussion of the normal distribution that about 68% of the area under the normal curve is included by a range $\mu_o \pm \sigma_o$. This means that somewhat less than 1 σ_o in either direction would be required to encompass 50% of the area (corresponding to the probability of .5) under the normal curve.

In fact, we can use the normal area table to find precisely what distance on either side of the mean (measured in standard deviation units) would include 50% of the total area—25% on either side of the mean. Using the normal area table backward, we see that an area of 25% on either side would require a distance of somewhere between .67 and .68 σ_o.

This means that the 10-unit estimating error on which our decision maker was willing to give 50-50 odds represents, say, .67 σ_o, or roughly 2/3 of the standard deviation of his prior estimating distribution. Since

$$.67\sigma_o = 10,$$
$$\sigma_o = \frac{10}{.67} = 15$$

and 15 is the σ_o for the normal prior distribution. This technique, of course, is not limited to the use of 50-50 odds. A σ_o could be derived in similar fashion from any probability statement concerning the magnitude of estimating error. Once obtained, the σ_o can be used to derive other probability statements concerning estimating errors, which then may be checked against the decision maker's intuitive feel for these errors.[1]

Let us now apply the use of a normal prior distribution to a specific decision situation.

A DECISION PROBLEM IN COMPUTER LEASING

Suppose that a mail-order firm with 900 retail outlets is contemplating the installation of a centralized data processing system in its home office with tape input units in each of the retail outlets. The total system including the inputs could be leased from the office equipment manufacturer for a two-year period at a cost of $180,000 per month (or $4,320,000 for the entire period). It is designed to provide more efficient accounts receivable and inventory record keeping. Since the firm believes that its current accounting, billing, and inventory control practices are providing satisfactory levels of customer service, economic justification for the facility must be made on the basis of a saving in clerical effort. Management feels that the elimination of clerical labor hours could be accomplished without creating serious personnel problems. Some of these hours are now spent by part-time and temporary employees, and normal attrition of the clerical work force could be expected to take care of the remaining reduction in the work force.

There is, of course, some uncertainty as to the dollar savings that will actually be achieved by the computer system. The customer representative for the computer manufacturer has estimated that monthly savings of $250 in clerical costs could be achieved for each retail branch. If so, this would mean total savings for the 900 branches of 900 × $250 = $225,000. For the 24-month period of the lease arrangement the estimated savings would be $225,000 × 24 = $5,400,000.

[1] If a σ_o derived in the above manner produces statements with which the decision maker cannot roughly agree, then this simply implies that his prior distribution is not normal, and other methods, some of which may be found in the bibliography, must be used.

Since the total leasing costs are $4,320,000, this estimate pictures the installation as quite profitable.[2]

The firm's president has asked his own systems analysis group to study the validity of the manufacturer's estimates. While they agree that $250/month/branch represents a reasonable "best guess" as to the clerical cost reductions, including wages, fringe benefits, and reducible overhead, the chief analyst has pointed out the possibility of a sizable error in this estimate. Differences in the operations of the individual branches are apt to produce considerable dispersion among the results actually achieved, and some basic doubts regarding the system's operating effectiveness when integrated with other company procedures makes the cost savings figure subject to considerable uncertainty.

The chief analyst points out that there is *some* chance, although he believes it rather unlikely, that total labor costs could be *increased* as a result of the change. Pressed to provide a "feel" for the underlying uncertainty, he estimates that the chances are about 50-50 that the average cost savings (per branch per month) will actually be between $150 and $350 (i.e., $250 $\pm$ $100).

The systems group also reports that the two-year period for which the lease is contemplated represents a reasonable period for decision-making purposes. Changes in the technology of the type of equipment being considered are rapid, and it seems unlikely that the decision made now will have any measurable impact on future decisions in this area.

BREAK-EVEN POINT AND LOSS FUNCTIONS

Under the foregoing circumstances, the company faces a decision problem where the conditional payoffs of the decision to lease depend on the average cost savings per month per branch for the entire company over the two-year period. We can, in fact, calculate the value of this average which would allow the firm to break even on the lease. The average savings per branch per month, which we can designate in the problem as μ (the mean of our basic random variable) times 900 branches times 24 months will give the total cost savings resulting from the leased equipment. In order to break even, the firm must have total savings equaling the total lease payments, $4,320,000. Therefore, the break-even value μ_b will be such that

$$\mu_b \times 900 \times 24 = \$4{,}320{,}000$$

and

$$\mu_b = \frac{4{,}320{,}000}{900 \times 24} = \$200/\text{branch}/\text{month}$$

[2] The time value of money is not considered here. It could be considered—although this would make the problem more complicated—by appropriate discounting of the cash flows, but the decision theory analysis would not be altered.

Thus, should the true value of μ turn out to be greater than \$200/branch/month, the lease would prove profitable. However, should μ in fact be less than \$200, the decision to lease will prove in retrospect to be an incorrect decision, and the firm will incur a loss. A general statement of the potential opportunity losses involved in this decision situation is given in Table 11.1. Notice the symmetrical character of the opportunity

Table 11.1

True value of μ	*Correct decision*	*Incorrect decision*	*Opportunity loss*
$\mu \geq \mu_b$	Lease	Do not lease	$(\mu - \mu_b)900 \times 24$
$\mu < \mu_b$	Do not lease	Lease	$(\mu_b - \mu)900 \times 24$

loss functions. They imply, for example, that a decision to lease with a true μ of \$100 (an incorrect decision) results in the same magnitude of opportunity loss (\$100 $\times$ 900 $\times$ 24 = \$2,160,000) as a decision *not* to lease with a true μ of \$300 (also an incorrect decision). Putting this another way, we can say that errors in estimating μ are just as serious in one direction as in the other. It is also true that the size of the opportunity loss is proportional to the size of the estimating error, resulting in a decision situation we describe technically as possessing *linear* loss functions.

Although symmetrical linear loss functions are not characteristic of *all* decision problems, such functions *are* found in many practical applications of business decision theory. In any case, to simplify a discussion that is already rather complex, we shall restrict ourselves to consideration of this type of problem in this chapter and the next.

All this discussion does help emphasize one point that was probably clear in the beginning: The proper decision for the firm to make depends on the value of μ, the average savings per branch per month. The true value of μ is, of course, unknown, even though the firm has collected substantial information that is relevant to estimating it. This information could be summarized in the form of a normal prior probability distribution. From the previous statement of the problem, the mean of the prior estimating distribution μ_o should be taken as \$250. This was regarded as the best estimate of obtainable cost savings. The σ_o for this estimating distribution could be obtained from the statement that the chances are about 50-50 that this average cost savings will be between \$150 and \$350. We saw on page 201 that 50-50 odds of including the true value in an interval estimate implied about $.67\sigma_o$ each direction from the μ_o. Since $.67\sigma_o = \$100$, for our problem, $\sigma_o = \$100/.67 = \$150$.

DECISION MAKING WITH A NORMAL PRIOR DISTRIBUTION

We are now ready to apply our prior estimating distribution to the actual decision process. Remember that the firm should decide to lease the data processing equipment if $\mu \geq \$200$. Since μ_o, the best estimate of μ, equals \$250, which is greater than \$200, and since the opportunity losses are symmetrical (equally severe in both directions), there is really no reason *not* to proceed with leasing the equipment. In fact, *in any problem where the opportunity losses are symmetrical in both directions from the break-even value of* μ *and where the prior distribution is also symmetrical, the decision rests on a simple, commonsense comparison of the mean of the estimating distribution with the break-even value.* Here, since $\mu_o > \mu_b$, the decision (to lease) would be made accordingly.

Note that when the loss functions and the prior distribution are symmetrical, it is only the mean of the estimating distribution that is important. The form of the estimating distribution we have used (in this case, normal) and its other parameters (in this case σ_o) have no relevance in making the type of decision considered here. Indeed, it is difficult to see how we have used any statistical decision theory at all, up to this point, to supplement commonsense reasoning. The fact is, we have not. Statistical theory and the additional information we have obtained relative to the estimating distribution of μ are useful only in the solution of two important related problems:

1. How to combine knowledge or judgment in the form of a prior distribution with information obtained from a sample.
2. How to determine the economic desirability of obtaining sample information prior to making a decision.

The first of these problems is considered in the following section; the second is reserved for the next chapter.

REVISION OF NORMAL PRIOR PROBABILITIES

A procedure was explained in Chap. 7 for revising a decision maker's prior estimate of probabilities. This procedure, based on Bayes' rule, provided a means for incorporating sample evidence along with prior beliefs in decision problems where the values of the random variable—the source of the uncertainty in the decision problem—were discrete or point values. Here a procedure will be developed which enables us to revise prior beliefs that are represented by a continuous probability distribution, namely, the normal, using sample results obtained from a normal sampling distribution. The revised estimating distribution for μ will represent the combined effects of the prior estimating distribution (often subjective) and the sampling distribution (objective).

What are the implications of the requirement that the sampling distribution also be normal? Remember that a particular sample mean $\bar{X}$ is only one of many possible $\bar{X}$ values that would be obtained from different random samples of a given size drawn from a population. Also, recall that these $\bar{X}$ values are approximately normally distributed around the true population mean μ as long as the sample size is reasonably large. The distribution of sample means will likewise be approximately normal for even smaller values of n as long as the population is close to symmetrically distributed.[3] The mean of the sampling distribution will be μ, and its standard deviation will be $\sigma_{\bar{X}}$, the standard error of the mean, given by the formula $\sigma_{\bar{X}} = \sigma_X/\sqrt{n}$. Where the population standard deviation σ_X is unknown, $s_{\bar{X}}$ can be used to estimate $\sigma_{\bar{X}}$ (as in Chaps. 9 and 10):

$$s_{\bar{X}} = \frac{s_X}{\sqrt{n}}$$

where s_X is the estimate of the population standard deviation σ_X, based on sample data.

Now the revised distribution could be obtained by breaking down the prior and sampling distributions into discrete chunks and proceeding exactly as in Chap. 7, where Bayes' rule was used to revise a discrete prior distribution. However, as the student may recall, that procedure was cumbersome. It would be made even more so here by the additional step of first converting a continuous probability distribution into a discrete one. The beauty of using normal distributions to represent the prior distribution and sample evidence is that the computations required to obtain the revised distributions are greatly simplified. In fact with normal prior and sampling distributions *the revised estimating distribution will also be normal,* and its mean and variance can be easily obtained.

INFORMATION CONTENT

To explain the procedures involved in obtaining the characteristics of the revised distribution, we shall first find it useful to define a new concept, *information content,* denoted by the symbol IC. It is generally equal to the reciprocal of the variance of a distribution. For the prior distribution,

$$IC_o = \frac{1}{\sigma_o^2} \tag{11.1}$$

[3] Actually, if the *parent* (not the prior) distribution from which the samples are drawn is normal, the sampling distribution will be normal for even small samples. Recall that if $s_{\bar{X}}$ is used as an estimate of $\sigma_{\bar{X}}$, the t distribution is applicable (see Chap. 9, pp. 171–172 and the final section of this chapter). Here, for simplicity, we assume normality of the sampling distribution.

As the formula implies, the greater the variance of a distribution, the less the informational content. A decision maker who is rather unsure of his prior estimates of a variable will represent his beliefs with an estimating distribution with a large variance. It makes sense that such a distribution should be described as having relatively low informational content. Of course the IC value really provides no additional description of the distribution beyond that given by the variance. It is a useful concept primarily because it simplifies the relationships among prior, sampling, and revised distributions, making these relationships intuitively easier to understand.

The information content of a sample, $IC_{\bar{X}}$, will be equal to the reciprocal of the variance of the sampling distribution:

$$IC_{\bar{X}} = \frac{1}{\sigma_{\bar{X}}^2} = \frac{1}{(\sigma_X/\sqrt{n})^2} = \frac{n}{\sigma_X^2} \tag{11.2}$$

Note that the information content of a sample is proportional to its size, logically enough, and inversely proportional to the variance of the population from which the sample is drawn.

CHARACTERISTICS OF THE REVISED DISTRIBUTION

We now state without proof the following important result: If the prior estimating distribution is normal, with mean μ_o and information content IC_o, and if the sampling distribution is normal with sample information content $IC_{\bar{X}}$, then the revised distribution is also normal with a mean μ_r given by

$$\mu_r = \frac{IC_o\mu_o + IC_{\bar{X}}\bar{X}}{IC_o + IC_{\bar{X}}} \tag{11.3}$$

Note that the revised mean is an ordinary *weighted average* of the prior mean and sample mean, where the weights used are the information contents of the prior distribution and sample, respectively.

An added advantage of the information content concept is that the IC_r for the revised distribution, and hence its variance, can be obtained simply. As might be expected, the information content in the revised distribution is the sum of information provided by the prior and sampling distributions:

$$IC_r = IC_o + IC_{\bar{X}} \tag{11.4}$$

If we wish to know the variance of the revised distribution, this expression can be rewritten as

$$\frac{1}{\sigma_r^2} = \frac{1}{\sigma_o^2} + \frac{1}{\sigma_{\bar{X}}^2} \tag{11.5}$$

(since IC was defined as the reciprocal of the variance). Then,

$$\sigma_r^2 = \frac{\sigma_o^2 \, \sigma_{\bar{X}}^2}{\sigma_o^2 + \sigma_{\bar{X}}^2} \tag{11.6}$$

A word of caution is in order concerning the use of these formulas. There are three variances involved here—all pertaining to distributions used in *estimating* μ, namely, the prior, sampling, and revised distributions. It is all too easy to get one or more of these variances confused with the population variance σ_X^2, which measures the dispersion of values within the population itself, or with the sample estimate of it, s_X^2, which is based on the dispersion of individual values making up a particular sample. The dispersion or spread among individual values comprising a population or sample is something entirely different from the dispersion of a distribution used to *estimate* the population mean. Essentially σ_o, $\sigma_{\bar{X}}$, and σ_r measure the precision of various estimates of μ; σ_X^2, or its "stand-in" s_X^2, which measures the dispersion of actual observations, is used in determining $\sigma_{\bar{X}}^2$, but that is the only way it is involved in the revision process. All this may be clearer in the context of the examples which follow.

AN EXAMPLE OF THE NORMAL REVISION PROCESS

To illustrate the method of revising a normal distribution, let us use the normal prior distribution of the computer-leasing problem described earlier in this chapter. It was determined that the firm should lease the equipment if it produced an average savings of $200 or more per branch for the 900 branches. The prior estimate formulated by company staff was represented by a normal probability distribution with a mean μ_o of $250 (the "best guess") and standard deviation of $150.

While this estimate of μ indicates that the company should lease, the relatively large σ_o for the estimating distribution is disquieting. Suppose the company finds it possible to have a month's trial run with a randomly selected sample of 30 of its branches to determine the cost savings available.

Assume that there is no seasonal pattern to savings achieved and that the company can take the information derived from the sample as representative of the entire period of the proposed lease. Then assume that the following results are calculated from the 30 individual values of monthly cost savings in the sample:

$$\bar{X} = \$194.20$$
$$s_X = \$251.55$$

From the latter value[4] we can estimate the standard deviation of the sampling distributions as

$$s_{\bar{X}} = \frac{s_X}{\sqrt{n}} = \frac{251.55}{\sqrt{30}} = 45$$

We are now prepared to put together the company's prior estimates and the sample information to obtain a revised estimating distribution. First,

$$IC_o = \frac{1}{150^2} = \frac{1}{22{,}500} = .0000444$$

$$IC_{\bar{X}} = \frac{1}{45^2} = \frac{1}{2025} = .0004938$$

Then the mean of the revised distribution μ_r is obtained from the weighted average

$$\begin{aligned} \mu_r &= \frac{\mu_o IC_o + \bar{X} IC_{\bar{X}}}{IC_o + IC_{\bar{X}}} \\ &= \frac{250(.0000444) + 194.20(.0004938)}{.0000444 + .0004938} \\ &= \$198.62 \end{aligned}$$

The revised distribution will have an information content of

$$\begin{aligned} IC_r &= IC_o + IC_{\bar{X}} \\ &= .0000444 + .0004938 \\ &= .0005382 \end{aligned}$$

and a standard deviation σ_r of

$$\begin{aligned} \sigma_r &= \sqrt{\frac{1}{IC_r}} \\ &= \sqrt{\frac{1}{.0005382}} \\ &= \sqrt{1858} \\ &= \$43.10 \end{aligned}$$

DECISION MAKING WITH THE REVISED DISTRIBUTION

We now know that the revised distribution for estimating μ is normal, with a mean of \$198.62 and a standard deviation of \$43.10. Even though the preceding computations have been rather involved, the revised

[4] The s_X larger than $\bar{X}$ indicates that the sample probably contains some negative X's, i.e., branches where the cost *savings* are negative due to an actual increase in costs.

distribution is used for decision-making purposes in the same common-sense way as was the prior distribution. Recall that in the absence of sample information the prior mean μ_o was simply compared with the economic break-even point μ_b to determine the proper decision. (Since $\mu_o = \$250$ and $\mu_b = \$200$, estimated savings were sufficient to justify a decision to lease the equipment.)

The *revised* "best estimate" of cost savings per branch, taking the information obtained from the sample of 30 branches into account, is \$198.62. Since this μ_r value is *less* than μ_b, that is, $\$198.62 < \$200$, the proper decision at this point would be to reject the lease arrangement. As before, it is the simple comparison of the *mean* of the revised estimating distribution with the break-even value that governs the decision. The σ_r for the revised distribution is important only in connection with *further* revision in the light of additional sample information.

Now the sample evidence was in this case sufficient to swing the decision from acceptance of the lease arrangement to rejection. Needless to say, this will not always happen. The sample evidence, properly weighted, may fail to pull the revised mean past the break-even point—it just barely did in the illustration—or it may support the prior estimate, causing the decision maker to be more sure than ever of his judgments. What is important is that we now have at our disposal a systematic method for combining the results of a sample with subjective prior estimates (business judgments) that can be represented by normal estimating distributions. Since the revised distribution is also normal, further sample evidence can be incorporated as it becomes available by repeating the revision process, treating this revised distribution as if it were a prior distribution.

REVISED DISTRIBUTIONS AND CONFIDENCE INTERVALS

It may prove useful to contrast the more traditional confidence interval estimating procedure discussed earlier in this book (Chap. 9 for normal sampling) with the revised estimating distribution of the preceding section. The sample of 30 branches could have been used as the basis for, say, a 95% confidence interval estimate of average cost savings per branch:

$$\begin{aligned}
95\% \text{ confidence interval} &= \bar{X} \pm 1.96 s_{\bar{X}} \\
&= \bar{X} \pm 1.96 \frac{s_X}{\sqrt{n}} \\
&= \$194.20 \pm 1.96(45) \\
&= \$194.20 \pm \$88.20
\end{aligned}$$

(To be strictly correct, a t value of 2.045 should have been used in place of $z = 1.96$ since s_X was used to estimate α_X. However, the normality of the sampling distribution is assumed in obtaining the revised distribution, so it seems more reasonable to base a confidence interval on the same assumption for comparative purposes. For an n as large as 30, the difference is small anyway.)

One interpretation of this interval is that the decision maker can be 95% sure that the range \$106.00 to \$282.40 contains the true value of average savings.

Using the revised estimating distribution, on the other hand, which is normal with $\mu_r = \$198.62$ and $\sigma_r = \$43.10$, the decision maker would obtain the probability that μ was in the interval \$106 to \$282.40 as follows:

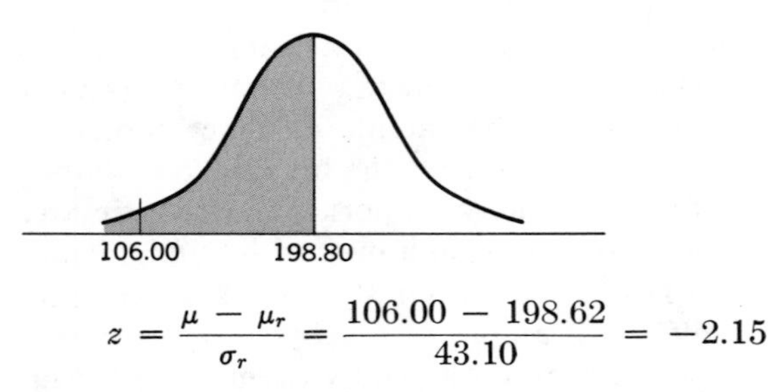

$$z = \frac{\mu - \mu_r}{\sigma_r} = \frac{106.00 - 198.62}{43.10} = -2.15$$

The area from the normal table corresponding to $z = -2.15$ is .4842. Therefore $P(106 < \mu < 198.80) = .4842$. Likewise, for the upper part of the range,

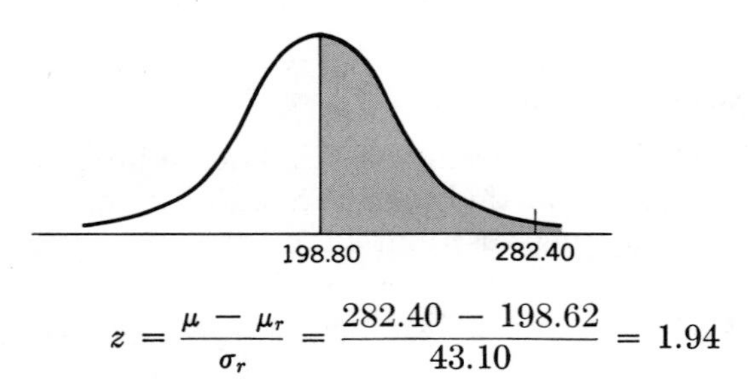

$$z = \frac{\mu - \mu_r}{\sigma_r} = \frac{282.40 - 198.62}{43.10} = 1.94$$

The area from the normal table corresponding to $z = 1.94$ is .4738. Thus, $P(106.00 < \mu < 282.40) = .4842 + .4738 = .9580$ as opposed to the confidence coefficient of .9500.

Alternatively, using the revised distribution, the decision maker could be 95% sure that the true average savings were between \$114.14, or $198.62 - 1.96(43.10)$, and \$283.10, or $198.62 + 1.96(43.10)$, compared with the confidence interval of 106.00 to 282.40. What causes the difference in these estimating procedures? Why is the revised probability that μ is within the confidence interval different from the confidence coefficient?

The answer, of course, is that the revised distribution incorporates prior information, whereas the confidence interval estimate does not. In fact, the only time that the use of a revised distribution and classical interval estimation will lead to similar results is when absolutely no prior information is available. This means that the decision maker, before sampling, would have to consider *all* possible values of the random variable equally likely. His prior estimating distribution would have infinite variance and zero information content. Under these circumstances, his revised distribution for estimating μ would have a mean equal to $\bar{X}$ and standard deviation equal to $\sigma_{\bar{X}}$, as in Fig. 11.1.

Notice that this curve has the exact properties of the distribution of sample means (for samples of size n drawn from a population with mean μ and standard deviation σ_X) with one important conceptual difference. It is also normal and has a standard deviation $\sigma_{\bar{X}}$, but the mean of the pictured distribution is the sample mean $\bar{X}$, whereas the mean of the sampling distribution is the true population mean μ.

Basically what has happened is that the random variable has been switched. The revised distribution in Fig. 11.1 is an estimating distribution constructed for the purpose of estimating the true value of μ, which is treated as if it were a random variable. The best estimate of μ in the absence of any prior information is $\bar{X}$, the mean of the sample. The sampling distribution of $\bar{X}$ on the other hand, is an abstraction describing the manner in which the values of a random variable $\bar{X}$, which are the means of all possible samples of a given size drawn from a population, are distributed around the true population mean.

Note that the type of distribution appearing in Fig. 11.1, although it incorporates no prior information, was not drawn in Chap. 4 or in Chap. 9 in connection with the discussion of classical estimation procedures. The reason is the classical objection, discussed at length in Chap. 4, to the interpretation of a population parameter such as μ as a random

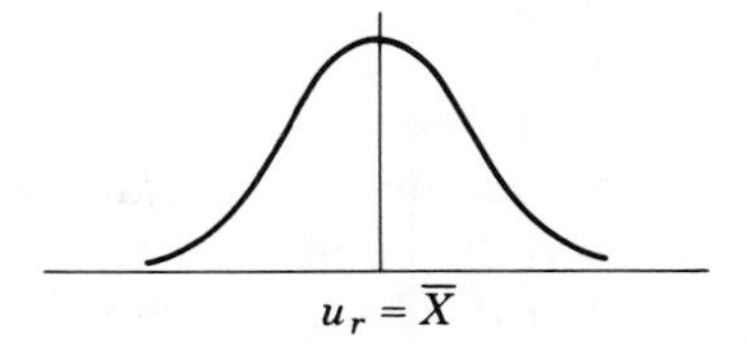

Fig. 11.1 Revised distribution for estimating μ when no prior information is available ($\sigma_o = \infty$; $IC_o = 0$; $\sigma_r = \sigma_{\bar{X}} = \sigma_X/\sqrt{n}$).

variable. The Bayesian, while he would favor such an interpretation, might object to a revised distribution such as that shown in Fig. 11.1 on other grounds. He would probably argue that situations where absolutely no prior information is available or where all values of a decision variable are equally likely occur rarely, if at all. If the prior information is vague and prior estimates are uncertain, the information content of the prior will reflect this. The Bayesian would simply take the position that it is not necessary to go to the extreme of ignoring prior information altogether.

DEPARTURES FROM NORMALITY

The results of the previous sections rest on the fundamental assumption that both the prior and sampling distributions are normal. What of the situation where this assumption is not valid?

Consider first the effects of a nonnormal prior distribution. If, as is usually the case, the information content of the prior distribution is small relative to that of the sampling distribution, the shape of the prior distribution will have little effect on either the shape of the revised distribution or the numerical values calculated as its parameters. Unless the decision maker's prior estimates are very definite (small σ_o^2 and high IC_o) and quite nonnormal, the formulas developed above for the normal case can be used without a serious loss of accuracy.

The situation is a little more complicated when nonnormal sampling distributions are considered. A distribution of sample means can be nonnormal for either of two reasons. First, the parent population from which the samples are drawn can depart seriously from the normal distribution. Under this circumstance, the sampling distribution will be very close to normal if the sample is large, but it may not be for small samples. Remember that the central limit theorem only promises an approach to normality as the sample size is increased.

Second, the distribution of sample means may be treated as strictly normal only when the true population standard deviation is known. In almost all practical problems it is necessary to estimate the population standard deviation from the sample standard deviation. Where s_X is used in place of σ (with the appropriate correction for the loss of a degree of freedom), sample means will be distributed according to the t distribution described in Chap. 9. Here again, however, we may note that the t distribution approaches normality as the sample size increases.

The situation may then be summarized as follows: An adequate approximation to normal sampling distributions will be obtained regardless of other circumstances as long as the sample size is reasonably large—a good rule of thumb here would be $n \geq 30$, although this depends on the nonnormality of the parent distribution. The revision formulas of this chapter may be used without hesitation for large samples. Although they are often used with smaller samples, the student should be aware of the theoretical limitations involved when the prior and sampling distributions are nonnormal. A feel for the magnitude of errors involved may be obtained by a study of Appendix 11A, where continuous methods are applied to a problem discussed earlier in which the normality assumptions are unwarranted.

Appendix 11A

Application of Normal Distribution Analysis to Decision Problems Involving Discrete Prior Distributions

Revision of prior distributions for estimating a population proportion using Bayes' rule and binomial tables was described at length in Chap. 7. The procedure involved, although simple enough in concept, suffers from two drawbacks: (1) The prior and revised distributions used are discrete, implying that only certain specified values of the random variable p are possible; (2) the necessary arithmetic is burdensome and time-consuming.

The purpose of this appendix is to consider an alternative method of revising discrete prior distributions of p or other random variables which treats them as *continuous* rather than discrete. Specifically, the method explained here converts a prior distribution of p to normal form and then utilizes the normal revision procedure explained in Chap. 11. The method is illustrated by applying it to the decision problem (the product development situation) used earlier to explain discrete revision procedures.

AN ALTERNATIVE ANALYSIS OF THE PRODUCT DEVELOPMENT PROBLEM

In Chaps. 6 and 7 a problem involving a decision whether or not to develop a new product was posed. To reiterate the more important facts of that problem, it was economically desirable to develop the product if gross profits per unit of $500 could more than cover fixed development costs of $500,000. The firm would thus have to sell 1000 units of the product among its 20,000 regular customers. Our previous analysis of this problem, cast in a binomial framework, set up the break-even point in terms of the proportion of customers who would have to buy the product, that is, $p = 1000/20{,}000 = .05$.

Suppose we now recast the problem in a continuous framework, replacing the proportion of customers buying, p, the random variable (and source of uncertainty in the problem), with the *average* dollar profit *per customer*, μ. The break-even value of this variable, μ_b, would be $\$500{,}000/20{,}000 = \$25$ per customer.

The subjectively derived prior distribution of the proportion of customers expected to purchase (Table 6.1):

Proportion of customers purchasing	*Probability*
.02	.1
.04	.3
.06	.3
.08	.2
.10	.1

can be recast as follows:

Average profit per customer	*Probability*
$10	.1
20	.3
30	.3
40	.2
50	.1

This is simply a different way of expressing the same managerial judgments regarding prospects for the product that were selected in the "proportion purchasing" distribution. While the new distribution is not strictly normal, it is symmetrical and bell-shaped enough to reasonably approximate a normal prior distribution. The parameters of this distribution may be calculated as $\mu_o = \$29.00$ and $\sigma_o = \$11.36$. (It is good practice for the student to verify these figures.)

A comparison of the prior mean profit per customer of $29.00 with the breakeven value of $\mu_b = \$25.00$ indicates that in the absence of any further information, the product *should* be developed. This is the same decision reached earlier in the *EOL* analysis (without sampling) of Table 6.4.

The real purpose here, however, is to consider the applicability of the normal *revision* process to this problem. Now notice that the distribution of profit per customer is *not* normal. Indeed, by the nature of this particular problem, all customers either buy the product, in which case the resulting profit is $500, or don't buy, in which case the profit is 0. Instead of being anywhere near normal, the distribution of profits by customers consists of just the two values 500 and 0, e.g.:

Customer number	*Gross profit realized*
1	$ 0
2	0
3	0
4	500
5	0
.	.
.	.
.	.
20,000	0

Actually, the nonnormality of this *parent* distribution, or population, in itself does not matter. In the revision process described in Chap. 11, we are concerned with the normality of the prior and *sampling* distributions. Of course, with a parent population as violently nonnormal as the one described above and a sample size as small as 20, the sampling distribution will hardly be exactly normal. Nevertheless, we shall proceed here to assume that the sampling distribution *is* normal and to carry out the normal analysis of the product-development problem. The results of this analysis can then be compared with the results previously obtained by discrete methods to see what errors are introduced by the normality assumptions. If the errors are not serious, the normal methods afford a desirable alternative approach because of their relative computational ease.

Since from the prior distribution the expected value of p is .058, we can estimate $\sigma_{\bar{p}}$ as[5]

$$\sigma_{\bar{p}} = \sqrt{\frac{p(1-p)}{n}} = \sqrt{\frac{(.058)(.942)}{20}}$$
$$= .0523$$

[5] Estimating $\sigma_{\bar{p}}$ according to the prior best estimate of p is generally superior to using the sample p in the estimate. In the problem under discussion, the sample proportion buying was 0, which would if used in the formula lead to an estimate of $\sigma_{\bar{p}} = 0$, which would in turn cause the entire procedure to break down!

This can be translated into terms of dollar sales per customer (our continuous variable), giving

$$\sigma_{\bar{X}} = \$26.15$$

then

$$\begin{aligned}\sigma_r &= \sqrt{\frac{\sigma_o^2\sigma_{\bar{X}}^2}{\sigma_o^2 + \sigma_{\bar{X}}^2}} \\ &= \sqrt{\frac{(11.36)^2(26.15)^2}{(11.36)^2 + (26.15)^2}} \\ &= \$10.42\end{aligned}$$

Also,

$$IC_o = \frac{1}{(11.35)^2} = .00775$$

and

$$IC_{\bar{X}} = \frac{1}{(26.15)^2} = .00146$$

Now since 0 buyers were actually found in the sample of 20 discussed in Chap. 7, the sample average profit per customer $\bar{X}$ is also 0, and

$$\begin{aligned}\mu_r &= \frac{IC_o(\mu_o) + IC_{\bar{X}}(\bar{X})}{IC_o + IC_{\bar{X}}} \\ &= \frac{(.00775)(29.00) + (.00146)(0)}{.00775 + .00146} \\ &= \$24.40\end{aligned}$$

Thus, using the normal analysis, the sample of (n = 20, r = 0) or (n = 20, $\bar{X}$ = 0) leads to a revised estimating distribution, assumed to be normal, with a mean of \$24.40 and a standard deviation of \$10.42. Using the sample prior distribution and sample data in discrete form in Chap. 7, we obtained the following revised distribution:

Proportion purchasing, p	*P(p) (revised)*
.02	.1985
.04	.3943
.06	.2588
.08	.1122
.10	.0362

As before, we can express proportion purchasing in terms of average profit per customer, as follows:

Average profit per customer	*Probability (revised)*
\$10	.1985
20	.3943
30	.2588
40	.1122
50	.0362

Calculation of the mean and standard deviation of this distribution, which the student can also verify, gives μ_r = \$23.93 (as compared with μ_r = \$24.40 using normal methods) and σ_r = \$10.38 (as compared with σ_r = \$10.42 using normal methods). The difference in results between the normal and discrete revision methods is insignificant, even though the normality assumptions were violated, particularly with respect to the sampling distribution. Of course, this one illustration does not in itself prove the adequacy of the normal analysis of seemingly "nonnormal" discrete problems, and it is not possible to generalize regarding the accuracy of the approximation obtained. Still, it does seem to provide remarkably close results in many practical decision situations, and its relative simplicity has much to recommend it. Certainly it makes sense to utilize the normal revision methods as a "first pass" in discrete decision situations. Should the decision prove borderline, the more accurate but more complex discrete methods could then be applied.

PROBLEMS

11.1 Acme Products is considering the addition of a new product to its line. The product would increase the company's fixed cost by \$2000 per year. The selling price is \$15 and variable costs are \$11 per unit. The market research department estimates that demand will be 600 units per year but that there is a 25% chance that sales will fall below the level of break-even profitability.

(*a*) What is the break-even level of demand?

(*b*) What are the characteristics of the company's demand estimating distribution? (Assume that a normal distribution is appropriate.)

(*c*) What decision should the company make?

11.2 Distinguish among the following variances, identifying the distribution for which each measures dispersion:

(*a*) σ_o^2

(*b*) σ_X^2

(*c*) s_X^2

(*d*) $\sigma_{\bar{X}}^2$

(*e*) σ_r^2

11.3 A normal prior estimating distribution has $\mu_o = 42$ and $\sigma_o = 1$. A sample of size 49 is taken with $\bar{X} = 41$ and $s_X = 14$. For the revised estimating distribution, compute:

(*a*) μ_r
(*b*) σ_r
(*c*) $P(\mu_X \leq 40)$

11.4 (*a*) In Prob. 11.3, how large would an additional sample have to be to reduce the standard deviation of the revised distribution σ_r to .5?

(*b*) What assumption did you have to make to answer (*a*)?

(*c*) Can you generalize these results? Is the reduction in σ_r, i.e., the improvement in the precision of your estimating distribution, proportional to the increase in sample size?

11.5 Spend 'n Save, a department store chain, wishes to estimate the average size of a charge sale. The credit manager estimates an average of \$12, and indicates that he is about 50% sure that the average would be between \$10 and \$14. To supplement his judgment, he draws a random sample of 100 charge slips from last year's records and computes $\bar{X} = \$9.64$ and $s_X = \$3.10$.

(*a*) Construct a 95% confidence interval estimate of μ_X, the mean size of charge sale.

(*b*) Use the credit manager's estimates to construct a prior estimating distribution for μ_X.

(*c*) Revise the estimating distribution to reflect the sample results.

(*d*) Based on the revised distribution obtained in (*c*), you can be 95% sure that μ_X is between ________ and ________.

(*e*) Compare the answers to (*a*) and (*d*).

(*f*) What general statement can you make regarding classical and Bayesian estimating procedures?

11.6 D. H. Roberts recently purchased a small manufacturing company. Among the company's assets are accounts receivable carried on the company's balance sheet at \$180,000. Mr. Roberts has been skeptical regarding the collectibility of these accounts, which represent balances owed by a total of 1440 different customers and many of which are long overdue. He is considering selling the accounts to a "factor" who takes full responsibility for collection as well as the risk of noncollectibility. The factor has offered 50% of the book value, or \$90,000, for the accounts.

After carefully looking over the records, Mr. Roberts estimates that if he were to attempt to collect these accounts himself, he would have to spend about \$30 per customer in collection expenses. He is uncertain, because of the low credit ratings of many customers and the large number of charges which have apparently been disputed by customers, as to how much can actually be collected. He estimates that it should run about \$120 per customer but could run as low as \$50 per customer (about a 10% chance).

(*a*) Should Mr. Roberts sell the accounts receivable or try to collect them?

(*b*) The company controller suggests trying to collect a random sample of the accounts before the decision is made. Thirty accounts are selected, with \$6010 being collected. Collection expenses for these accounts are \$2110. Would these results alter the decision? (If you think you lack some information necessary to analyze this part of the problem, see whether you can make an intelligent guess at the answer.)

11.7 Suppose the sample of 30 accounts in Prob. 11.6 yields net collections (gross amount collected less collection expense) with a mean of $130 per account and s_X = $60.

(*a*) Obtain a revised normal estimating distribution for net collections per account.

(*b*) Should the accounts receivable be sold to a factor?

11.8 A mining company is investigating the desirability of buying and developing an ore body. The ore body is estimated to contain 5 million tons of ore. It will cost $2,000,000 to purchase and develop the field, including the erection of a processing plant on the site. Variable costs of mining and processing are $50 per ton of ore. The selling price of the metal to be recovered is 24 cents per pound. To simplify the problem do not worry about discounting future cash flows, and assume that all the figures used above are certain.

The random variable in the problem is the average grade of the ore (the percent of the metal in the ore). We can assume that all the metal in the ore is recoverable and that there are no by-products of any value.

On the basis of past experience and preliminary site testing, management estimates that the average grade of the ore body $\mu_o = 12\%$. They also believe that it is reasonable to assume a normal prior, with a 50-50 chance that the grade will be within $\pm 1.0\%$ from μ_o.

Recognizing that there is a fairly large chance that the true mean could be below the break-even value, the management decides to drill 25 test cores in a random pattern into the ore body to check the grade of the ore. When they do, they find that $\bar{X}$, the average ore grade from the 25 cores, is 9.5% with $s_X = 2.5\%$.

Taking into consideration all the evidence they have accumulated up to this point, should they decide to mine the body or not?

11.9 (*a*) In designing a sampling procedure for a normal prior distribution decision problem (see chap. 12) the optimum decision criterion $\bar{X}_{AL}$ is not generally specified in advance of taking the sample. Can you surmise why?

(*b*) How *is* the sample result used in this case to make the decision?

11.10 In the computer-leasing problem discussed in the text, the sample evidence was responsible for changing the decision that would have been made without sampling.

(*a*) What is the lowest value of mean cost savings for the sample that would have left the decision without sampling—to lease the equipment—unchanged?

(*b*) How might a different s_X value for the sample have changed the final decision?

(*c*) How might a similar sample result (same $\bar{X}$ and s_X) from a larger or smaller sample have changed the decision?

11.11 XL Tire and Rubber, Inc., distributes its products through 700 retail outlets. To stimulate slumping sales, the company president is considering a large promotional campaign involving the use of local radio and newspaper advertising and the use of "loss leaders." With the golf season at its peak and enthusiasm for the sport running high, the president believes that the sale of high-quality, name-brand golf balls at "give away" prices will attract customers to his retail outlets. He is hopeful, of course, that these customers will buy tires or other products once they are in the store.

The golf balls would cost the company \$6 per dozen. The proposed plan is to sell the balls at \$.99 per package of 3 on a one-package-to-a-customer basis, with 200 dozen balls being allocated to each retail outlet. This price should be low enough to attract customer traffic and to assure that all the golf balls will be sold during the promotion period. Selling expenses, including inventory carrying costs, shipping, etc., are estimated at 15 cents per package of 3. Advertising expenses for the promotion would involve an agency fee of \$30,000 to plan the campaign and local expenditures of \$1000 for each retail outlet.

(*a*) Assuming the XL gross profit margin (contribution to profit and fixed overhead) averages 25% on sales, how much additional merchandise would each golf ball purchaser have to buy (on the average) to make the promotion a success?

(*b*) What specific assumptions did you have to make to answer (*a*)?

(*c*) Formulate *your own* normal prior estimating distribution of average sales per golf-ball purchaser. (You don't have to know anything about the tire business—just base your μ_o on your best estimate as to how this sort of promotion would work out. If you are not sure, this can be reflected by a large σ_o for your estimating distribution.)

(*d*) What decision regarding the promotion would *you* make?

11.12 The Instant Wealth investment advisory service is considering expanding its weekly market letter that is mailed to subscribers to include additional statistical material and recommendations. Since this material is supplementary in nature, there would be no market for it outside its existing list of subscribers. The Instant Wealth president believes that the new supplement can be sold to about half of the firm's 12,000 subscribers but concedes that there is a 10% chance that as few as one-quarter may buy and a 10% chance that as many as three-quarters may buy it. These estimates assume pricing the supplement at \$50 per year.

The variable cost of producing this supplement is estimated at \$30/subscriber/year, but it would involve initial development costs (including research, purchase of data, computer programming, etc.) of \$80,000. The president believes that these development costs must be recovered quickly since competition will copy the supplement, probably forcing him to lower the price to a much less attractive level within two years.

(*a*) Express the president's estimate of the proportion of customers who will buy the supplement as a normal prior distribution.

(*b*) Based on the above information alone, what should be done?

11.13 In the problems considered earlier involving work sampling (see Probs. 5.2 and 10.8), 24 employees were observed in written communication out of the 100 spot checks. Management, surprised at these results and aware of similar studies done elsewhere, believes that the true percentage is probably around 20%, with only a 10% chance that it could run as high as 24% (or as low as 16%).

(*a*) Obtain an estimating distribution incorporating both the management estimate and the previous sample results.

(*b*) What amount of information is contained in the prior estimating distribution? How does it compare with the information content of the sample?

11.14 In Prob. 7.4, the prior distribution assumed for p was a discrete probability distribution.

(*a*) Do the best you can to represent this prior information by a normal distribution.

(*b*) Use the normal revision process to incorporate the sample results ($n = 100$, $r = 12$).

(*c*) How does the mean of the revised normal distribution in part (*b*) compare with the mean of the revised discrete distribution in Prob. 7.4?

(*d*) Is the normal approximation accurate enough to be useful? Explain.

11.15 Give some examples of practical situations in which you think the normal revision process outlined in this chapter would *not* be applicable. Indicate in each case whether you think it is the normality assumption concerning the prior distribution or concerning the sampling distribution (or some other assumption) that has been violated.

12
The Economics of Sampling: The Normal Case

The questions of whether additional information in the form of a sample should be purchased before making a final decision and, if so, how large a sample should be obtained were considered in Chap. 6. The analysis therein enabled us to compute the expected value of sample information ($EVSI$) for various sizes of samples, which could then be compared with the cost of the various sizes to determine the economic desirability of each in a decision problem. However, the analysis was limited to cases in which the decision maker's prior probability distribution was discrete, and the proposed sampling was binomial, i.e., drawn from a Bernoulli process. The purpose of this chapter is to extend the economic analysis of sampling alternatives to the normal case—where the prior and sampling distributions are normal.

EXPECTED VALUE OF PERFECT INFORMATION

As a first step in assessing the value of sample information, let us examine the method for computing the value of *perfect* information ($EVPI$) where the probability distribution of the random variable is normal. It should be remembered that the *EVPI* in a decision problem is equal to the cost of uncertainty, which is in turn defined as the expected opportunity loss (*EOL*) of the optimal act.

Suppose the decision maker in the computer-leasing problem of the last chapter, armed with only the prior information (in the form of a normal distribution) supplied by his staff, wishes to know the cost of the uncertainty with which he is faced. Remember that the prior best estimate μ_o of \$250 average savings per branch per month would lead him to decide in favor of leasing the equipment. Let us compute the *EOL* for this (optimal) decision.

As long as the average savings realized was greater than the economic break-even value μ_b of \$200, the decision to lease would prove correct, and no opportunity loss would be experienced. Should the true value of the average savings μ be less than \$200, however, the decision would (in retrospect) be incorrect. It was shown in Chap. 11 (page 203) that the dollar magnitude of the opportunity loss under these circumstances was $(\mu_b - \mu)(900)(24)$, or $(200 - \mu)(21{,}600)$. The entire opportunity loss function for the decision to lease, which is linear with a slope of $-21{,}600$ for the $\mu < \$200$ portion and which is simply equal to 0 for values of $\mu \geq 200$, is shown in Figure 12.1.

Now the procedure that has been previously used to evaluate *EOL*s is to multiply the opportunity loss conditional on each state of nature (or value of the random variable) by the probability that each state of nature will occur. These products are summed over all possible values of the random variable to obtain the *EOL* for the decision in question. The difficulty in applying this procedure here is that the random variable has an infinite number of possible values. Whereas, before, our analysis was limited to several possible states of nature representing discrete values of the random variable, its distribution is now being regarded as *continuous*. Specifically, it is assumed to be normally distributed, with $\mu_o = 250$

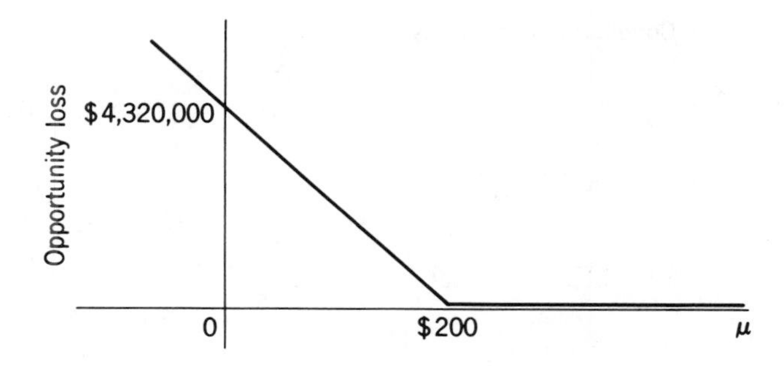

Fig. 12.1 Opportunity loss for the decision to lease.

and $\sigma_o = 150$. This distribution is shown superimposed on the opportunity loss function in Fig. 12.2.

Of course, the *EOL* could be computed in straightforward fashion by the previously used method if the continuous probability distribution were first broken up into discrete values. This can be accomplished by using discrete values equal to the midpoint of arbitrarily selected intervals to represent the entire interval in the calculations. This is analogous to using the midpoint of each class interval to represent all the values in the class in computing the mean or standard deviation of a frequency distribution (see Appendix 8A). Suppose, for example, that the range of values for μ is broken up into \$50 intervals, as shown in Fig. 12.2. Any interval, such as the shaded range from 150 to 200, could be represented by its midpoint, in this case 175. The *COL* for $\mu = 175$ (it would be \$540,000) would then be multiplied by the probability of the range (150 to 200), which the point 175 represents. Probabilities for each interval such as $P(150 < \mu < 200)$ can of course be obtained from the normal area tables and in turn can be multiplied by their respective midpoint *COL*s. Intervals to the right of \$200, the break-even point, can be ignored, since the *COL* term in the product is 0 for all $\mu \geq \$200$. Likewise, at some point in the left tail of the distribution the probability term for μ falling within a stated interval becomes 0 for practical purposes (even though the normal distribution theoretically extends to infinity). Thus the calculations, as shown in Table 12.1, need only be made for μ values less than 200 and greater than, say, -300.

The sum of these products of *COL* times probability is the *EOL* of the decision to lease. This figure is of course an approximation since the procedure used in Table 12.1 was formulated by breaking up the continuum of possible values for μ into a series of intervals and treating

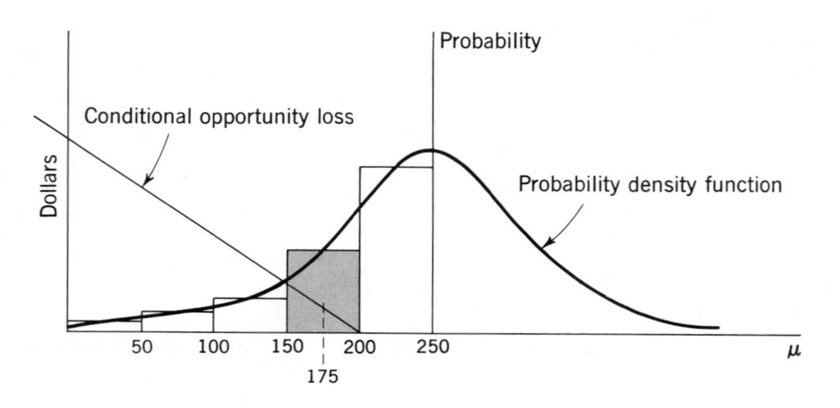

Fig. 12.2

Table 12.1 Approximate computation of expected opportunity loss (*EOL*) for the decision to lease without sampling

Interval	*Midpoint*	*COL*	*Probability*	*COL* × *Probability*
$150 < \mu < 200$	175	\$ 540,000	.1193	\$ 64,422
$100 < \mu < 150$	125	1,620,000	.0927	150,174
$50 < \mu < 100$	75	2,700,000	.0669	180,630
$0 < \mu < 50$	25	3,780,000	.0443	167,454
$-50 < \mu < 0$	−25	4,860,000	.0247	120,042
$-100 < \mu < -50$	−75	5,940,000	.0128	76,032
$-150 < \mu < -100$	−125	7,020,000	.0061	42,822
$-200 < \mu < -150$	−175	8,100,000	.0024	19,440
$-250 < \mu < -200$	−225	9,180,000	.0013	11,934
$-300 < \mu < -250$	−275	10,260,000	.0004	4,104
				\$837,054

them as if they were discrete values. Now this approximation could be made more accurate by using a narrower interval, but the volume of calculations would be correspondingly increased, and it is cumbersome enough for the 50-unit interval used in Table 12.1. As the interval is made narrower and narrower, ultimately approaching the continuous case that this procedure is designed to approximate, the arithmetic burden continues to expand.

Fortunately, mathematics comes to our aid in this situation. The use of calculus makes it possible to circumvent the numerical approximation above and to obtain a theoretically correct result through the use of a simple formula. If the prior estimating distribution is normal and the opportunity loss function is linear, the *EOL* of the optimal act—also the cost of uncertainty and *EVPI*—can be shown to be

$$EOL = L\sigma_o N(D_o) \tag{12.1}$$

where L is the absolute slope of the non-zero portion of the opportunity loss function and σ_o is the standard deviation of the prior distribution. The final factor in the formula, $N(D_o)$, called the normal loss integral, has a value which can be determined from the table given in Appendix D at the end of the book. First, the argument D_o is determined:

$$D_o = \frac{|\mu_o - \mu_b|}{\sigma_o} \tag{12.2}$$

Logically enough, the D_o value is based on the *difference* between the economic break-even and best estimate values of μ which determines the relative positions of the normal estimating distribution and the opportunity loss line. This difference is "normalized" by the customary step, dividing by σ_o, so that it is expressed in terms of a number of standard deviation units. Once obtained, the D_o value is used to look up the value of the function $N(D_o)$ in Appendix D.

The use of the formula is simplified by the fact that algebraic signs are irrelevant. It is the *absolute value* of the slope of the opportunity loss line (L) and the absolute difference $|\mu_o - \mu_b|$ that are required. Application to the computer-leasing problem should demonstrate how easy it really is to use this approach. L, the absolute slope of the COL line, is 21,600—remember that the function was $(200 - \mu)$ (21,600)—and σ_o is 150. Also

$$D_o = \frac{|\mu_o - \mu_b|}{\sigma_o} = \frac{|250 - 200|}{150} = .33$$

and from Appendix D, $N(D_o) = .2555$. Then for the (optimal) decision to lease the equipment, the EOL^* is

$$\begin{aligned} EOL^* &= L\sigma_o N(D_o) \\ &= 21{,}600(150)(.2555) \\ &= \$828{,}000 \end{aligned}$$

This figure is of course superior to the approximation of about \$837,000 obtained by the procedure of Table 12.1.

As we have noted at several previous points in this book, the EOL^* may also be interpreted as the *cost of uncertainty* with which the decision maker is faced. More important, it may also be regarded as the $EVPI$. While *perfect* information is never available in a practical situation, the $EVPI$ figure at least provides an upper limit on the value of prospective sample information. Since

$$EVPI = EOL^* = \$828{,}000$$

we at least know that no more than \$828,000 should be spent for additional information.

Before we turn to the problems of evaluating less-than-perfect sample information, let us reconsider several concepts used earlier in the light of the normal distribution analysis used here. One concept originally developed in Chap. 2, the expected profit under conditions of absolute certainty (EPC), can be formulated in the present context as

$$EPC = L\sigma_o[D_o + N(D_o)] \tag{12.3}$$

which, substituting our leasing problem data, gives

$$\begin{aligned} EPC &= (21{,}600)(150)(.3333 + .2555) \\ &= \$1{,}908{,}000 \end{aligned}$$

This figure, not to be confused with $EVPI$, describes the amount of profit (in this case, cost savings) the decision maker could expect to realize if he had available a perfect forecast of the uncertain random variable in his decision problem. In the problem at hand, given the uncertainty regarding the cost savings per branch per month, the decision maker's expected profit (savings), or EMV, is

$$\begin{aligned} EMV &= (900 \text{ branches}) \ (24 \text{ months}) \ (\$250/\text{branch/month}) - \$4{,}320{,}000 \\ &= \$5{,}400{,}000 - \$4{,}320{,}000 \\ &= \$1{,}080{,}000 \end{aligned}$$

As before, $EMV + EVPI$ should equal EPC. That is, the expected profit given uncertainty plus the cost of that uncertainty, $EVPI$, equals the expected profit under certain conditions. Here

$$\begin{aligned} EMV + EVPI &= 1{,}080{,}000 + 828{,}000 \\ &= \$1{,}908{,}000 \\ &= EPC \end{aligned}$$

which checks with our previous result, as it should.

EXPECTED VALUE OF SAMPLE INFORMATION

In Chap. 6, we defined the expected value of sample information ($EVSI$) as the difference between $EVPI$ and the EOL resulting from the use of the *best* decision criterion in conjunction with a particular sample size. Another way of putting this is that the value of a sample is reflected in the reduction in the cost of uncertainty that it produces. Although this concept is straightforward enough, the computation of the $EVSI$ for the discrete case (Chap. 6) was very involved, partly because the minimum EOL for a given sample size was a function of the value of the criterion number c used, and partly because each individual point in the discrete probability distribution occupied a distinct place in the computational procedure.

Here also the normal distribution analysis is seen to have the advantage of greater simplicity. For a normal prior distribution and normal sampling—i.e., a distribution of sample means which is expected to be normal—$EVSI$ is given by a now familiar type of formula:

$$EVSI = L\sigma_I N(D_I) \tag{12.4}$$

Note that the only difference between this formula and the one for $EVPI$ (or EOL^*) is the subscripts on the σ and D terms. The σ_I used here represents the degree of improvement in the estimate (of μ) that is made as a result of the sample information. Specifically, we define σ_I^2 as the improvement, or *reduction* in variance, between the prior estimating distribution and the revised distribution which takes into account the sample evidence, i.e.,

$$\sigma_I^2 = \sigma_o^2 - \sigma_r^2 \tag{12.5}$$

Of course σ_r^2, the variance of the revised distribution, is not *known* before the sample results are obtained, but it *can* be estimated by using an estimate of $\sigma_{\bar{X}}^2$ and the relationship from Chap. 11

$$\sigma_r^2 = \frac{\sigma_{\bar{X}}^2 \sigma_o^2}{\sigma_o^2 + \sigma_{\bar{X}}^2}$$

The $\sigma_{\bar{X}}^2$ estimate in turn requires that the variance of the original population σ_X^2 be estimated, either from earlier sampling, from experience with similar data, or perhaps from pure judgment. Remember that

$$\sigma_{\bar{X}}^2 = \frac{\sigma_X^2}{n}$$

By substitution for σ_r^2, Eq. (12.5) can be rewritten as

$$\begin{aligned}\sigma_I^2 &= \sigma_o^2 - \frac{\sigma_{\bar{X}}^2 \sigma_o^2}{\sigma_o^2 + \sigma_{\bar{X}}^2} \\ &= \frac{\sigma_o^2 \sigma_o^2}{\sigma_o^2 + \sigma_{\bar{X}}^2}\end{aligned} \tag{12.6}$$

Then the σ_I of the *EVSI* expression [Eq. (12.4)] can be obtained as

$$\sigma_I = \sqrt{\frac{\sigma_o^2 \sigma_o^2}{\sigma_o^2 + \sigma_{\bar{X}}^2}} \tag{12.7}$$

The D_I of Eq. (12.4) is defined as was D_o before, with only the substitution of σ_I for σ_o:

$$D_I = \frac{|\mu_o - \mu_b|}{\sigma_I} \tag{12.8}$$

The calculation of *EVSI* may now be illustrated for the leasing problem. Let us determine the expected value of a sample of branches of size 30 (such as the one actually taken and used to revise the prior distribution in Chap. 11) on an a priori basis, i.e., *before* any such sample is taken. Values are needed to put into the equation

$$EVSI = L\sigma_I N(D_I)$$

L is \$21,600, the same value used in the calculation of *EVPI*. To get σ_I, we must first estimate the population standard deviation σ_X. Remember that this σ_X is a measure of the dispersion or spread of the individual items in the parent population, in this case the cost savings of individual branches. It is *not* the same as σ_o, which measures the expected accuracy of the estimate of *average* savings. Although in the last chapter σ_X was estimated by the s_X value of \$251.55, the s_X value is calculated directly from the sample data and would not be available *before* the sample is taken. Let us suppose that the company is able to estimate σ_X as \$300 based on the experience of the computer manufacturer or other information, implying that roughly two-thirds of the per branch per month savings will fall within $\pm$\$300 from the average savings. Then

$$\sigma_{\bar{X}} = \frac{\sigma_X}{\sqrt{n}} = \frac{\$300}{\sqrt{30}} = \$54.80$$

$$\sigma_I = \sqrt{\frac{\sigma_o^2\sigma_o^2}{\sigma_o^2 + \sigma_{\bar{X}}^2}}$$

$$= \sqrt{\frac{150^2 150^2}{150^2 + 54.8^2}} = \$141$$

$$D_I = \frac{|\mu_o - \mu_b|}{\sigma_I} = \frac{|250 - 200|}{141}$$

$$= \frac{50}{141} = .355$$

and from Appendix D,

$$N(D_I) = .2463$$

Finally,

$$EVSI = L\sigma_I N(D_I)$$
$$= (21{,}600)(141)(.2463) = \$750{,}000$$

FACTORS AFFECTING *EVSI*

The *EVSI* for a sample of only 30 in the leasing problem was \$750,000, which may seem surprisingly high and close to the *EVPI* of \$828,000. Why should the value of a modest size sample be so great in this situation? A closer examination of the formula for *EVSI* provides some clues to the answer. Partially, of course, the large *EVSI* is due to the relatively large L (the unit increase in opportunity loss per unit decrease in average cost savings). However, L also appears in the formula for *EVPI*, so this in itself cannot explain the size of *EVSI* relative to *EVPI*.

The real key to the relatively large *EVSI* is the σ_I, a measure of the improvement in the prior estimate *expected* to be produced by the sample information. The σ_I enters the formula in two ways. First, it appears directly as the second factor in the equation, so that the larger the σ_I, the larger the *EVSI*. Second, it appears in the denominator of the expression for D_I,

$$D_I = \frac{|\mu_o - \mu_b|}{\sigma_I}$$

so that the larger the σ_I, the smaller the D_I. However, an examination of Appendix D shows that $N(D)$ is inversely related to D; $N(D)$ decreases as D increases, so that the larger the σ_I, the *larger* the function $N(D_I)$. Thus, increases in σ_I affect *EVSI* directly through both the second and third terms in the equation.

The question might then be raised: What produces larger σ_I values? Recall the expression:

$$\sigma_I = \sqrt{\frac{\sigma_o^2\sigma_o^2}{\sigma_o^2 + \sigma_{\bar{X}}^2}}$$

which could also be written

$$\sigma_I = \sqrt{\frac{\sigma_o^2\sigma_o^2}{\sigma_o^2 + \sigma_X^2/n}}$$

A careful examination of this expression will reveal that σ_I is directly related to σ_o, directly related to n, and inversely related to σ_X. That is to say, the potential or expected value of sample information will be greatest in cases where the prior estimating variance is large (which means that the decision maker has little prior information), the sample size is large (which is logical), and the parent population variance is small (which minimizes sampling errors). These results are all in agreement with what intuition would tell us about the sampling process, which should make the seemingly "mystical" formula for *EVSI* somewhat less so.

One further point might be noted. D_I depends not only on σ_I but on $|\mu_o - \mu_b|$, the absolute difference between the prior best estimate and the break-even point, as well. The larger this difference, the larger the D_I and the smaller the $N(D_I)$. *EVSI* will hence be less when the prior best estimate is well above or below the economic break-even point. This again agrees with intuition. When a decision appears relatively clear-cut, sample information is potentially less valuable than when the decision is borderline.

EXPECTED VERSUS ACTUAL VALUE OF SAMPLE INFORMATION

The point that the expected value of sample information is not generally equal to its actual value was emphasized in Chap. 7, but it bears repeating here. The actual value of a sample in a decision problem depends on how much it reduces the cost of uncertainty. The *EOL* of the best decision, given the revised information, must be compared with the *EOL* of the best decision that could be made on the basis of prior information. This difference, observed with the benefit of hindsight, is *not* necessarily equal to the value the sample is *expected* to have beforehand. In the leasing example, the cost of uncertainty (also *EVPI*) based on prior information was \$828,000. Using the values from the estimating distribution as *revised* (for the results of the sample of 30 actually obtained in place of the prior parameters), we get:

$$\begin{aligned}\text{Revised cost of uncertainty} &= L\sigma_r N(D_r)\\ &= (21{,}600)(43.10)N\left[\frac{198.62 - 200}{43.10}\right]\\ &= (21{,}600)(43.10)(.3841)\\ &= \$358{,}000\end{aligned}$$

Thus the actual reduction in the cost of uncertainty—and hence the value of the sample—once this particular sample was actually taken was \$828,000 − 358,000 = \$470,000. This compares with an *expected* value *EVSI* of \$750,000. The sample simply turned out to be, in retrospect, less valuable than anticipated.

SPECIFICATION OF A DECISION RULE IN ADVANCE OF SAMPLING

The sample of 30 branches taken in the leasing-decision problem was used (in Chap. 11) to revise the prior probability distribution. The decision not to lease was based on a comparison of the mean of the revised estimating distribution with the economic break-even point. Instead of proceeding in this fashion, we could have formulated a statistical decision rule that would have specified in advance the action to be taken as a result of various possible sample outcomes. This would entail using the relationship for revising a prior mean:

$$\mu_r = \frac{\mu_o IC_o + \bar{X} IC_{\bar{X}}}{IC_o + IC_{\bar{X}}}$$

and solving for the sample mean $\bar{X}$ that would make the revised mean just equal to the economic break-even point μ_b. Manipulation of the above equation gives

$$\bar{X} = \frac{\mu_r(IC_o + IC_{\bar{X}}) - \mu_o IC_o}{IC_{\bar{X}}}$$

Substitution of μ_b for μ_r provides an expression for the action limit $\bar{X}_{\text{AL}}$ for the sample mean:

$$\bar{X}_{\text{AL}} = \frac{\mu_b(IC_o + IC_{\bar{X}}) - \mu_o IC_o}{IC_{\bar{X}}}$$

Notice that one term in this expression, namely, $IC_{\bar{X}}$, is generally unknown before the sample is taken. $IC_{\bar{X}}$, the information content of the sample, is equal to $1/\sigma_{\bar{X}}^2$ or $1/(\sigma_X^2/n)$. The variance of the population σ_X^2 is generally unknown in sample situations, usually being estimated by the s_X^2 statistic calculated from sample data. In a case where σ_X *is* known, or can be estimated accurately from available data or judgment, a decision rule could be formulated in advance. However, since it is usually more reasonable to estimate σ_X^2 from sample data and since the revision process for the normal case is relatively straightforward, the actual revision is usually carried out instead for the sample data on an after-the-fact basis, as in Chap. 11.

OPTIMAL SAMPLE SIZE

To this point we have analyzed the expected benefit of only one sample size ($n = 30$). Although its $EVSI$ was impressively high, the cost of obtaining it was not discussed. There is certainly no assurance that when both values and costs are considered, this particular sample size will be optimal. The optimal sample size can be determined, as in Chap. 6, by computing the *net gain from sampling* for various possible sample sizes. This net gain, it will be recalled, is the difference between the $EVSI$ and the actual cost of obtaining the sample information.

Suppose that in the computer-leasing problem the trial run from which sample information is obtained is available at a fixed setup cost of \$60,000 and an estimated net cost per branch (or item in the sample) of \$2000; that is,

$$\text{Sample cost} = 60{,}000 + 2000n$$

Table 12.2 provides a systematic framework for computing the net gain from sampling. The variance of the sampling distribution $\sigma_{\bar{X}}^2$ is computed in column 2 for each sample size. These values are entered into the formula for σ_I (along with the prior variance σ_o^2, which is a constant in any given problem) in column 3. D_I is computed in column 4 by dividing the constant $|\mu_o - \mu_b|$ difference by the various σ_I values. $N(D_I)$ is then obtained from the table and $EVSI$ calculated as the product of L (a constant) times σ_I times $N(D_I)$. The final "net gain from sampling" column is the difference between $EVSI$ (column 6) and the cost of the sample (column 7).

The maximum net gain from sampling does occur at about $n = 30$. Notice, however, that the net gain is relatively insensitive to the sample size. This also implies that the subjective estimate of σ_x that had to be made to carry out the calculations could be somewhat in error without

Table 12.2 Determination of net gain from sampling, computer-leasing problem

(1)	(2)	(3)	(4)
Sample size, n	$\sigma_{\bar{X}}^2 = \frac{300^2}{n}$	$\sigma_I = \sqrt{\frac{(150)^2(150)^2}{(150)^2 + \sigma_{\bar{X}}^2}}$	$D_I = \frac{\lvert 250 - 200 \rvert}{\sigma_I}$
20	4500	137	.365
30	3000	141	.355
40	2250	143	.350
50	1800	144	.347

(5)	(6)	(7)	(8)
$N(D_I)$	$EVSI =$ 21,600 $\sigma_I N(D_I)$	*Sample cost,* 60,000 + 2000*n*	*Net gain from sampling*
.2427	$718,000	$100,000	$618,000
.2463	750,000	120,000	630,000
.2481	766,000	140,000	626,000
.2493	775,000	160,000	615,000

any serious effect in the decision to purchase additional information. For this problem, as is often the case, sampling per se appears very valuable, but the exact size of the sample is not crucial.

Appendix 12A

Use of the Normal Distribution to Estimate Optimal Sample Size in Discrete Binomial Decision Problems

Appendix 11A described the use of normal distribution analysis to revise a discrete prior probability distribution to reflect sample information actually obtained through a binomial sampling process. Specifically, the normal analysis was applied to the product-development problem of Chaps. 6 and 7. Despite the fact that normality assumptions were not strictly valid, the results obtained were extremely close to those obtained by the more cumbersome discrete revision methods described in Chap. 7.

This appendix seeks to apply normal analysis to evaluating the economics of sampling in binomial-type sampling situations. While discrete methods for direct use are available (as explained in Chap. 6), calculation of *EVPI* and *EVSI* by the analysis of Chap. 12 is so much simpler and quicker that its applicability to problems posed earlier should be considered. Here, we shall once again examine the economics for sampling for the product-development problem, comparing the results obtained with those obtained in Chap. 6 to evaluate their accuracy.

EXPECTED VALUE OF PERFECT INFORMATION

Where the prior distribution may be assumed normal, the $EVPI$ is given by

$$EVPI = L\sigma_o N(D_o)$$

It was shown in Appendix 11A that the decision maker's prior information in the product-development problem could be described by a distribution of average profit per customer that was normal with $u_o = \$29$ and $\sigma_o = \$11.36$. The opportunity loss function will be given by:

$$(\mu - \$25)(20{,}000) \qquad \mu \geq \$25$$

and

$$(\$25 - \mu)(20{,}000) \qquad \mu < \$25$$

since μ represents average sales per customer, \$25 is the break-even value of average sales, and the firm has 20,000 customers. L, the absolute slope of this function, is 20,000. Then

$$\begin{aligned} EVPI &= 20{,}000(\$11.36)N\left[\frac{|29 - 25|}{11.36}\right] \\ &= 20{,}000(\$11.36)(.2474) \\ &\doteq \$56{,}200 \end{aligned}$$

This compares with an $EVPI$ calculated by discrete methods in Chap. 6 of \$60,000. The discrepancy, which is relatively minor for practical purposes, arises because the discrete prior distribution in this problem does depart somewhat from normal.

EXPECTED VALUE OF SAMPLE INFORMATION

The fact that the sampling distribution in this problem would *not* be closely approximated by a normal distribution was discussed at length in Appendix 11A. Nevertheless, let us calculate the $EVSI$ for various sample sizes in the manner of Table 12.2. The only important difference in the procedure is that the expected variance of the sampling distribution $\sigma_{\bar{X}}^2$ must be obtained by first obtaining $\sigma_{\bar{p}}^2$ for various sample sizes on the assumption that p is .058 (the expected value of p from the prior estimating distribution):

Sample size, n	$\sigma_{\bar{p}}^2 = \frac{p(1-p)}{n} = \frac{.058(.942)}{n}$
10	.00546
20	.00273
50	.00109
100	.000546

Now the relationship of average profit per customer to proportion of customers buying is:

$$\text{Average profit/customer} = \frac{(\text{prop. buying})(20{,}000 \text{ customers})(\$500 \text{ profit/unit})}{20{,}000 \text{ customers}}$$
$$= p(\$500)$$

To convert the *variance* of proportion of customers into average profit per customer, we should multiply not by 500, but by $(500)^2$, that is,

$$\sigma_{\bar{X}}^2 = \sigma_{\bar{p}}^2(250{,}000)$$

Therefore we estimate:

n	$\sigma_{\bar{X}}^2$
10	(.00546)(250,000) = 1365
20	(.00273)(250,000) = 682
50	(.00109)(250,000) = 272
100	(.000546)(250,000) = 136

These values are inputs to column 2 of the format in Table 12.3, which is similar to Table 12.2. Taking the sample costs from Table 7.9, we can obtain net gain from sampling as shown in Table 12.4.

This analysis suggests that, of the sample sizes considered, $n = 50$ represents the optimum. This is the same optimal size determined by the discrete analysis in Chap. 6. The net gain from sampling for $n = 50$ computed here, \$2,070 compares with an earlier figure of \$2737 (Table

Table 12.3 Normal approximation for $EVSI$, product development problem

(1) *Sample size*	(2) $\sigma_{\bar{X}}{}^2$	(3) $\sigma_I = \sqrt{\dfrac{11.36^2 \times 11.36^2}{11.36^2 + \sigma_{\bar{X}}{}^2}}$	(4) $D_I = \dfrac{29 - 25}{\sigma_I}$	(5) $N(D_I)$	(6) $EVSI = 20{,}00\sigma_I N(D_I)$
10	1365	.334	1.197	.0561	$ 3,750
20	682	4.53	.883	.1036	9,390
50	272	6.45	.620	.1633	21,070
100	136	7.93	.504	.1966	31,180

Table 12.4 Normal approximation for net gain from sampling, product-development problem

Sample size, n	*EVSI*	*Sample cost*	*Net gain from sampling*
10	$ 3,750	$ 7,000	$−3,250
20	9,390	10,000	−610
50	21,070	19,000	+2,070
100	31,180	34,000	−2,820

6.9). Although the $EVSI$ figures calculated by the two methods are somewhat different, the *conclusions* regarding the amount of additional information that should be purchased are the same.

Although it is impossible to generalize as to when the normal analysis will be completely adequate for discrete problems of the type considered here, it will almost always provide a useful starting point. If net gain from sampling is "flat" in the region of the optimum, i.e., if the gain does not appear very sensitive to sample size, then the choice of an exact n does not matter much anyway. If the net gain does change rapidly with sample size, a complete discrete analysis should be done in the region of the optimum. At least it will save considerable time and effort to use normal analysis to locate this optimal region.

PROBLEMS

12.1 Give two examples each where the *COL* function in a business decision situation is

(*a*) linear

(*b*) nonlinear

(*c*) In your answers to part (*b*), are the departures from linearity serious? Do you think the methods of this chapter could be used as an approximate means of solving such problems?

12.2 Refer to Prob. 11.1. Suppose the market for the proposed product will only last for one year.

(*a*) What is the maximum amount Acme could profitably spend on market research to better ascertain demand?

(*b*) As a practical matter, would you recommend spending that much? Why?

12.3 Refer to Prob. 11.11. Suppose the advertising agency, in an effort to land the contract to manage the entire golf-ball promotion, offers to conduct a pilot study involving a random sample of 10 of the XL branches for a fee of $10,000. The agency will pay all expenses (including the cost and selling expenses of the golf balls) of the promotion. In addition, it will maintain and analyze records necessary to determine the amount of additional purchases made by customers who would not have visited the stores were it not for the promotion.

(*a*) Would you buy the pilot study? (*Note:* In Prob. 11.11 you were asked to formulate your own prior distribution. Use it here also.)

(*b*) What is your *EVPI*?

(*c*) Do you think a larger pilot study might be desirable? Explain.

12.4 In the computer-leasing problem described in the text, the *EVPI* was calculated as $828,000. What would the *EVPI* have been if:

(*a*) σ_o were $100 instead of $150

(*b*) μ_b were $250 instead of $200

(*c*) L were $43,200 instead of $21,600

Write out generalizations for the type of changes in (*a*), (*b*), and (*c*). For each case, describe the relationship of the variable in question to *EVPI*.

12.5 Repeat parts (*a*), (*b*), and (*c*) of the previous problem for the effect on *EVSI* for samples of size 30, 40, and 50. Is $n = 30$ still the optimum size sample to take in each case?

12.6 A computation of the *EVSI* using the method described in this chapter requires certain data inputs. List these inputs, and state the source from which each would customarily be obtained.

12.7 You are given the task of explaining to an executive who knows no statistics the concept of the value of sample information in a decision situation. Describe, in nonstatistical terms, factors which contribute to a high (or low) *EVSI*.

12.8 Why is the actual value of sample information that has been obtained different from the *EVSI* for that sample size?

12.9 Churn & Churn, a stock brokerage firm, is contemplating a change in their commission charges on convertible bond transactions. Currently, they are charging $2.50 per bond, the minimum commission allowable under New York Stock Exchange rules. Their controller has estimated that their out-of-pocket costs on such transactions are $6.00 fixed cost (regardless of the size of the order) plus $1.25 per bond. Clearly, they are not even breaking even on one or two bond orders. They are considering raising the minimum charge on bond orders to $10.00. Although they believe that many customers will no longer place one or two bond orders with the firm, they are not concerned about losing this business since it is unprofitable anyway. The real concern is that these customers will direct *other* brokerage business, which is profitable, elsewhere.

A check of customer accounts reveals that about 4000 of the firm's customers had convertible bond transactions during the last year. The firm's partners were called together to make estimates of the amount of *net* revenues that would be gained or lost because of the changes. The consensus was that about $20.00 per convertible bond customer would be *gained* in net revenues in the coming year. Specifically, 8 of the firm's 12 partners felt that the net effect would be between 0 and $40.00 per customer for this year. It was agreed that by the end of the coming year, competing firms would have to make similar changes, so that the situation would have to be reappraised at that time. For this reason and because of the turnover in customer accounts the partners did not attempt to forecast any longer-run effects.

One of the younger partners, a recent business school graduate by the name of Churn, suggests that a *sample* of the customers involved should be studied through a combination of detailed analyses of account records and personal interviews.

Perusal of the records could show bond and nonbond commissions generated by the customer and a careful interview with him could reveal his attitude toward the proposed change and his intentions regarding the future conduct of his investment affairs. Measurement could thus be made of the net effect on the firm's revenues for each customer sampled.

Churn believes that he can get one of his former professors to perform such a study at a cost of $2000 plus $40 per customer contained in the sample.

The professor agrees to the terms, but warns the partners not to expect too much since a preliminary examination of customer accounts convinces him that there will be considerable variability in the net revenue effect from customer to customer. He is heard to mumble, "Population standard deviation must be at least $100."

What should Churn & Churn do?

12.10 Refer to Prob. 11.12. The president of Instant Wealth is having second thoughts about making the initial outlay necessary to produce the new supplement. One of his junior executives has suggested including an advertisement of the supplement and an invitation to purchase it in the current mailing to all subscribers. The president is reluctant to do this, however, since he feels it would destroy the firm's well-established image if the response from subscribers was not sufficiently favorable and the supplement had to be cancelled. After some discussion, he does agree to including the advertising in a mailing to a sample of 200 subscribers.

How much can Instant Wealth afford to spend on development of promotional materials, etc., for the sample of 200?

12.11 Refer to Prob. 12.10. Suppose the cost of sampling is $2000 plus $6 per customer included. Would some other size sample be more desirable than the 200 to which the Instant Wealth president has agreed? How would you convince him to change his mind?

12.12 In the computer-leasing problem described in the text, a sample of 30 branches was taken, and the prior distribution was revised accordingly (see Chap. 11). The best decision at that point was to reject the leasing arrangement. Suppose a *further* sample was being considered before making a decision. If the cost of obtaining this sample was (\$60,000 + 2000n), how large an additional sample would you recommend?

Note: The solution to a problem exactly like this occupies much of Chap. 12, *except* that the revised distribution obtained in Chap. 11 will be used in place of the original prior distribution.

12.13 For the mining problem presented in Prob. 11.8, find:

(*a*) The expected opportunity loss of the optimal act without sampling

(*b*) The expected profit under certainty

(*c*) The expected monetary value of the optimal act

Note: You should be able to check your answers for (*a*), (*b*), and (*c*) by using the relationship $EMV + EOL = EPC$.

12.14 For the data of Prob. 11.8 and 12.13, assume that before any sample is taken, management's best estimate of σ_X is .03.

Find the optimal sample size for this problem, assuming that the cost of sampling is 10,000 + 4000n. (To simplify the problem, consider only the alternatives n = 20, 30, 40, 50, and 100.)

12.15 Why might the method used in this chapter to determine the optimum sample size in a decision situation give an answer that is only approximately correct? Is the departure from the true optimum serious? Explain.

12.16 The prior distribution in Prob. 6.10 only very roughly resembles a normal distribution. Represent this prior distribution as best you can by a normal distribution, and use normal methods to determine the optimal size sample to take. For purposes of comparison with the earlier results, use only n values of 10, 20, 50, and 100.

12.17 (*a*) What are the advantages of using the "normal" methods of Chap. 12 to determine optimal sample size as compared to the discrete methods of Chap. 6?

(*b*) Under what circumstances would you feel justified in using the normal methods to approximate the optimum sample size for a discrete problem?

Bibliography

I. PROBABILITY AND MATHEMATICAL STATISTICS

Feller, William: "Probability Theory and Its Applications," vol. I, 2d ed., John Wiley & Sons, Inc., New York, 1957.

Goldberg, Samuel: "Probability," Prentice-Hall, Inc., Englewood Cliffs, N.J., 1960.

Hoel, Paul G.: "Introduction to Mathematical Statistics," 3d ed., John Wiley & Sons, Inc., New York, 1962.

Mood, Alexander M., and Franklin A. Graybill: "Introduction to the Theory of Statistics," 2d ed., McGraw-Hill Book Company, New York, 1963.

Parzen, Emanuel: "Modern Probability Theory and Its Applications," John Wiley & Sons, Inc., New York, 1960.

II. DECISION THEORY AND BAYESIAN STATISTICS

Chernoff, Herman, and Lincoln Moses: "Elementary Decision Theory," John Wiley & Sons, Inc., New York, 1959.

Hadley, G.: "Introduction to Probability and Statistical Decision Theory," Holden Day, San Francisco, 1967.

Luce, R. Duncan, and Howard Raiffa: "Games and Decisions," John Wiley & Sons, Inc., New York, 1957.

Raiffa, Howard, and Robert Schlaifer: "Applied Statistical Decision Theory," Harvard Graduate School of Business Administration, Division of Research, Boston, 1961.

Savage, L. J.: "Foundations of Statistics," John Wiley & Sons, Inc., New York, 1954.

Schlaifer, Robert: "Introduction to Statistics for Business Decisions," McGraw-Hill Book Company, New York, 1961.

———: "Probability and Statistics for Business Decisions," McGraw-Hill Book Company, New York, 1959.

III. CLASSICAL STATISTICAL INFERENCE

Dixon, W. J., and F. J. Massey, Jr.: "Introduction to Statistical Analysis," 2d ed., McGraw-Hill Book Company, New York, 1957.

Guenther, William C.: "Concepts of Statistical Inference," McGraw-Hill Book Company, New York, 1965.

Wallis, W. Allen, and Harry V. Roberts: "Statistics: A New Approach," The Free Press of Glencoe, New York, 1956.

appendix A

Cumulative Binomial Probabilities

The following table lists cumulative binomial probabilities for values of p (by increments of .01) for values of n from 1 through 20, 50, and 100. For values of $p \leq .50$, the table shows the probability of r *or more* successes in n trials. For values of $p > .50$, the same table can be used to find the probability of r *or fewer* successes in n trials.

We shall illustrate the use of the table with the following examples:

1. For $n = 3$ and $p = .10$ find the probability of *two or more* successes.
   Find the section of the table for $n = 3$. Since $p < .50$, look down the r column at the *left* margin to find $r = 2$. Then look across this row to find the cell below $p = .10$. The value of .0280 in this cell is the binomial probability of two or more successes, given $n = 3$ and $p = .10$.

2. For $n = 3$ and $p = .90$ find the probability of *one or fewer* successes.
   Find the section of the table for $n = 3$. Since $p > .50$, look down the r column at the *right* margin to find $r = 1$, and look across this row to the cell below a $1 - p$ value of .10 (since $p = .90$, $1 - p = .10$). The value in this cell, .0280, is the probability of *one or fewer* successes, given $n = 3$ and $p = .90$.
   Observe that this probability is exactly the same as that for two or more successes, given $n = 3$ and $p = .10$ found earlier.

3. For $n = 3$ and $p = .90$, find the probability of *two or more* successes.
   The probability of two or more successes, given $n = 3$ and $p = .9$, is simply 1 minus the probability of obtaining one or fewer successes, given $n = 3$, $p = .90$. Therefore, the probability is $1.0000 - .0280 = .9720$.

Cumulative binomial probabilities

If $p \leq .50$	*If* $p > .50$
Use these r values to find the probability of r *or more* successes in n trials	Use these r values to find the probability of r *or fewer* successes in n trials
$\Sigma_r^n C(n,r)_p{}^r(1-p)^{n-r}$	$\Sigma_o^r C(n,r)_p{}^r(1-p)^{n-r}$

r					$n = 1$						r
	p = 01	02	03	04	05	06	07	08	09	10 = $(1-p)$	
1	0100	0200	0300	0400	0500	0600	0700	0800	0900	1000	0
	p = 11	12	13	14	15	16	17	18	19	20 = $(1-p)$	
1	1100	1200	1300	1400	1500	1600	1700	1800	1900	2000	0
	p = 21	22	23	24	25	26	27	28	29	30 = $(1-p)$	
1	2100	2200	2300	2400	2500	2600	2700	2800	2900	3000	0
	p = 31	32	33	34	35	36	37	38	39	40 = $(1-p)$	
1	3100	3200	3300	3400	3500	3600	3700	3800	3900	4000	0
	p = 41	42	43	44	45	46	47	48	49	50 = $(1-p)$	
1	4100	4200	4300	4400	4500	4600	4700	4800	4900	5000	0

r					$n = 2$						r
	p = 01	02	03	04	05	06	07	08	09	10 = $(1-p)$	
1	0199	0396	0591	0784	0975	1164	1351	1536	1719	1900	1
2	0001	0004	0009	0016	0025	0036	0049	0064	0081	0100	0
	p = 11	12	13	14	15	16	17	18	19	20 = $(1-p)$	
1	2079	2256	2431	2604	2775	2944	3111	3276	3439	3600	1
2	0121	0144	0169	0196	0225	0256	0289	0324	0361	0400	0
	p = 21	22	23	24	25	26	27	28	29	30 = $(1-p)$	
1	3759	3916	4071	4224	4375	4524	4671	4816	4959	5100	1
2	0441	0484	0529	0576	0625	0676	0729	0784	0841	0900	0
	p = 31	32	33	34	35	36	37	38	39	40 = $(1-p)$	
1	5239	5376	5511	5644	5775	5904	6031	6156	6279	6400	1
2	0961	1024	1089	1156	1225	1296	1369	1444	1521	1600	0
	p = 41	42	43	44	45	46	47	48	49	50 = $(1-p)$	
1	6519	6636	6751	6864	6975	7084	7191	7296	7399	7500	1
2	1681	1764	1849	1936	2025	2116	2209	2304	2401	2500	0

r					$n = 3$						r
	p = 01	02	03	04	05	06	07	08	09	10 = $(1-p)$	
1	0297	0588	0873	1153	1426	1694	1956	2213	2464	2710	2
2	0003	0012	0026	0047	0073	0104	0140	0182	0228	0280	1
3				0001	0001	0002	0003	0005	0007	0010	0
	p = 11	12	13	14	15	16	17	18	19	20 = $(1-p)$	
1	2950	3185	3415	3639	3859	4073	4282	4486	4686	4880	2
2	0336	0397	0463	0533	0608	0686	0769	0855	0946	1040	1
3	0013	0017	0022	0027	0034	0041	0049	0058	0069	0080	0

Cumulative binomial probabilities (Continued)

r	$n = 3$ (*Continued*)										r
	$p = 21$	22	23	24	25	26	27	28	29	$30 = (1 - p)$	
1	5070	5254	5435	5610	5781	5948	6110	6268	6421	6570	2
2	1138	1239	1344	1452	1563	1676	1793	1913	2035	2160	1
3	0093	0106	0122	0138	0156	0176	0197	0220	0244	0270	0
	$p = 31$	32	33	34	35	36	37	38	39	$40 = (1 - p)$	
1	6715	6856	6992	7125	7254	7379	7500	7617	7730	7840	2
2	2287	2417	2548	2682	2818	2955	3094	3235	3377	3520	1
3	0298	0328	0359	0393	0429	0467	0507	0549	0593	0640	0
	$p = 41$	42	43	44	45	46	47	48	49	$50 = (1 - p)$	
1	7946	8049	8148	8244	8336	8425	8511	8594	8673	8750	2
2	3665	3810	3957	4104	4253	4401	4551	4700	4850	5000	1
3	0689	0741	0795	0852	0911	0973	1038	1106	1176	1250	0

r	$n = 4$										r
	$p = 01$	02	03	04	05	06	07	08	09	$10 = (1 - p)$	
1	0394	0776	1147	1507	1855	2193	2519	2836	3143	3439	3
2	0006	0023	0052	0091	0140	0199	0267	0344	0430	0523	2
3			0001	0002	0005	0008	0013	0019	0027	0037	1
4									0001	0001	0
	$p = 11$	12	13	14	15	16	17	18	19	$20 = (1 - p)$	
1	3726	4003	4271	4530	4780	5021	5254	5479	5695	5904	3
2	0624	0732	0847	0968	1095	1228	1366	1509	1656	1808	2
3	0049	0063	0079	0098	0120	0144	0171	0202	0235	0272	1
4	0001	0002	0003	0004	0005	0007	0008	0010	0013	0016	0
	$p = 21$	22	23	24	25	26	27	28	29	$30 = (1 - p)$	
1	6105	6298	6485	6664	6836	7001	7160	7313	7459	7599	3
2	1963	2122	2285	2450	2617	2787	2959	3132	3307	3483	2
3	0312	0356	0403	0453	0508	0566	0628	0694	0763	0837	1
4	0019	0023	0028	0033	0039	0046	0053	0061	0071	0081	0
	$p = 31$	32	33	34	35	36	37	38	39	$40 = (1 - p)$	
1	7733	7862	7985	8103	8215	8322	8425	8522	8615	8704	3
2	3660	3837	4015	4193	4370	4547	4724	4900	5075	5248	2
3	0915	0996	1082	1171	1265	1362	1464	1569	1679	1792	1
4	0092	0105	0119	0134	0150	0168	0187	0209	0231	0256	0
	$p = 41$	42	43	44	45	46	47	48	49	$50 = (1 - p)$	
1	8788	8868	8944	9017	9085	9150	9211	9269	9323	9375	3
2	5420	5590	5759	5926	6090	6252	6412	6569	6724	6875	2
3	1909	2030	2155	2283	2415	2550	2689	2831	2977	3125	1
4	0283	0311	0342	0375	0410	0448	0488	0531	0576	0625	0

r	$n = 5$										r
	$p = 01$	02	03	04	05	06	07	08	09	$10 = (1 - p)$	
1	0490	0961	1413	1846	2262	2661	3043	3409	3760	4095	4
2	0010	0038	0085	0148	0226	0319	0425	0544	0674	0815	3
3		0001	0003	0006	0012	0020	0031	0045	0063	0086	2
4						0001	0001	0002	0003	0005	1

Cumulative binomial probabilities (Continued)

r					n = 5 (Continued)						r
	p = 11	12	13	14	15	16	17	18	19	20 = (1 − p)	
1	4416	4723	5016	5296	5563	5818	6061	6293	6513	6723	4
2	0965	1125	1292	1467	1648	1835	2027	2224	2424	2627	3
3	0112	0143	0179	0220	0266	0318	0375	0437	0505	0579	2
4	0007	0009	0013	0017	0022	0029	0036	0045	0055	0067	1
5				0001	0001	0001	0001	0002	0002	0003	0
	p = 21	22	23	24	25	26	27	28	29	30 = (1 − p)	
1	6923	7113	7293	7464	7627	7781	7927	8065	8196	8319	4
2	2833	3041	3251	3461	3672	3883	4093	4303	4511	4718	3
3	0659	0744	0836	0933	1035	1143	1257	1376	1501	1631	2
4	0081	0097	0114	0134	0156	0181	0208	0238	0272	0308	1
5	0004	0005	0006	0008	0010	0012	0014	0017	0021	0024	0
	p = 31	32	33	34	35	36	37	38	39	40 = (1 − p)	
1	8436	8546	8650	8748	8840	8926	9008	9084	9155	9222	4
2	4923	5125	5325	5522	5716	5906	6093	6276	6455	6630	3
3	1766	1905	2050	2199	2352	2509	2670	2835	3003	3174	2
4	0347	0390	0436	0486	0540	0598	0660	0726	0796	0870	1
5	0029	0034	0039	0045	0053	0060	0069	0079	0090	0102	0
	p = 41	42	43	44	45	46	47	48	49	50 = (1 − p)	
1	9285	9344	9398	9449	9497	9541	9582	9620	9655	9688	4
2	6801	6967	7129	7286	7438	7585	7728	7865	7998	8125	3
3	3349	3525	3705	3886	4069	4253	4439	4625	4813	5000	2
4	0949	1033	1121	1214	1312	1415	1522	1635	1753	1875	1
5	0116	0131	0147	0165	0185	0206	0229	0255	0282	0313	0

r					n = 6						r
	p = 01	02	03	04	05	06	07	08	09	10 = (1 − p)	
1	0585	1142	1670	2172	2649	3101	3530	3936	4321	4686	5
2	0015	0057	0125	0216	0328	0459	0608	0773	0952	1143	4
3		0002	0005	0012	0022	0038	0058	0085	0118	0159	3
4					0001	0002	0003	0005	0008	0013	2
5										0001	1
	p = 11	12	13	14	15	16	17	18	19	20 = (1 − p)	
1	5030	5356	5664	5954	6229	6487	6731	6960	7176	7379	5
2	1345	1556	1776	2003	2235	2472	2713	2956	3201	3446	4
3	0206	0261	0324	0395	0473	0560	0655	0759	0870	0989	3
4	0018	0025	0034	0045	0059	0075	0094	0116	0141	0170	2
5	0001	0001	0002	0003	0004	0005	0007	0010	0013	0016	1
6										0001	0
	p = 21	22	23	24	25	26	27	28	29	30 = (1 − p)	
1	7569	7748	7916	8073	8220	8358	8487	8607	8719	8824	5
2	3692	3937	4180	4422	4661	4896	5128	5356	5580	5798	4
3	1115	1250	1391	1539	1694	1856	2023	2196	2374	2557	3
4	0202	0239	0280	0326	0376	0431	0492	0557	0628	0705	2
5	0020	0025	0031	0038	0046	0056	0067	0079	0093	0109	1
6	0001	0001	0001	0002	0002	0003	0004	0005	0006	0007	0

Cumulative binomial probabilities (Continued)

n = 6 (*Continued*)

r	p = 31	32	33	34	35	36	37	38	39	40 = $(1-p)$	r
1	8921	9011	9095	9173	9246	9313	9375	9432	9485	9533	5
2	6012	6220	6422	6619	6809	6994	7172	7343	7508	7667	4
3	2744	2936	3130	3328	3529	3732	3937	4143	4350	4557	3
4	0787	0875	0969	1069	1174	1286	1404	1527	1657	1792	2
5	0127	0148	0170	0195	0223	0254	0288	0325	0365	0410	1
6	0009	0011	0013	0015	0018	0022	0026	0030	0035	0041	0
	p = 41	42	43	44	45	46	47	48	49	50 = $(1-p)$	
1	9578	9619	9657	9692	9723	9752	9778	9802	9824	9844	5
2	7819	7965	8105	8238	8364	8485	8599	8707	8810	8906	4
3	4764	4971	5177	5382	5585	5786	5985	6180	6373	6563	3
4	1933	2080	2232	2390	2553	2721	2893	3070	3252	3438	2
5	0458	0510	0566	0627	0692	0762	0837	0917	1003	1094	1
6	0048	0055	0063	0073	0083	0095	0108	0122	0138	0156	0

n = 7

r	p = 01	02	03	04	05	06	07	08	09	10 = $(1-p)$	r
1	0679	1319	1920	2486	3017	3515	3983	4422	4832	5217	6
2	0020	0079	0171	0294	0444	0618	0813	1026	1255	1497	5
3		0003	0009	0020	0038	0063	0097	0140	0193	0257	4
4				0001	0002	0004	0007	0012	0018	0027	3
5								0001	0001	0002	2
	p = 11	12	13	14	15	16	17	18	19	20 = $(1-p)$	
1	5577	5913	6227	6521	6794	7049	7286	7507	7712	7903	6
2	1750	2012	2281	2556	2834	3115	3396	3677	3956	4233	5
3	0331	0416	0513	0620	0738	0866	1005	1154	1313	1480	4
4	0039	0054	0072	0094	0121	0153	0189	0231	0279	0333	3
5	0003	0004	0006	0009	0012	0017	0022	0029	0037	0047	2
6					0001	0001	0001	0002	0003	0004	1
	p = 21	22	23	24	25	26	27	28	29	30 = $(1-p)$	
1	8080	8243	8395	8535	8665	8785	8895	8997	9090	9176	6
2	4506	4775	5040	5298	5551	5796	6035	6266	6490	6706	5
3	1657	1841	2033	2231	2436	2646	2861	3081	3304	3529	4
4	0394	0461	0536	0617	0706	0802	0905	1016	1134	1260	3
5	0058	0072	0088	0107	0129	0153	0181	0213	0248	0288	2
6	0005	0006	0008	0011	0013	0017	0021	0026	0031	0038	1
7					0001	0001	0001	0001	0002	0002	0
	p = 31	32	33	34	35	36	37	38	39	40 = $(1-p)$	
1	9255	9328	9394	9454	9510	9560	9606	9648	9686	9720	6
2	6914	7113	7304	7487	7662	7828	7987	8137	8279	8414	5
3	3757	3987	4217	4447	4677	4906	5134	5359	5581	5801	4
4	1394	1534	1682	1837	1998	2167	2341	2521	2707	2898	3
5	0332	0380	0434	0492	0556	0625	0701	0782	0869	0963	2
6	0046	0055	0065	0077	0090	0105	0123	0142	0164	0188	1
7	0003	0003	0004	0005	0006	0008	0009	0011	0014	0016	0

Cumulative binomial probabilities (Continued)

n = 7 (*Continued*)

r	p = 41	42	43	44	45	46	47	48	49	50 = (1 − p)	r
1	9751	9779	9805	9827	9848	9866	9883	9897	9910	9922	6
2	8541	8660	8772	8877	8976	9068	9153	9233	9307	9375	5
3	6017	6229	6436	6638	6836	7027	7213	7393	7567	7734	4
4	3094	3294	3498	3706	3917	4131	4346	4563	4781	5000	3
5	1063	1169	1282	1402	1529	1663	1803	1951	2105	2266	2
6	0216	0246	0279	0316	0357	0402	0451	0504	0562	0625	1
7	0019	0023	0027	0032	0037	0044	0051	0059	0068	0078	0

n = 8

r	p = 01	02	03	04	05	06	07	08	09	10 = (1 − p)	r
1	0773	1492	2163	2786	3366	3904	4404	4868	5297	5695	7
2	0027	0103	0223	0381	0572	0792	1035	1298	1577	1869	6
3	0001	0004	0013	0031	0058	0096	0147	0211	0289	0381	5
4			0001	0002	0004	0007	0013	0022	0034	0050	4
5							0001	0001	0003	0004	3

r	p = 11	12	13	14	15	16	17	18	19	20 = (1 − p)	r
1	6063	6404	6718	7008	7275	7521	7748	7956	8147	8322	7
2	2171	2480	2794	3111	3428	3744	4057	4366	4670	4967	6
3	0487	0608	0743	0891	1052	1226	1412	1608	1815	2031	5
4	0071	0097	0129	0168	0214	0267	0328	0397	0476	0563	4
5	0007	0010	0015	0021	0029	0038	0050	0065	0083	0104	3
6		0001	0001	0002	0002	0003	0005	0007	0009	0012	2
7									0001	0001	1

r	p = 21	22	23	24	25	26	27	28	29	30 = (1 − p)	r
1	8483	8630	8764	8887	8999	9101	9194	9278	9354	9424	7
2	5257	5538	5811	6075	6329	6573	6807	7031	7244	7447	6
3	2255	2486	2724	2967	3215	3465	3718	3973	4228	4482	5
4	0659	0765	0880	1004	1138	1281	1433	1594	1763	1941	4
5	0129	0158	0191	0230	0273	0322	0377	0438	0505	0580	3
6	0016	0021	0027	0034	0042	0052	0064	0078	0094	0113	2
7	0001	0002	0002	0003	0004	0005	0006	0008	0010	0013	1
8									0001	0001	0

r	p = 31	32	33	34	35	36	37	38	39	40 = (1 − p)	r
1	9486	9543	9594	9640	9681	9719	9752	9782	9808	9832	7
2	7640	7822	7994	8156	8309	8452	8586	8711	8828	8936	6
3	4736	4987	5236	5481	5722	5958	6189	6415	6634	6846	5
4	2126	2319	2519	2724	2936	3153	3374	3599	3828	4059	4
5	0661	0750	0846	0949	1061	1180	1307	1443	1586	1737	3
6	0134	0159	0187	0218	0253	0293	0336	0385	0439	0498	2
7	0016	0020	0024	0030	0036	0043	0051	0061	0072	0085	1
8	0001	0001	0001	0002	0002	0003	0004	0004	0005	0007	0

Cumulative binomial probabilities (Continued)

$n = 8$ *(Continued)*

r	p = 41	42	43	44	45	46	47	48	49	50 = $(1-p)$	r
1	9853	9872	9889	9903	9916	9928	9938	9947	9954	9961	7
2	9037	9130	9216	9295	9368	9435	9496	9552	9602	9648	6
3	7052	7250	7440	7624	7799	7966	8125	8276	8419	8555	5
4	4292	4527	4762	4996	5230	5463	5694	5922	6146	6367	4
5	1895	2062	2235	2416	2604	2798	2999	3205	3416	3633	3
6	0563	0634	0711	0794	0885	0982	1086	1198	1318	1445	2
7	0100	0117	0136	0157	0181	0208	0239	0272	0310	0352	1
8	0008	0010	0012	0014	0017	0020	0024	0028	0033	0039	0

$n = 9$

r	p = 01	02	03	04	05	06	07	08	09	10 = $(1-p)$	r
1	0865	1663	2398	3075	3698	4270	4796	5278	5721	6126	8
2	0034	0131	0282	0478	0712	0978	1271	1583	1912	2252	7
3	0001	0006	0020	0045	0084	0138	0209	0298	0405	0530	6
4			0001	0003	0006	0013	0023	0037	0057	0083	5
5						0001	0002	0003	0005	0009	4
6										0001	3

r	p = 11	12	13	14	15	16	17	18	19	20 = $(1-p)$	r
1	6496	6835	7145	7427	7684	7918	8131	8324	8499	8658	8
2	2599	2951	3304	3657	4005	4348	4685	5012	5330	5638	7
3	0672	0833	1009	1202	1409	1629	1861	2105	2357	2618	6
4	0117	0158	0209	0269	0339	0420	0512	0615	0730	0856	5
5	0014	0021	0030	0041	0056	0075	0098	0125	0158	0196	4
6	0001	0002	0003	0004	0006	0009	0013	0017	0023	0031	3
7						0001	0001	0002	0002	0003	2

r	p = 21	22	23	24	25	26	27	28	29	30 = $(1-p)$	r
1	8801	8931	9048	9154	9249	9335	9411	9480	9542	9596	8
2	5934	6218	6491	6750	6997	7230	7452	7660	7856	8040	7
3	2885	3158	3434	3713	3993	4273	4552	4829	5102	5372	6
4	0994	1144	1304	1475	1657	1849	2050	2260	2478	2703	5
5	0240	0291	0350	0416	0489	0571	0662	0762	0870	0988	4
6	0040	0051	0065	0081	0100	0122	0149	0179	0213	0253	3
7	0004	0006	0008	0010	0013	0017	0022	0028	0035	0043	2
8			0001	0001	0001	0001	0002	0003	0003	0004	1

r	p = 31	32	33	34	35	36	37	38	39	40 = $(1-p)$	r
1	9645	9689	9728	9762	9793	9820	9844	9865	9883	9899	8
2	8212	8372	8522	8661	8789	8908	9017	9118	9210	9295	7
3	5636	5894	6146	6390	6627	6856	7076	7287	7489	7682	6
4	2935	3173	3415	3662	3911	4163	4416	4669	4922	5174	5
5	1115	1252	1398	1553	1717	1890	2072	2262	2460	2666	4
6	0298	0348	0404	0467	0536	0612	0696	0787	0886	0994	3
7	0053	0064	0078	0094	0112	0133	0157	0184	0215	0250	2
8	0006	0007	0009	0011	0014	0017	0021	0026	0031	0038	1
9				0001	0001	0001	0001	0002	0002	0003	0

Cumulative binomial probabilities (Continued)

r	$n = 9$ *(Continued)*										r
	p = 41	42	43	44	45	46	47	48	49	50 = $(1 - p)$	
1	9913	9926	9936	9946	9954	9961	9967	9972	9977	9980	8
2	9372	9442	9505	9563	9615	9662	9704	9741	9775	9805	7
3	7866	8039	8204	8359	8505	8642	8769	8889	8999	9102	6
4	5424	5670	5913	6152	6386	6614	6836	7052	7260	7461	5
5	2878	3097	3322	3551	3786	4024	4265	4509	4754	5000	4
6	1109	1233	1366	1508	1658	1817	1985	2161	2346	2539	3
7	0290	0334	0383	0437	0498	0564	0637	0717	0804	0898	2
8	0046	0055	0065	0077	0091	0107	0125	0145	0169	0195	1
9	0003	0004	0005	0006	0008	0009	0011	0014	0016	0020	0

r	$n = 10$										r
	p = 01	02	03	04	05	06	07	08	09	10 = $(1 - p)$	
1	0956	1829	2626	3352	4013	4614	5160	5656	6106	6513	9
2	0043	0162	0345	0582	0861	1176	1517	1879	2254	2639	8
3	0001	0009	0028	0062	0115	0188	0283	0401	0540	0702	7
4			0001	0004	0010	0020	0036	0058	0088	0128	6
5					0001	0002	0003	0006	0010	0016	5
6									0001	0001	4
	p = 11	12	13	14	15	16	17	18	19	20 = $(1 - p)$	
1	6882	7215	7516	7787	8031	8251	8448	8626	8784	8926	9
2	3028	3417	3804	4184	4557	4920	5270	5608	5932	6242	8
3	0884	1087	1308	1545	1798	2064	2341	2628	2922	3222	7
4	0178	0239	0313	0400	0500	0614	0741	0883	1039	1209	6
5	0025	0037	0053	0073	0099	0130	0168	0213	0266	0328	5
6	0003	0004	0006	0010	0014	0020	0027	0037	0049	0064	4
7			0001	0001	0001	0002	0003	0004	0006	0009	3
8									0001	0001	2
	p = 21	22	23	24	25	26	27	28	29	30 = $(1 - p)$	
1	9053	9166	9267	9357	9437	9508	9570	9626	9674	9718	9
2	6536	6815	7079	7327	7560	7778	7981	8170	8345	8507	8
3	3526	3831	4137	4442	4744	5042	5335	5622	5901	6172	7
4	1391	1587	1794	2012	2241	2479	2726	2979	3239	3504	6
5	0399	0479	0569	0670	0781	0904	1037	1181	1337	1503	5
6	0082	0104	0130	0161	0197	0239	0287	0342	0404	0473	4
7	0012	0016	0021	0027	0035	0045	0056	0070	0087	0106	3
8	0001	0002	0002	0003	0004	0006	0007	0010	0012	0016	2
9							0001	0001	0001	0001	1
	p = 31	32	33	34	35	36	37	38	39	40 = $(1 - p)$	
1	9755	9789	9818	9843	9865	9885	9902	9916	9929	9940	9
2	8656	8794	8920	9035	9140	9236	9323	9402	9473	9536	8
3	6434	6687	6930	7162	7384	7595	7794	7983	8160	8327	7
4	3772	4044	4316	4589	4862	5132	5400	5664	5923	6177	6
5	1679	1867	2064	2270	2485	2708	2939	3177	3420	3669	5
6	0551	0637	0732	0836	0949	1072	1205	1348	1500	1662	4
7	0129	0155	0185	0220	0260	0305	0356	0413	0477	0548	3
8	0020	0025	0032	0039	0048	0059	0071	0086	0103	0123	2
9	0002	0003	0003	0004	0005	0007	0009	0011	0014	0017	1
10								0001	0001	0001	0

Cumulative binomial probabilities (Continued)

r	$n = 10$ *(Continued)*										r
	$p = 41$	42	43	44	45	46	47	48	49	$50 = (1 - p)$	
1	9949	9957	9964	9970	9975	9979	9983	9986	9988	9990	9
2	9594	9645	9691	9731	9767	9799	9827	9852	9874	9893	8
3	8483	8628	8764	8889	9004	9111	9209	9298	9379	9453	7
4	6425	6665	6898	7123	7340	7547	7745	7933	8112	8281	6
5	3922	4178	4436	4696	4956	5216	5474	5730	5982	6230	5
6	1834	2016	2207	2407	2616	2832	3057	3288	3526	3770	4
7	0626	0712	0806	0908	1020	1141	1271	1410	1560	1719	3
8	0146	0172	0202	0236	0274	0317	0366	0420	0480	0547	2
9	0021	0025	0031	0037	0045	0054	0065	0077	0091	0107	1
10	0001	0002	0002	0003	0003	0004	0005	0006	0008	0010	0
r	$n = 11$										r
	$p = 01$	02	03	04	05	06	07	08	09	$10 = (1 - p)$	
1	1047	1993	2847	3618	4312	4937	5499	6004	6456	6862	10
2	0052	0195	0413	0692	1019	1382	1772	2181	2601	3026	9
3	0002	0012	0037	0083	0152	0248	0370	0519	0695	0896	8
4			0002	0007	0016	0030	0053	0085	0129	0185	7
5					0001	0003	0005	0010	0017	0028	6
6								0001	0002	0003	5
	$p = 11$	12	13	14	15	16	17	18	19	$20 = (1 - p)$	
1	7225	7549	7839	8097	8327	8531	8712	8873	9015	9141	10
2	3452	3873	4286	4689	5078	5453	5811	6151	6474	6779	9
3	1120	1366	1632	1915	2212	2521	2839	3164	3494	3826	8
4	0256	0341	0442	0560	0694	0846	1013	1197	1397	1611	7
5	0042	0061	0087	0119	0159	0207	0266	0334	0413	0504	6
6	0005	0008	0012	0018	0027	0037	0051	0068	0090	0117	5
7		0001	0001	0002	0003	0005	0007	0010	0014	0020	4
8							0001	0001	0002	0002	3
	$p = 21$	22	23	24	25	26	27	28	29	$30 = (1 - p)$	
1	9252	9350	9436	9511	9578	9636	9686	9730	9769	9802	10
2	7065	7333	7582	7814	8029	8227	8410	8577	8730	8870	9
3	4158	4488	4814	5134	5448	5753	6049	6335	6610	6873	8
4	1840	2081	2333	2596	2867	3146	3430	3719	4011	4304	7
5	0607	0723	0851	0992	1146	1313	1493	1685	1888	2103	6
6	0148	0186	0231	0283	0343	0412	0490	0577	0674	0782	5
7	0027	0035	0046	0059	0076	0095	0119	0146	0179	0216	4
8	0003	0005	0007	0009	0012	0016	0021	0027	0034	0043	3
9			0001	0001	0001	0002	0002	0003	0004	0006	2

Cumulative binomial probabilities (Continued)

r	n = 11 (Continued)										r
	p = 31	32	33	34	35	36	37	38	39	40 = (1 − p)	
1	9831	9856	9878	9896	9912	9926	9938	9948	9956	9964	10
2	8997	9112	9216	9310	9394	9470	9537	9597	9650	9698	9
3	7123	7361	7587	7799	7999	8186	8360	8522	8672	8811	8
4	4598	4890	5179	5464	5744	6019	6286	6545	6796	7037	7
5	2328	2563	2807	3059	3317	3581	3850	4122	4397	4672	6
6	0901	1031	1171	1324	1487	1661	1847	2043	2249	2465	5
7	0260	0309	0366	0430	0501	0581	0670	0768	0876	0994	4
8	0054	0067	0082	0101	0122	0148	0177	0210	0249	0293	3
9	0008	0010	0013	0016	0020	0026	0032	0039	0048	0059	2
10	0001	0001	0001	0002	0002	0003	0004	0005	0006	0007	1
	p = 41	42	43	44	45	46	47	48	49	50 = (1 − p)	
1	9970	9975	9979	9983	9986	9989	9991	9992	9994	9995	10
2	9739	9776	9808	9836	9861	9882	9900	9916	9930	9941	9
3	8938	9055	9162	9260	9348	9428	9499	9564	9622	9673	8
4	7269	7490	7700	7900	8089	8266	8433	8588	8733	8867	7
5	4948	5223	5495	5764	6029	6288	6541	6787	7026	7256	6
6	2690	2924	3166	3414	3669	3929	4193	4460	4729	5000	5
7	1121	1260	1408	1568	1738	1919	2110	2312	2523	2744	4
8	0343	0399	0461	0532	0610	0696	0791	0895	1009	1133	3
9	0072	0087	0104	0125	0148	0175	0206	0241	0282	0327	2
10	0009	0012	0014	0018	0022	0027	0033	0040	0049	0059	1
11	0001	0001	0001	0001	0002	0002	0002	0003	0004	0005	0

r	n = 12										r
	p = 01	02	03	04	05	06	07	08	09	10 = (1 − p)	
1	1136	2153	3062	3873	4596	5241	5814	6323	6775	7176	11
2	0062	0231	0486	0809	1184	1595	2033	2487	2948	3410	10
3	0002	0015	0048	0107	0196	0316	0468	0652	0866	1109	9
4		0001	0003	0010	0022	0043	0075	0120	0180	0256	8
5				0001	0002	0004	0009	0016	0027	0043	7
6							0001	0002	0003	0005	6
7										0001	5
	p = 11	12	13	14	15	16	17	18	19	20 = (1 − p)	
1	7530	7843	8120	8363	8578	8766	8931	9076	9202	9313	11
2	3867	4314	4748	5166	5565	5945	6304	6641	6957	7251	10
3	1377	1667	1977	2303	2642	2990	3344	3702	4060	4417	9
4	0351	0464	0597	0750	0922	1114	1324	1552	1795	2054	8
5	0065	0095	0133	0181	0239	0310	0393	0489	0600	0726	7
6	0009	0014	0022	0033	0046	0065	0088	0116	0151	0194	6
7	0001	0002	0003	0004	0007	0010	0015	0021	0029	0039	5
8					0001	0001	0002	0003	0004	0006	4
9										0001	3

Cumulative binomial probabilities (Continued)

r	$n = 12$ (*Continued*)										r
	$p = 21$	22	23	24	25	26	27	28	29	$30 = (1 - p)$	
1	9409	9493	9566	9629	9683	9730	9771	9806	9836	9862	11
2	7524	7776	8009	8222	8416	8594	8755	8900	9032	9150	10
3	4768	5114	5450	5778	6093	6397	6687	6963	7225	7472	9
4	2326	2610	2904	3205	3512	3824	4137	4452	4765	5075	8
5	0866	1021	1192	1377	1576	1790	2016	2254	2504	2763	7
6	0245	0304	0374	0453	0544	0646	0760	0887	1026	1178	6
7	0052	0068	0089	0113	0143	0178	0219	0267	0322	0386	5
8	0008	0011	0016	0021	0028	0036	0047	0060	0076	0095	4
9	0001	0001	0002	0003	0004	0005	0007	0010	0013	0017	3
10						0001	0001	0001	0002	0002	2
	$p = 31$	32	33	34	35	36	37	38	39	$40 = (1 - p)$	
1	9884	9902	9918	9932	9943	9953	9961	9968	9973	9978	11
2	9256	9350	9435	9509	9576	9634	9685	9730	9770	9804	10
3	7704	7922	8124	8313	8487	8648	8795	8931	9054	9166	9
4	5381	5681	5973	6258	6533	6799	7053	7296	7528	7747	8
5	3032	3308	3590	3876	4167	4459	4751	5043	5332	5618	7
6	1343	1521	1711	1913	2127	2352	2588	2833	3087	3348	6
7	0458	0540	0632	0734	0846	0970	1106	1253	1411	1582	5
8	0118	0144	0176	0213	0255	0304	0359	0422	0493	0573	4
9	0022	0028	0036	0045	0056	0070	0086	0104	0127	0153	3
10	0003	0004	0005	0007	0008	0011	0014	0018	0022	0028	2
11				0001	0001	0001	0001	0002	0002	0003	1
	$p = 41$	42	43	44	45	46	47	48	49	$50 = (1 - p)$	
1	9982	9986	9988	9990	9992	9994	9995	9996	9997	9998	11
2	9834	9860	9882	9901	9917	9931	9943	9953	9961	9968	10
3	9267	9358	9440	9513	9579	9637	9688	9733	9773	9807	9
4	7953	8147	8329	8498	8655	8801	8934	9057	9168	9270	8
5	5899	6175	6443	6704	6956	7198	7430	7652	7862	8062	7
6	3616	3889	4167	4448	4731	5014	5297	5577	5855	6128	6
7	1765	1959	2164	2380	2607	2843	3089	3343	3604	3872	5
8	0662	0760	0869	0988	1117	1258	1411	1575	1751	1938	4
9	0183	0218	0258	0304	0356	0415	0481	0555	0638	0730	3
10	0035	0043	0053	0065	0079	0095	0114	0137	0163	0193	2
11	0004	0005	0007	0009	0011	0014	0017	0021	0026	0032	1
12				0001	0001	0001	0001	0001	0002	0002	0

r	$n = 13$										r
	$p = 01$	02	03	04	05	06	07	08	09	$10 = (1 - p)$	
1	1225	2310	3270	4118	4867	5526	6107	6617	7065	7458	12
2	0072	0270	0564	0932	1354	1814	2298	2794	3293	3787	11
3	0003	0020	0062	0135	0245	0392	0578	0799	1054	1339	10
4		0001	0005	0014	0031	0060	0103	0163	0242	0342	9
5				0001	0003	0007	0013	0024	0041	0065	8
6						0001	0001	0003	0005	0009	7
7									0001	0001	6

Cumulative binomial probabilities (Continued)

r	n = 13 (*Continued*)										r
	p = 11	12	13	14	15	16	17	18	19	20 = (1 − p)	
1	7802	8102	8364	8592	8791	8963	9113	9242	9354	9450	12
2	4270	4738	5186	5614	6017	6396	6751	7080	7384	7664	11
3	1651	1985	2337	2704	3080	3463	3848	4231	4611	4983	10
4	0464	0609	0776	0967	1180	1414	1667	1939	2226	2527	9
5	0097	0139	0193	0260	0342	0438	0551	0681	0827	0991	8
6	0015	0024	0036	0053	0075	0104	0139	0183	0237	0300	7
7	0002	0003	0005	0008	0013	0019	0027	0038	0052	0070	6
8			0001	0001	0002	0003	0004	0006	0009	0012	5
9								0001	0001	0002	4
	p = 21	22	23	24	25	26	27	28	29	30 = (1 − p)	
1	9533	9604	9666	9718	9762	9800	9833	9860	9883	9903	12
2	7920	8154	8367	8559	8733	8889	9029	9154	9265	9363	11
3	5347	5699	6039	6364	6674	6968	7245	7505	7749	7975	10
4	2839	3161	3489	3822	4157	4493	4826	5155	5478	5794	9
5	1173	1371	1585	1816	2060	2319	2589	2870	3160	3457	8
6	0375	0462	0562	0675	0802	0944	1099	1270	1455	1654	7
7	0093	0120	0154	0195	0243	0299	0365	0440	0527	0624	6
8	0017	0024	0032	0043	0056	0073	0093	0118	0147	0182	5
9	0002	0004	0005	0007	0010	0013	0018	0024	0031	0040	4
10			0001	0001	0001	0002	0003	0004	0005	0007	3
11									0001	0001	2
	p = 31	32	33	34	35	36	37	38	39	40 = (1 − p)	
1	9920	9934	9945	9955	9963	9970	9975	9980	9984	9987	12
2	9450	9527	9594	9653	9704	9749	9787	9821	9849	9874	11
3	8185	8379	8557	8720	8868	9003	9125	9235	9333	9421	10
4	6101	6398	6683	6957	7217	7464	7698	7917	8123	8314	9
5	3760	4067	4376	4686	4995	5301	5603	5899	6188	6470	8
6	1867	2093	2331	2581	2841	3111	3388	3673	3962	4256	7
7	0733	0854	0988	1135	1295	1468	1654	1853	2065	2288	6
8	0223	0271	0326	0390	0462	0544	0635	0738	0851	0977	5
9	0052	0065	0082	0102	0126	0154	0187	0225	0270	0321	4
10	0009	0012	0015	0020	0025	0032	0040	0051	0063	0078	3
11	0001	0001	0002	0003	0003	0005	0006	0008	0010	0013	2
12							0001	0001	0001	0001	1
	p = 41	42	43	44	45	46	47	48	49	50 = (1 − p)	
1	9990	9992	9993	9995	9996	9997	9997	9998	9998	9999	12
2	9895	9912	9928	9940	9951	9960	9967	9974	9979	9983	11
3	9499	9569	9630	9684	9731	9772	9808	9838	9865	9888	10
4	8492	8656	8807	8945	9071	9185	9288	9381	9464	9539	9
5	6742	7003	7254	7493	7721	7935	8137	8326	8502	8666	8
6	4552	4849	5146	5441	5732	6019	6299	6573	6838	7095	7
7	2524	2770	3025	3290	3563	3842	4127	4415	4707	5000	6
8	1114	1264	1426	1600	1788	1988	2200	2424	2659	2905	5
9	0379	0446	0520	0605	0698	0803	0918	1045	1183	1334	4
10	0096	0117	0141	0170	0203	0242	0287	0338	0396	0461	3
11	0017	0021	0027	0033	0041	0051	0063	0077	0093	0112	2
12	0002	0002	0003	0004	0005	0007	0009	0011	0014	0017	1
13							0001	0001	0001	0001	0

Cumulative binomial probabilities (Continued)

r	n = 14										r
	p = 01	02	03	04	05	06	07	08	09	10 = (1 − p)	
1	1313	2464	3472	4353	5123	5795	6380	6888	7330	7712	13
2	0084	0310	0645	1059	1530	2037	2564	3100	3632	4154	12
3	0003	0025	0077	0167	0301	0478	0698	0958	1255	1584	11
4		0001	0006	0019	0042	0080	0136	0214	0315	0441	10
5				0002	0004	0010	0020	0035	0059	0092	9
6						0001	0002	0004	0008	0015	8
7									0001	0002	7
	p = 11	12	13	14	15	16	17	18	19	20 = (1 − p)	
1	8044	8330	8577	8789	8972	9129	9264	9379	9477	9560	13
2	4658	5141	5599	6031	6433	6807	7152	7469	7758	8021	12
3	1939	2315	2708	3111	3521	3932	4341	4744	5138	5519	11
4	0594	0774	0979	1210	1465	1742	2038	2351	2679	3018	10
5	0137	0196	0269	0359	0467	0594	0741	0907	1093	1298	9
6	0024	0038	0057	0082	0115	0157	0209	0273	0349	0439	8
7	0003	0006	0009	0015	0022	0032	0046	0064	0087	0116	7
8		0001	0001	0002	0003	0005	0008	0012	0017	0024	6
9						0001	0001	0002	0003	0004	5
	p = 21	22	23	24	25	26	27	28	29	30 = (1 − p)	
1	9631	9691	9742	9786	9822	9852	9878	9899	9917	9932	13
2	8259	8473	8665	8837	8990	9126	9246	9352	9444	9525	12
3	5887	6239	6574	6891	7189	7467	7727	7967	8188	8392	11
4	3366	3719	4076	4432	4787	5136	5479	5813	6137	6448	10
5	1523	1765	2023	2297	2585	2884	3193	3509	3832	4158	9
6	0543	0662	0797	0949	1117	1301	1502	1718	1949	2195	8
7	0152	0196	0248	0310	0383	0467	0563	0673	0796	0933	7
8	0033	0045	0060	0079	0103	0132	0167	0208	0257	0315	6
9	0006	0008	0011	0016	0022	0029	0038	0050	0065	0083	5
10	0001	0001	0002	0002	0003	0005	0007	0009	0012	0017	4
11						0001	0001	0001	0002	0002	3
	p = 31	32	33	34	35	36	37	38	39	40 = (1 − p)	
1	9945	9955	9963	9970	9976	9981	9984	9988	9990	9992	13
2	9596	9657	9710	9756	9795	9828	9857	9881	9902	9919	12
3	8577	8746	8899	9037	9161	9271	9370	9457	9534	9602	11
4	6747	7032	7301	7556	7795	8018	8226	8418	8595	8757	10
5	4486	4813	5138	5458	5773	6080	6378	6666	6943	7207	9
6	2454	2724	3006	3297	3595	3899	4208	4519	4831	5141	8
7	1084	1250	1431	1626	1836	2059	2296	2545	2805	3075	7
8	0381	0458	0545	0643	0753	0876	1012	1162	1325	1501	6
9	0105	0131	0163	0200	0243	0294	0353	0420	0497	0583	5
10	0022	0029	0037	0048	0060	0076	0095	0117	0144	0175	4
11	0003	0005	0006	0008	0011	0014	0019	0024	0031	0039	3
12		0001	0001	0001	0001	0002	0003	0003	0005	0006	2
13										0001	1

r					*n* = 14 (*Continued*)						r
	p = 41	42	43	44	45	46	47	48	49	50 = (1 − *p*)	
1	9994	9995	9996	9997	9998	9998	9999	9999	9999	9999	13
2	9934	9946	9956	9964	9971	9977	9981	9985	9988	9991	12
3	9661	9713	9758	9797	9830	9858	9883	9903	9921	9935	11
4	8905	9039	9161	9270	9368	9455	9532	9601	9661	9713	10
5	7459	7697	7922	8132	8328	8510	8678	8833	8974	9102	9
6	5450	5754	6052	6344	6627	6900	7163	7415	7654	7880	8
7	3355	3643	3937	4236	4539	4843	5148	5451	5751	6047	7
8	1692	1896	2113	2344	2586	2840	3105	3380	3663	3953	6
9	0680	0789	0910	1043	1189	1348	1520	1707	1906	2120	5
10	0212	0255	0304	0361	0426	0500	0583	0677	0782	0898	4
11	0049	0061	0076	0093	0114	0139	0168	0202	0241	0287	3
12	0008	0010	0013	0017	0022	0027	0034	0042	0053	0065	2
13	0001	0001	0001	0002	0003	0003	0004	0006	0007	0009	1
14										0001	0

r					*n* = 15						r
	p = 01	02	03	04	05	06	07	08	09	10 = (1 − *p*)	
1	1399	2614	3667	4579	5367	6047	6633	7137	7570	7941	14
2	0096	0353	0730	1191	1710	2262	2832	3403	3965	4510	13
3	0004	0030	0094	0203	0362	0571	0829	1130	1469	1841	12
4		0002	0008	0024	0055	0104	0175	0273	0399	0556	11
5			0001	0002	0006	0014	0028	0050	0082	0127	10
6					0001	0001	0003	0007	0013	0022	9
7								0001	0002	0003	8
	p = 11	12	13	14	15	16	17	18	19	20 = (1 − *p*)	
1	8259	8530	8762	8959	9126	9269	9389	9490	9576	9648	14
2	5031	5524	5987	6417	6814	7179	7511	7813	8085	8329	13
3	2238	2654	3084	3520	3958	4392	4819	5234	5635	6020	12
4	0742	0959	1204	1476	1773	2092	2429	2782	3146	3518	11
5	0187	0265	0361	0478	0617	0778	0961	1167	1394	1642	10
6	0037	0057	0084	0121	0168	0227	0300	0387	0490	0611	9
7	0006	0010	0015	0024	0036	0052	0074	0102	0137	0181	8
8	0001	0001	0002	0004	0006	0010	0014	0021	0030	0042	7
9					0001	0001	0002	0003	0005	0008	6
10									0001	0001	5
	p = 21	22	23	24	25	26	27	28	29	30 = (1 − *p*)	
1	9709	9759	9802	9837	9866	9891	9911	9928	9941	9953	14
2	8547	8741	8913	9065	9198	9315	9417	9505	9581	9647	13
3	6385	6731	7055	7358	7639	7899	8137	8355	8553	8732	12
4	3895	4274	4650	5022	5387	5742	6086	6416	6732	7031	11
5	1910	2195	2495	2810	3135	3469	3810	4154	4500	4845	10
6	0748	0905	1079	1272	1484	1713	1958	2220	2495	2784	9
7	0234	0298	0374	0463	0566	0684	0817	0965	1130	1311	8
8	0058	0078	0104	0135	0173	0219	0274	0338	0413	0500	7
9	0011	0016	0023	0031	0042	0056	0073	0094	0121	0152	6
10	0002	0003	0004	0006	0008	0011	0015	0021	0028	0037	5
11			0001	0001	0001	0002	0002	0003	0005	0007	4
12									0001	0001	3

Cumulative binomial probabilities (Continued)

r	n = 15 (*Continued*)										r
	p = 31	32	33	34	35	36	37	38	39	40 = (1 − p)	
1	9962	9969	9975	9980	9984	9988	9990	9992	9994	9995	14
2	9704	9752	9794	9829	9858	9883	9904	9922	9936	9948	13
3	8893	9038	9167	9281	9383	9472	9550	9618	9678	9729	12
4	7314	7580	7829	8060	8273	8469	8649	8813	8961	9095	11
5	5187	5523	5852	6171	6481	6778	7062	7332	7587	7827	10
6	3084	3393	3709	4032	4357	4684	5011	5335	5654	5968	9
7	1509	1722	1951	2194	2452	2722	3003	3295	3595	3902	8
8	0599	0711	0837	0977	1132	1302	1487	1687	1902	2131	7
9	0190	0236	0289	0351	0422	0504	0597	0702	0820	0950	6
10	0048	0062	0079	0099	0124	0154	0190	0232	0281	0338	5
11	0009	0012	0016	0022	0028	0037	0047	0059	0075	0093	4
12	0001	0002	0003	0004	0005	0006	0009	0011	0015	0019	3
13					0001	0001	0001	0002	0002	0003	2
	p = 41	42	43	44	45	46	47	48	49	50 = (1 − p)	
1	9996	9997	9998	9998	9999	9999	9999	9999	10000	10000	14
2	9958	9966	9973	9979	9983	9987	9990	9992	9994	9995	13
3	9773	9811	9843	9870	9893	9913	9929	9943	9954	9963	12
4	9215	9322	9417	9502	9576	9641	9697	9746	9788	9824	11
5	8052	8261	8454	8633	8796	8945	9080	9201	9310	9408	10
6	6274	6570	6856	7131	7392	7641	7875	8095	8301	8491	9
7	4214	4530	4847	5164	5478	5789	6095	6394	6684	6964	8
8	2374	2630	2898	3176	3465	3762	4065	4374	4686	5000	7
9	1095	1254	1427	1615	1818	2034	2265	2510	2767	3036	6
10	0404	0479	0565	0661	0769	0890	1024	1171	1333	1509	5
11	0116	0143	0174	0211	0255	0305	0363	0430	0506	0592	4
12	0025	0032	0040	0051	0063	0079	0097	0119	0145	0176	3
13	0004	0005	0007	0009	0011	0014	0018	0023	0029	0037	2
14			0001	0001	0001	0002	0002	0003	0004	0005	1

r	n = 16										r
	p = 01	02	03	04	05	06	07	08	09	10 = (1 − p)	
1	1485	2762	3857	4796	5599	6284	6869	7366	7789	8147	15
2	0109	0399	0818	1327	1892	2489	3098	3701	4289	4853	14
3	0005	0037	0113	0242	0429	0673	0969	1311	1694	2108	13
4		0002	0011	0032	0070	0132	0221	0342	0496	0684	12
5			0001	0003	0009	0019	0038	0068	0111	0170	11
6					0001	0002	0005	0010	0019	0033	10
7							0001	0001	0003	0005	9
8										0001	8

Cumulative binomial probabilities (Continued)

r	n = 16 (Continued)										r
	p = 11	12	13	14	15	16	17	18	19	20 = (1 − p)	
1	8450	8707	8923	9105	9257	9386	9493	9582	9657	9719	15
2	5386	5885	6347	6773	7161	7513	7830	8115	8368	8593	14
3	2545	2999	3461	3926	4386	4838	5277	5698	6101	6482	13
4	0907	1162	1448	1763	2101	2460	2836	3223	3619	4019	12
5	0248	0348	0471	0618	0791	0988	1211	1458	1727	2018	11
6	0053	0082	0120	0171	0235	0315	0412	0527	0662	0817	10
7	0009	0015	0024	0038	0056	0080	0112	0153	0204	0267	9
8	0001	0002	0004	0007	0011	0016	0024	0036	0051	0070	8
9			0001	0001	0002	0003	0004	0007	0010	0015	7
10							0001	0001	0002	0002	6
	p = 21	22	23	24	25	26	27	28	29	30 = (1 − p)	
1	9770	9812	9847	9876	9900	9919	9935	9948	9958	9967	15
2	8791	8965	9117	9250	9365	9465	9550	9623	9686	9739	14
3	6839	7173	7483	7768	8029	8267	8482	8677	8851	9006	13
4	4418	4814	5203	5583	5950	6303	6640	6959	7260	7541	12
5	2327	2652	2991	3341	3698	4060	4425	4788	5147	5501	11
6	0992	1188	1405	1641	1897	2169	2458	2761	3077	3402	10
7	0342	0432	0536	0657	0796	0951	1125	1317	1526	1753	9
8	0095	0127	0166	0214	0271	0340	0420	0514	0621	0744	8
9	0021	0030	0041	0056	0075	0098	0127	0163	0206	0257	7
10	0004	0006	0008	0012	0016	0023	0031	0041	0055	0071	6
11	0001	0001	0001	0002	0003	0004	0006	0008	0011	0016	5
12						0001	0001	0001	0002	0003	4
	p = 31	32	33	34	35	36	37	38	39	40 = (1 − p)	
1	9974	9979	9984	9987	9990	9992	9994	9995	9996	9997	15
2	9784	9822	9854	9880	9902	9921	9936	9948	9959	9967	14
3	9144	9266	9374	9467	9549	9620	9681	9734	9778	9817	13
4	7804	8047	8270	8475	8661	8830	8982	9119	9241	9349	12
5	5846	6181	6504	6813	7108	7387	7649	7895	8123	8334	11
6	3736	4074	4416	4759	5100	5438	5770	6094	6408	6712	10
7	1997	2257	2531	2819	3119	3428	3746	4070	4398	4728	9
8	0881	1035	1205	1391	1594	1813	2048	2298	2562	2839	8
9	0317	0388	0470	0564	0671	0791	0926	1076	1242	1423	7
10	0092	0117	0148	0185	0229	0280	0341	0411	0491	0583	6
11	0021	0028	0037	0048	0062	0079	0100	0125	0155	0191	5
12	0004	0005	0007	0010	0013	0017	0023	0030	0038	0049	4
13		0001	0001	0001	0002	0003	0004	0005	0007	0009	3
14								0001	0001	0001	2

Cumulative binomial probabilities (Continued)

$n = 16$ (*Continued*)

r	$p = 41$	42	43	44	45	46	47	48	49	$50 = (1-p)$	r
1	9998	9998	9999	9999	9999	9999	10000	10000	10000	10000	15
2	9974	9979	9984	9987	9990	9992	9994	9995	9997	9997	14
3	9849	9876	9899	9918	9934	9947	9958	9966	9973	9979	13
4	9444	9527	9600	9664	9719	9766	9806	9840	9869	9894	12
5	8529	8707	8869	9015	9147	9265	9370	9463	9544	9616	11
6	7003	7280	7543	7792	8024	8241	8441	8626	8795	8949	10
7	5058	5387	5711	6029	6340	6641	6932	7210	7476	7728	9
8	3128	3428	3736	4051	4371	4694	5019	5343	5665	5982	8
9	1619	1832	2060	2302	2559	2829	3111	3405	3707	4018	7
10	0687	0805	0936	1081	1241	1416	1607	1814	2036	2272	6
11	0234	0284	0342	0409	0486	0574	0674	0786	0911	1051	5
12	0062	0078	0098	0121	0149	0183	0222	0268	0322	0384	4
13	0012	0016	0021	0027	0035	0044	0055	0069	0086	0106	3
14	0002	0002	0003	0004	0006	0007	0010	0013	0016	0021	2
15					0001	0001	0001	0001	0002	0003	1

$n = 17$

r	$p = 01$	02	03	04	05	06	07	08	09	$10 = (1-p)$	r
1	1571	2907	4042	5004	5819	6507	7088	7577	7988	8332	16
2	0123	0446	0909	1465	2078	2717	3362	3995	4604	5182	15
3	0006	0044	0134	0286	0503	0782	1118	1503	1927	2382	14
4		0003	0014	0040	0088	0164	0273	0419	0603	0826	13
5			0001	0004	0012	0026	0051	0089	0145	0221	12
6					0001	0003	0007	0015	0027	0047	11
7							0001	0002	0004	0008	10
8										0001	9

r	$p = 11$	12	13	14	15	16	17	18	19	$20 = (1-p)$	r
1	8621	8862	9063	9230	9369	9484	9579	9657	9722	9775	16
2	5723	6223	6682	7099	7475	7813	8113	8379	8613	8818	15
3	2858	3345	3836	4324	4802	5266	5711	6133	6532	6904	14
4	1087	1383	1710	2065	2444	2841	3251	3669	4091	4511	13
5	0321	0446	0598	0778	0987	1224	1487	1775	2087	2418	12
6	0075	0114	0166	0234	0319	0423	0548	0695	0864	1057	11
7	0014	0023	0037	0056	0083	0118	0163	0220	0291	0377	10
8	0002	0004	0007	0011	0017	0027	0039	0057	0080	0109	9
9		0001	0001	0002	0003	0005	0008	0012	0018	0026	8
10						0001	0001	0002	0003	0005	7
11										0001	6

Cumulative binomial probabilities (Continued)

r	n = 17 (Continued)										r
	p = 21	22	23	24	25	26	27	28	29	30 = (1 − p)	
1	9818	9854	9882	9906	9925	9940	9953	9962	9970	9977	16
2	8996	9152	9285	9400	9499	9583	9654	9714	9765	9807	15
3	7249	7567	7859	8123	8363	8578	8771	8942	9093	9226	14
4	4927	5333	5728	6107	6470	6814	7137	7440	7721	7981	13
5	2766	3128	3500	3879	4261	4643	5023	5396	5760	6113	12
6	1273	1510	1770	2049	2347	2661	2989	3329	3677	4032	11
7	0479	0598	0736	0894	1071	1268	1485	1721	1976	2248	10
8	0147	0194	0251	0320	0402	0499	0611	0739	0884	1046	9
9	0037	0051	0070	0094	0124	0161	0206	0261	0326	0403	8
10	0007	0011	0016	0022	0031	0042	0057	0075	0098	0127	7
11	0001	0002	0003	0004	0006	0009	0013	0018	0024	0032	6
12				0001	0001	0002	0002	0003	0005	0007	5
13									0001	0001	4
	p = 31	32	33	34	35	36	37	38	39	40 = (1 − p)	
1	9982	9986	9989	9991	9993	9995	9996	9997	9998	9998	16
2	9843	9872	9896	9917	9933	9946	9957	9966	9973	9979	15
3	9343	9444	9532	9608	9673	9728	9775	9815	9849	9877	14
4	8219	8437	8634	8812	8972	9115	9241	9353	9450	9536	13
5	6453	6778	7087	7378	7652	7906	8142	8360	8559	8740	12
6	4390	4749	5105	5458	5803	6139	6465	6778	7077	7361	11
7	2536	2838	3153	3479	3812	4152	4495	4839	5182	5522	10
8	1227	1426	1642	1877	2128	2395	2676	2971	3278	3595	9
9	0492	0595	0712	0845	0994	1159	1341	1541	1757	1989	8
10	0162	0204	0254	0314	0383	0464	0557	0664	0784	0919	7
11	0043	0057	0074	0095	0120	0151	0189	0234	0286	0348	6
12	0009	0013	0017	0023	0030	0040	0051	0066	0084	0106	5
13	0002	0002	0003	0004	0006	0008	0011	0015	0019	0025	4
14				0001	0001	0001	0002	0002	0003	0005	3
15										0001	2
	p = 41	42	43	44	45	46	47	48	49	50 = (1 − p)	
1	9999	9999	9999	9999	10000	10000	10000	10000	10000	10000	16
2	9984	9987	9990	9992	9994	9996	9997	9998	9998	9999	15
3	9900	9920	9935	9948	9959	9968	9975	9980	9985	9988	14
4	9610	9674	9729	9776	9816	9849	9877	9901	9920	9936	13
5	8904	9051	9183	9301	9404	9495	9575	9644	9704	9755	12
6	7628	7879	8113	8330	8529	8712	8878	9028	9162	9283	11
7	5856	6182	6499	6805	7098	7377	7641	7890	8122	8338	10
8	3920	4250	4585	4921	5257	5590	5918	6239	6552	6855	9
9	2238	2502	2780	3072	3374	3687	4008	4335	4667	5000	8
10	1070	1236	1419	1618	1834	2066	2314	2577	2855	3145	7
11	0420	0503	0597	0705	0826	0962	1112	1279	1462	1662	6
12	0133	0165	0203	0248	0301	0363	0434	0517	0611	0717	5
13	0033	0042	0054	0069	0086	0108	0134	0165	0202	0245	4
14	0006	0008	0011	0014	0019	0024	0031	0040	0050	0064	3
15	0001	0001	0002	0002	0003	0004	0005	0007	0009	0012	2
16							0001	0001	0001	0001	1

r	$n = 18$										r
	p = 01	02	03	04	05	06	07	08	09	10 = $(1 - p)$	
1	1655	3049	4220	5204	6028	6717	7292	7771	8169	8499	17
2	0138	0495	1003	1607	2265	2945	3622	4281	4909	5497	16
3	0007	0052	0157	0333	0581	0898	1275	1702	2168	2662	15
4		0004	0018	0050	0109	0201	0333	0506	0723	0982	14
5			0002	0006	0015	0034	0067	0116	0186	0282	13
6				0001	0002	0005	0010	0021	0038	0064	12
7							0001	0003	0006	0012	11
8									0001	0002	10
	p = 11	12	13	14	15	16	17	18	19	20 = $(1 - p)$	
1	8773	8998	9185	9338	9464	9566	9651	9719	9775	9820	17
2	6042	6540	6992	7398	7759	8080	8362	8609	8824	9009	16
3	3173	3690	4206	4713	5203	5673	6119	6538	6927	7287	15
4	1282	1618	1986	2382	2798	3229	3669	4112	4554	4990	14
5	0405	0558	0743	0959	1206	1482	1787	2116	2467	2836	13
6	0102	0154	0222	0310	0419	0551	0708	0889	1097	1329	12
7	0021	0034	0054	0081	0118	0167	0229	0306	0400	0513	11
8	0003	0006	0011	0017	0027	0041	0060	0086	0120	0163	10
9		0001	0002	0003	0005	0008	0013	0020	0029	0043	9
10					0001	0001	0002	0004	0006	0009	8
11								0001	0001	0002	7
	p = 21	22	23	24	25	26	27	28	29	30 = $(1 - p)$	
1	9856	9886	9909	9928	9944	9956	9965	9973	9979	9984	17
2	9169	9306	9423	9522	9605	9676	9735	9784	9824	9858	16
3	7616	7916	8187	8430	8647	8839	9009	9158	9288	9400	15
4	5414	5825	6218	6591	6943	7272	7578	7860	8119	8354	14
5	3220	3613	4012	4414	4813	5208	5594	5968	6329	6673	13
6	1586	1866	2168	2488	2825	3176	3538	3907	4281	4656	12
7	0645	0799	0974	1171	1390	1630	1891	2171	2469	2783	11
8	0217	0283	0363	0458	0569	0699	0847	1014	1200	1407	10
9	0060	0083	0112	0148	0193	0249	0316	0395	0488	0596	9
10	0014	0020	0028	0039	0054	0073	0097	0127	0164	0210	8
11	0003	0004	0006	0009	0012	0018	0025	0034	0046	0061	7
12		0001	0001	0002	0002	0003	0005	0007	0010	0014	6
13						0001	0001	0001	0002	0003	5
	p = 31	32	33	34	35	36	37	38	39	40 = $(1 - p)$	
1	9987	9990	9993	9994	9996	9997	9998	9998	9999	9999	17
2	9886	9908	9927	9942	9954	9964	9972	9978	9983	9987	16
3	9498	9581	9652	9713	9764	9807	9843	9873	9897	9918	15
4	8568	8759	8931	9083	9217	9335	9439	9528	9606	9672	14
5	7001	7309	7598	7866	8114	8341	8549	8737	8907	9058	13
6	5029	5398	5759	6111	6450	6776	7086	7379	7655	7912	12
7	3111	3450	3797	4151	4509	4867	5224	5576	5921	6257	11
8	1633	1878	2141	2421	2717	3027	3349	3681	4021	4366	10
9	0720	0861	1019	1196	1391	1604	1835	2084	2350	2632	9
10	0264	0329	0405	0494	0597	0714	0847	0997	1163	1347	8

Cumulative binomial probabilities (Continued)

r					$n = 18$ (*Continued*)						r
	$p = 31$	32	33	34	35	36	37	38	39	40 $= (1 - p)$	
11	0080	0104	0133	0169	0212	0264	0325	0397	0480	0576	7
12	0020	0027	0036	0047	0062	0080	0102	0130	0163	0203	6
13	0004	0005	0008	0011	0014	0019	0026	0034	0044	0058	5
14	0001	0001	0001	0002	0003	0004	0005	0007	0010	0013	4
15						0001	0001	0001	0002	0002	3
	$p = 41$	42	43	44	45	46	47	48	49	50 $= (1 - p)$	
1	9999	9999	10000	10000	10000	10000	10000	10000	10000	10000	17
2	9990	9992	9994	9996	9997	9998	9998	9999	9999	9999	16
3	9934	9948	9959	9968	9975	9981	9985	9989	9991	9993	15
4	9729	9777	9818	9852	9880	9904	9923	9939	9952	9962	14
5	9193	9313	9418	9510	9589	9658	9717	9767	9810	9846	13
6	8151	8372	8573	8757	8923	9072	9205	9324	9428	9519	12
7	6582	6895	7193	7476	7742	7991	8222	8436	8632	8811	11
8	4713	5062	5408	5750	6085	6412	6728	7032	7322	7597	10
9	2928	3236	3556	3885	4222	4562	4906	5249	5591	5927	9
10	1549	1768	2004	2258	2527	2812	3110	3421	3742	4073	8
11	0686	0811	0951	1107	1280	1470	1677	1902	2144	2403	7
12	0250	0307	0372	0449	0537	0638	0753	0883	1028	1189	6
13	0074	0094	0118	0147	0183	0225	0275	0334	0402	0481	5
14	0017	0022	0029	0038	0049	0063	0079	0100	0125	0154	4
15	0003	0004	0006	0007	0010	0013	0017	0023	0029	0038	3
16		0001	0001	0001	0001	0002	0003	0004	0005	0007	2
17									0001	0001	1

r					$n = 19$						r
	$p = 01$	02	03	04	05	06	07	08	09	10 $= (1 - p)$	
1	1738	3188	4394	5396	6226	6914	7481	7949	8334	8649	18
2	0153	0546	1100	1751	2453	3171	3879	4560	5202	5797	17
3	0009	0061	0183	0384	0665	1021	1439	1908	2415	2946	16
4		0005	0022	0061	0132	0243	0398	0602	0853	1150	15
5			0002	0007	0020	0044	0085	0147	0235	0352	14
6				0001	0002	0006	0014	0029	0051	0086	13
7						0001	0002	0004	0009	0017	12
8								0001	0001	0003	11
	$p = 11$	12	13	14	15	16	17	18	19	20 $= (1 - p)$	
1	8908	9119	9291	9431	9544	9636	9710	9770	9818	9856	18
2	6342	6835	7277	7669	8015	8318	8581	8809	9004	9171	17
3	3488	4032	4568	5089	5587	6059	6500	6910	7287	7631	16
4	1490	1867	2275	2708	3159	3620	4085	4549	5005	5449	15
5	0502	0685	0904	1158	1444	1762	2107	2476	2864	3267	14
6	0135	0202	0290	0401	0537	0700	0891	1110	1357	1631	13
7	0030	0048	0076	0113	0163	0228	0310	0411	0532	0676	12
8	0005	0009	0016	0026	0041	0061	0089	0126	0173	0233	11
9	0001	0002	0003	0005	0008	0014	0021	0032	0047	0067	10
10				0001	0001	0002	0004	0007	0010	0016	9
11							0001	0001	0002	0003	8

Cumulative binomial probabilities (Continued)

r					$n = 19$ (*Continued*)						r
	$p = 21$	22	23	24	25	26	27	28	29	$30 = (1-p)$	
1	9887	9911	9930	9946	9958	9967	9975	9981	9985	9989	18
2	9313	9434	9535	9619	9690	9749	9797	9837	9869	9896	17
3	7942	8222	8471	8692	8887	9057	9205	9333	9443	9538	16
4	5877	6285	6671	7032	7369	7680	7965	8224	8458	8668	15
5	3681	4100	4520	4936	5346	5744	6129	6498	6848	7178	14
6	1929	2251	2592	2950	3322	3705	4093	4484	4875	5261	13
7	0843	1034	1248	1487	1749	2032	2336	2657	2995	3345	12
8	0307	0396	0503	0629	0775	0941	1129	1338	1568	1820	11
9	0093	0127	0169	0222	0287	0366	0459	0568	0694	0839	10
10	0023	0034	0047	0066	0089	0119	0156	0202	0258	0326	9
11	0005	0007	0011	0016	0023	0032	0044	0060	0080	0105	8
12	0001	0001	0002	0003	0005	0007	0010	0015	0021	0028	7
13				0001	0001	0001	0002	0003	0004	0006	6
14									0001	0001	5
	$p = 31$	32	33	34	35	36	37	38	39	$40 = (1-p)$	
1	9991	9993	9995	9996	9997	9998	9998	9999	9999	9999	18
2	9917	9935	9949	9960	9969	9976	9981	9986	9989	9992	17
3	9618	9686	9743	9791	9830	9863	9890	9913	9931	9945	16
4	8856	9022	9169	9297	9409	9505	9588	9659	9719	9770	15
5	7486	7773	8037	8280	8500	8699	8878	9038	9179	9304	14
6	5641	6010	6366	6707	7032	7339	7627	7895	8143	8371	13
7	3705	4073	4445	4818	5188	5554	5913	6261	6597	6919	12
8	2091	2381	2688	3010	3344	3690	4043	4401	4762	5122	11
9	1003	1186	1389	1612	1855	2116	2395	2691	3002	3325	10
10	0405	0499	0608	0733	0875	1035	1213	1410	1626	1861	9
11	0137	0176	0223	0280	0347	0426	0518	0625	0747	0885	8
12	0038	0051	0068	0089	0114	0146	0185	0231	0287	0352	7
13	0009	0012	0017	0023	0031	0041	0054	0070	0091	0116	6
14	0002	0002	0003	0005	0007	0009	0013	0017	0023	0031	5
15			0001	0001	0001	0002	0002	0003	0005	0006	4
16									0001	0001	3
	$p = 41$	42	43	44	45	46	47	48	49	$50 = (1-p)$	
1	10000	10000	10000	10000	10000	10000	10000	10000	10000	10000	18
2	9994	9995	9996	9997	9998	9999	9999	9999	9999	10000	17
3	9957	9967	9974	9980	9985	9988	9991	9993	9995	9996	16
4	9813	9849	9878	9903	9923	9939	9952	9963	9971	9978	15
5	9413	9508	9590	9660	9720	9771	9814	9850	9879	9904	14
6	8579	8767	8937	9088	9223	9342	9446	9537	9615	9682	13
7	7226	7515	7787	8039	8273	8488	8684	8862	9022	9165	12
8	5480	5832	6176	6509	6831	7138	7430	7706	7964	8204	11
9	3660	4003	4353	4706	5060	5413	5762	6105	6439	6762	10
10	2114	2385	2672	2974	3290	3617	3954	4299	4648	5000	9
11	1040	1213	1404	1613	1841	2087	2351	2631	2928	3238	8
12	0429	0518	0621	0738	0871	1021	1187	1372	1575	1796	7
13	0146	0183	0227	0280	0342	0415	0500	0597	0709	0835	6
14	0040	0052	0067	0086	0109	0137	0171	0212	0261	0318	5
15	0009	0012	0016	0021	0028	0036	0046	0060	0076	0096	4
16	0001	0002	0003	0004	0005	0007	0010	0013	0017	0022	3
17				0001	0001	0001	0001	0002	0003	0004	2

Cumulative binomial probabilities (Continued)

r	$n = 20$										r
	$p = 01$	02	03	04	05	06	07	08	09	$10 = (1 - p)$	
1	1821	3324	4562	5580	6415	7099	7658	8113	8484	8784	19
2	0169	0599	1198	1897	2642	3395	4131	4831	5484	6083	18
3	0010	0071	0210	0439	0755	1150	1610	2121	2666	3231	17
4		0006	0027	0074	0159	0290	0471	0706	0993	1330	16
5			0003	0010	0026	0056	0107	0183	0290	0432	15
6				0001	0003	0009	0019	0038	0068	0113	14
7						0001	0003	0006	0013	0024	13
8								0001	0002	0004	12
9										0001	11
	$p = 11$	12	13	14	15	16	17	18	19	$20 = (1 - p)$	
1	9028	9224	9383	9510	9612	9694	9759	9811	9852	9885	19
2	6624	7109	7539	7916	8244	8529	8773	8982	9159	9308	18
3	3802	4369	4920	5450	5951	6420	6854	7252	7614	7939	17
4	1710	2127	2573	3041	3523	4010	4496	4974	5439	5886	16
5	0610	0827	1083	1375	1702	2059	2443	2849	3271	3704	15
6	0175	0260	0370	0507	0673	0870	1098	1356	1643	1958	14
7	0041	0067	0103	0153	0219	0304	0409	0537	0689	0867	13
8	0008	0014	0024	0038	0059	0088	0127	0177	0241	0321	12
9	0001	0002	0005	0008	0013	0021	0033	0049	0071	0100	11
10			0001	0001	0002	0004	0007	0011	0017	0026	10
11						0001	0001	0002	0004	0006	9
12									0001	0001	8
	$p = 21$	22	23	24	25	26	27	28	29	$30 = (1 - p)$	
1	9910	9931	9946	9959	9968	9976	9982	9986	9989	9992	19
2	9434	9539	9626	9698	9757	9805	9845	9877	9903	9924	18
3	8230	8488	8716	8915	9087	9237	9365	9474	9567	9645	17
4	6310	6711	7085	7431	7748	8038	8300	8534	8744	8929	16
5	4142	4580	5014	5439	5852	6248	6625	6981	7315	7625	15
6	2297	2657	3035	3427	3828	4235	4643	5048	5447	5836	14
7	1071	1301	1557	1838	2142	2467	2810	3169	3540	3920	13
8	0419	0536	0675	0835	1018	1225	1455	1707	1982	2277	12
9	0138	0186	0246	0320	0409	0515	0640	0784	0948	1133	11
10	0038	0054	0075	0103	0139	0183	0238	0305	0385	0480	10
11	0009	0013	0019	0028	0039	0055	0074	0100	0132	0171	9
12	0002	0003	0004	0006	0009	0014	0019	0027	0038	0051	8
13			0001	0001	0002	0003	0004	0006	0009	0013	7
14							0001	0001	0002	0003	6

Cumulative binomial probabilities (Continued)

r	$n = 20$ (*Continued*)										r
	$p = 31$	32	33	34	35	36	37	38	39	$40 = (1 - p)$	
1	9994	9996	9997	9998	9998	9999	9999	9999	9999	10000	19
2	9940	9953	9964	9972	9979	9984	9988	9991	9993	9995	18
3	9711	9765	9811	9848	9879	9904	9924	9940	9953	9964	17
4	9092	9235	9358	9465	9556	9634	9700	9755	9802	9840	16
5	7911	8173	8411	8626	8818	8989	9141	9274	9390	9490	15
6	6213	6574	6917	7242	7546	7829	8090	8329	8547	8744	14
7	4305	4693	5079	5460	5834	6197	6547	6882	7200	7500	13
8	2591	2922	3268	3624	3990	4361	4735	5108	5478	5841	12
9	1340	1568	1818	2087	2376	2683	3005	3341	3688	4044	11
10	0591	0719	0866	1032	1218	1424	1650	1897	2163	2447	10
11	0220	0279	0350	0434	0532	0645	0775	0923	1090	1275	9
12	0069	0091	0119	0154	0196	0247	0308	0381	0466	0565	8
13	0018	0025	0034	0045	0060	0079	0102	0132	0167	0210	7
14	0004	0006	0008	0011	0015	0021	0028	0037	0049	0065	6
15	0001	0001	0001	0002	0003	0004	0006	0009	0012	0016	5
16						0001	0001	0002	0002	0003	4
	$p = 41$	42	43	44	45	46	47	48	49	$50 = (1 - p)$	
1	10000	10000	10000	10000	10000	10000	10000	10000	10000	10000	19
2	9996	9997	9998	9998	9999	9999	9999	10000	10000	10000	18
3	9972	9979	9984	9988	9991	9993	9995	9996	9997	9998	17
4	9872	9898	9920	9937	9951	9962	9971	9977	9983	9987	16
5	9577	9651	9714	9767	9811	9848	9879	9904	9924	9941	15
6	8921	9078	9217	9340	9447	9539	9619	9687	9745	9793	14
7	7780	8041	8281	8501	8701	8881	9042	9186	9312	9423	13
8	6196	6539	6868	7183	7480	7759	8020	8261	8482	8684	12
9	4406	4771	5136	5499	5857	6207	6546	6873	7186	7483	11
10	2748	3064	3394	3736	4086	4443	4804	5166	5525	5881	10
11	1480	1705	1949	2212	2493	2791	3104	3432	3771	4119	9
12	0679	0810	0958	1123	1308	1511	1734	1977	2238	2517	8
13	0262	0324	0397	0482	0580	0694	0823	0969	1133	1316	7
14	0084	0107	0136	0172	0214	0265	0326	0397	0480	0577	6
15	0022	0029	0038	0050	0064	0083	0105	0133	0166	0207	5
16	0004	0006	0008	0011	0015	0020	0027	0035	0046	0059	4
17	0001	0001	0001	0002	0003	0004	0005	0007	0010	0013	3
18						0001	0001	0001	0001	0002	2

Cumulative binomial probabilities (Continued)

r	$n = 50$										r
	p = 01	02	03	04	05	06	07	08	09	10 = $(1-p)$	
1	3950	6358	7819	8701	9231	9547	9734	9845	9910	9948	49
2	0894	2642	4447	5995	7206	8100	8735	9173	9468	9662	48
3	0138	0784	1892	3233	4595	5838	6892	7740	8395	8883	47
4	0016	0178	0628	1391	2396	3527	4673	5747	6697	7497	46
5	0001	0032	0168	0490	1036	1794	2710	3710	4723	5688	45
6		0005	0037	0144	0378	0776	1350	2081	2928	3839	44
7		0001	0007	0036	0118	0289	0583	1019	1596	2298	43
8			0001	0008	0032	0094	0220	0438	0768	1221	42
9				0001	0008	0027	0073	0167	0328	0579	41
10					0002	0007	0022	0056	0125	0245	40
11						0002	0006	0017	0043	0094	39
12							0001	0005	0013	0032	38
13								0001	0004	0010	37
14									0001	0003	36
15										0001	35
	p = 11	12	13	14	15	16	17	18	19	20 = $(1-p)$	
1	9971	9983	9991	9995	9997	9998	9999	10000	10000	10000	49
2	9788	9869	9920	9951	9971	9983	9990	9994	9997	9998	48
3	9237	9487	9661	9779	9858	9910	9944	9965	9979	9987	47
4	8146	8655	9042	9330	9540	9688	9792	9863	9912	9943	46
5	6562	7320	7956	8472	8879	9192	9428	9601	9726	9815	45
6	4760	5647	6463	7186	7806	8323	8741	9071	9327	9520	44
7	3091	3935	4789	5616	6387	7081	7686	8199	8624	8966	43
8	1793	2467	3217	4010	4812	5594	6328	6996	7587	8096	42
9	0932	1392	1955	2605	3319	4071	4832	5576	6280	6927	41
10	0435	0708	1074	1537	2089	2718	3403	4122	4849	5563	40
11	0183	0325	0535	0824	1199	1661	2203	2813	3473	4164	39
12	0069	0135	0242	0402	0628	0929	1309	1768	2300	2893	38
13	0024	0051	0100	0179	0301	0475	0714	1022	1405	1861	37
14	0008	0018	0037	0073	0132	0223	0357	0544	0791	1106	36
15	0002	0006	0013	0027	0053	0096	0164	0266	0411	0607	35
16	0001	0002	0004	0009	0019	0038	0070	0120	0197	0308	34
17			0001	0003	0007	0014	0027	0050	0087	0144	33
18				0001	0002	0005	0010	0019	0036	0063	32
19					0001	0001	0003	0007	0013	0025	31
20							0001	0002	0005	0009	30
21								0001	0002	0003	29
22										0001	28

Cumulative binomial probabilities (Continued)

r	n = 50 (*Continued*)										r
	p = 21	22	23	24	25	26	27	28	29	30 = $(1 - p)$	
1	10000	10000	10000	10000	10000	10000	10000	10000	10000	10000	49
2	9999	9999	10000	10000	10000	10000	10000	10000	10000	10000	48
3	9992	9995	9997	9998	9999	10000	10000	10000	10000	10000	47
4	9964	9978	9986	9992	9995	9997	9998	9999	9999	10000	46
5	9877	9919	9948	9967	9979	9987	9992	9995	9997	9998	45
6	9663	9767	9841	9893	9930	9954	9970	9981	9988	9993	44
7	9236	9445	9603	9720	9806	9868	9911	9941	9961	9975	43
8	8523	8874	9156	9377	9547	9676	9772	9842	9892	9927	42
9	7505	8009	8437	8794	9084	9316	9497	9635	9740	9817	41
10	6241	6870	7436	7934	8363	8724	9021	9260	9450	9598	40
11	4864	5552	6210	6822	7378	7871	8299	8663	8965	9211	39
12	3533	4201	4878	5544	6184	6782	7329	7817	8244	8610	38
13	2383	2963	3585	4233	4890	5539	6163	6749	7287	7771	37
14	1490	1942	2456	3023	3630	4261	4901	5534	6145	6721	36
15	0862	1181	1565	2013	2519	3075	3669	4286	4912	5532	35
16	0462	0665	0926	1247	1631	2075	2575	3121	3703	4308	34
17	0229	0347	0508	0718	0983	1306	1689	2130	2623	3161	33
18	0105	0168	0259	0384	0551	0766	1034	1359	1741	2178	32
19	0045	0075	0122	0191	0287	0418	0590	0809	1080	1406	31
20	0018	0031	0054	0088	0139	0212	0314	0449	0626	0848	30
21	0006	0012	0022	0038	0063	0100	0155	0232	0338	0478	29
22	0002	0004	0008	0015	0026	0044	0071	0112	0170	0251	28
23	0001	0001	0003	0006	0010	0018	0031	0050	0080	0123	27
24			0001	0002	0004	0007	0012	0021	0035	0056	26
25				0001	0001	0002	0004	0008	0014	0024	25
26						0001	0002	0003	0005	0009	24
27								0001	0002	0003	23
28									0001	0001	22
	p = 31	32	33	34	35	36	37	38	39	40 = $(1 - p)$	
1	10000	10000	10000	10000	10000	10000	10000	10000	10000	10000	49
2	10000	10000	10000	10000	10000	10000	10000	10000	10000	10000	48
3	10000	10000	10000	10000	10000	10000	10000	10000	10000	10000	47
4	10000	10000	10000	10000	10000	10000	10000	10000	10000	10000	46
5	9999	9999	10000	10000	10000	10000	10000	10000	10000	10000	45
6	9996	9997	9998	9999	9999	10000	10000	10000	10000	10000	44
7	9984	9990	9994	9996	9998	9999	9999	10000	10000	10000	43
8	9952	9969	9980	9987	9992	9995	9997	9998	9999	9999	42
9	9874	9914	9942	9962	9975	9984	9990	9994	9996	9998	41
10	9710	9794	9856	9901	9933	9955	9971	9981	9988	9992	40
11	9409	9563	9683	9773	9840	9889	9924	9949	9966	9978	39
12	8916	9168	9371	9533	9658	9753	9825	9878	9916	9943	38
13	8197	8564	8873	9130	9339	9505	9635	9736	9811	9867	37
14	7253	7732	8157	8524	8837	9097	9310	9481	9616	9720	36
15	6131	6698	7223	7699	8122	8491	8805	9069	9286	9460	35

Cumulative binomial probabilities (Continued)

r	$n = 50$ *(Continued)*										r
	$p = 31$	32	33	34	35	36	37	38	39	$40 = (1 - p)$	
16	4922	5530	6120	6679	7199	7672	8094	8462	8779	9045	34
17	3734	4328	4931	5530	6111	6664	7179	7649	8070	8439	33
18	2666	3197	3760	4346	4940	5531	6105	6653	7164	7631	32
19	1786	2220	2703	3227	3784	4362	4949	5533	6101	6644	31
20	1121	1447	1826	2257	2736	3255	3805	4376	4957	5535	30
21	0657	0882	1156	1482	1861	2289	2764	3278	3824	4390	29
22	0360	0503	0685	0912	1187	1513	1890	2317	2788	3299	28
23	0184	0267	0379	0525	0710	0938	1214	1540	1916	2340	27
24	0087	0133	0196	0282	0396	0544	0730	0960	1236	1562	26
25	0039	0061	0094	0141	0207	0295	0411	0560	0748	0978	25
26	0016	0026	0042	0066	0100	0149	0216	0305	0423	0573	24
27	0006	0011	0018	0029	0045	0070	0106	0155	0223	0314	23
28	0002	0004	0007	0012	0019	0031	0048	0074	0110	0160	22
29	0001	0001	0002	0004	0007	0012	0020	0032	0050	0076	21
30			0001	0002	0003	0005	0008	0013	0021	0034	20
31					0001	0002	0003	0005	0008	0014	19
32						0001	0001	0002	0003	0005	18
33								0001	0001	0002	17
34										0001	16
	$p = 41$	42	43	44	45	46	47	48	49	$50 = (1 - p)$	
1	10000	10000	10000	10000	10000	10000	10000	10000	10000	10000	49
2	10000	10000	10000	10000	10000	10000	10000	10000	10000	10000	48
3	10000	10000	10000	10000	10000	10000	10000	10000	10000	10000	47
4	10000	10000	10000	10000	10000	10000	10000	10000	10000	10000	46
5	10000	10000	10000	10000	10000	10000	10000	10000	10000	10000	45
6	10000	10000	10000	10000	10000	10000	10000	10000	10000	10000	44
7	10000	10000	10000	10000	10000	10000	10000	10000	10000	10000	43
8	10000	10000	10000	10000	10000	10000	10000	10000	10000	10000	42
9	9999	9999	10000	10000	10000	10000	10000	10000	10000	10000	41
10	9995	9997	9998	9999	9999	10000	10000	10000	10000	10000	40
11	9986	9991	9994	9997	9998	9999	9999	10000	10000	10000	39
12	9962	9975	9984	9990	9994	9996	9998	9999	9999	10000	38
13	9908	9938	9958	9973	9982	9989	9993	9996	9997	9998	37
14	9799	9858	9902	9933	9955	9970	9981	9988	9992	9995	36
15	9599	9707	9789	9851	9896	9929	9952	9968	9980	9987	35
16	9265	9443	9585	9696	9780	9844	9892	9926	9950	9967	34
17	8757	9025	9248	9429	9573	9687	9774	9839	9888	9923	33
18	8051	8421	8740	9010	9235	9418	9565	9680	9769	9836	32
19	7152	7617	8037	8406	8727	8998	9225	9410	9559	9675	31
20	6099	6638	7143	7608	8026	8396	8718	8991	9219	9405	30
21	4965	5539	6099	6635	7138	7602	8020	8391	8713	8987	29
22	3840	4402	4973	5543	6100	6634	7137	7599	8018	8389	28
23	2809	3316	3854	4412	4981	5548	6104	6636	7138	7601	27
24	1936	2359	2826	3331	3866	4422	4989	5554	6109	6641	26
25	1255	1580	1953	2375	2840	3343	3876	4431	4996	5561	25

Cumulative binomial probabilities (Continued)

r	n = 50 (*Continued*)										r
	p = 41	42	43	44	45	46	47	48	49	50 = $(1-p)$	
26	0762	0992	1269	1593	1966	2386	2850	3352	3885	4439	24
27	0432	0584	0772	1003	1279	1603	1975	2395	2858	3359	23
28	0229	0320	0439	0591	0780	1010	1286	1609	1981	2399	22
29	0113	0164	0233	0325	0444	0595	0784	1013	1289	1611	21
30	0052	0078	0115	0166	0235	0327	0446	0596	0784	1013	20
31	0022	0034	0053	0079	0116	0167	0236	0327	0445	0595	19
32	0009	0014	0022	0035	0053	0079	0116	0166	0234	0325	18
33	0003	0005	0009	0014	0022	0035	0053	0078	0114	0164	17
34	0001	0002	0003	0005	0009	0014	0022	0034	0052	0077	16
35		0001	0001	0002	0003	0005	0008	0014	0021	0033	15
36				0001	0001	0002	0003	0005	0008	0013	14
37						0001	0001	0002	0003	0005	13
38								0001	0001	0002	12

r	n = 100										r
	p = 01	02	03	04	05	06	07	08	09	10 = $(1-p)$	
1	6340	8674	9524	9831	9941	9979	9993	9998	9999	10000	99
2	2642	5967	8054	9128	9629	9848	9940	9977	9991	9997	98
3	0794	3233	5802	7679	8817	9434	9742	9887	9952	9981	97
4	0184	1410	3528	5705	7422	8570	9256	9633	9827	9922	96
5	0034	0508	1821	3711	5640	7232	8368	9097	9526	9763	95
6	0005	0155	0808	2116	3840	5593	7086	8201	8955	9424	94
7	0001	0041	0312	1064	2340	3936	5557	6968	8060	8828	93
8		0009	0106	0475	1280	2517	4012	5529	6872	7939	92
9		0002	0032	0190	0631	1463	2660	4074	5506	6791	91
10			0009	0068	0282	0775	1620	2780	4125	5487	90
11			0002	0022	0115	0376	0908	1757	2882	4168	89
12				0007	0043	0168	0469	1028	1876	2970	88
13				0002	0015	0069	0224	0559	1138	1982	87
14					0005	0026	0099	0282	0645	1239	86
15					0001	0009	0041	0133	0341	0726	85
16						0003	0016	0058	0169	0399	84
17						0001	0006	0024	0078	0206	83
18							0002	0009	0034	0100	82
19							0001	0003	0014	0046	81
20								0001	0005	0020	80
21									0002	0008	79
22									0001	0003	78
23										0001	77

Cumulative binomial probabilities (Continued)

r	$n = 100$ (*Continued*)										r
	$p = 11$	12	13	14	15	16	17	18	19	$20 = (1 - p)$	
1	10000	10000	10000	10000	10000	10000	10000	10000	10000	10000	99
2	9999	10000	10000	10000	10000	10000	10000	10000	10000	10000	98
3	9992	9997	9999	10000	10000	10000	10000	10000	10000	10000	97
4	9966	9985	9994	9998	9999	10000	10000	10000	10000	10000	96
5	9886	9947	9977	9990	9996	9998	9999	10000	10000	10000	95
6	9698	9848	9926	9966	9984	9993	9997	9999	10000	10000	94
7	9328	9633	9808	9903	9953	9978	9990	9996	9998	9999	93
8	8715	9239	9569	9766	9878	9939	9970	9986	9994	9997	92
9	7835	8614	9155	9508	9725	9853	9924	9962	9982	9991	91
10	6722	7743	8523	9078	9449	9684	9826	9908	9953	9977	90
11	5471	6663	7663	8440	9006	9393	9644	9800	9891	9943	89
12	4206	5458	6611	7591	8365	8939	9340	9605	9773	9874	88
13	3046	4239	5446	6566	7527	8297	8876	9289	9567	9747	87
14	2076	3114	4268	5436	6526	7469	8234	8819	9241	9531	86
15	1330	2160	3173	4294	5428	6490	7417	8177	8765	9196	85
16	0802	1414	2236	3227	4317	5420	6458	7370	8125	8715	84
17	0456	0874	1492	2305	3275	4338	5414	6429	7327	8077	83
18	0244	0511	0942	1563	2367	3319	4357	5408	6403	7288	82
19	0123	0282	0564	1006	1628	2424	3359	4374	5403	6379	81
20	0059	0147	0319	0614	1065	1689	2477	3395	4391	5398	80
21	0026	0073	0172	0356	0663	1121	1745	2525	3429	4405	79
22	0011	0034	0088	0196	0393	0710	1174	1797	2570	3460	78
23	0005	0015	0042	0103	0221	0428	0754	1223	1846	2611	77
24	0002	0006	0020	0051	0119	0246	0462	0796	1270	1891	76
25	0001	0003	0009	0024	0061	0135	0271	0496	0837	1314	75
26		0001	0004	0011	0030	0071	0151	0295	0528	0875	74
27			0001	0005	0014	0035	0081	0168	0318	0558	73
28			0001	0002	0006	0017	0041	0091	0184	0342	72
29				0001	0003	0008	0020	0048	0102	0200	71
30					0001	0003	0009	0024	0054	0112	70
31						0001	0004	0011	0027	0061	69
32						0001	0002	0005	0013	0031	68
33							0001	0002	0006	0016	67
34								0001	0003	0007	66
35									0001	0003	65
36										0001	64
37										0001	63

Cumulative binomial probabilities (Continued)

r	$n = 100$ (*Continued*)										r
	$p = 21$	22	23	24	25	26	27	28	29	$30 = (1 - p)$	
1	10000	10000	10000	10000	10000	10000	10000	10000	10000	10000	99
2	10000	10000	10000	10000	10000	10000	10000	10000	10000	10000	98
3	10000	10000	10000	10000	10000	10000	10000	10000	10000	10000	97
4	10000	10000	10000	10000	10000	10000	10000	10000	10000	10000	96
5	10000	10000	10000	10000	10000	10000	10000	10000	10000	10000	95
6	10000	10000	10000	10000	10000	10000	10000	10000	10000	10000	94
7	10000	10000	10000	10000	10000	10000	10000	10000	10000	10000	93
8	9999	10000	10000	10000	10000	10000	10000	10000	10000	10000	92
9	9996	9998	9999	10000	10000	10000	10000	10000	10000	10000	91
10	9989	9995	9998	9999	10000	10000	10000	10000	10000	10000	90
11	9971	9986	9993	9997	9999	9999	10000	10000	10000	10000	89
12	9933	9965	9983	9992	9996	9998	9999	10000	10000	10000	88
13	9857	9922	9959	9979	9990	9995	9998	9999	10000	10000	87
14	9721	9840	9911	9953	9975	9988	9994	9997	9999	9999	86
15	9496	9695	9823	9900	9946	9972	9986	9993	9997	9998	85
16	9153	9462	9671	9806	9889	9939	9967	9983	9992	9996	84
17	8668	9112	9430	9647	9789	9878	9932	9963	9981	9990	83
18	8032	8625	9074	9399	9624	9773	9867	9925	9959	9978	82
19	7252	7991	8585	9038	9370	9601	9757	9856	9918	9955	81
20	6358	7220	7953	8547	9005	9342	9580	9741	9846	9911	80
21	5394	6338	7189	7918	8512	8973	9316	9560	9726	9835	79
22	4419	5391	6320	7162	7886	8479	8943	9291	9540	9712	78
23	3488	4432	5388	6304	7136	7856	8448	8915	9267	9521	77
24	2649	3514	4444	5386	6289	7113	7828	8420	8889	9245	76
25	1933	2684	3539	4455	5383	6276	7091	7802	8393	8864	75
26	1355	1972	2717	3561	4465	5381	6263	7071	7778	8369	74
27	0911	1393	2009	2748	3583	4475	5380	6252	7053	7756	73
28	0588	0945	1429	2043	2776	3602	4484	5378	6242	7036	72
29	0364	0616	0978	1463	2075	2803	3621	4493	5377	6232	71
30	0216	0386	0643	1009	1495	2105	2828	3638	4501	5377	70
31	0123	0232	0406	0669	1038	1526	2134	2851	3654	4509	69
32	0067	0134	0247	0427	0693	1065	1554	2160	2873	3669	68
33	0035	0074	0144	0262	0446	0717	1091	1580	2184	2893	67
34	0018	0039	0081	0154	0276	0465	0739	1116	1605	2207	66
35	0009	0020	0044	0087	0164	0290	0482	0760	1139	1629	65
36	0004	0010	0023	0048	0094	0174	0303	0499	0780	1161	64
37	0002	0005	0011	0025	0052	0101	0183	0316	0515	0799	63
38	0001	0002	0005	0013	0027	0056	0107	0193	0328	0530	62
39		0001	0002	0006	0014	0030	0060	0113	0201	0340	61
40			0001	0003	0007	0015	0032	0064	0119	0210	60
41				0001	0003	0008	0017	0035	0068	0125	59
42				0001	0001	0004	0008	0018	0037	0072	58
43					0001	0002	0004	0009	0020	0040	57
44						0001	0002	0005	0010	0021	56
45							0001	0002	0005	0011	55
46								0001	0002	0005	54
47									0001	0003	53
48										0001	52
49										0001	51

Cumulative binomial probabilities (Continued)

r	$n = 100$ (*Continued*)										r
	$p = 31$	32	33	34	35	36	37	38	39	$40 = (1 - p)$	
1	10000	10000	10000	10000	10000	10000	10000	10000	10000	10000	99
2	10000	10000	10000	10000	10000	10000	10000	10000	10000	10000	98
3	10000	10000	10000	10000	10000	10000	10000	10000	10000	10000	97
4	10000	10000	10000	10000	10000	10000	10000	10000	10000	10000	96
5	10000	10000	10000	10000	10000	10000	10000	10000	10000	10000	95
6	10000	10000	10000	10000	10000	10000	10000	10000	10000	10000	94
7	10000	10000	10000	10000	10000	10000	10000	10000	10000	10000	93
8	10000	10000	10000	10000	10000	10000	10000	10000	10000	10000	92
9	10000	10000	10000	10000	10000	10000	10000	10000	10000	10000	91
10	10000	10000	10000	10000	10000	10000	10000	10000	10000	10000	90
11	10000	10000	10000	10000	10000	10000	10000	10000	10000	10000	89
12	10000	10000	10000	10000	10000	10000	10000	10000	10000	10000	88
13	10000	10000	10000	10000	10000	10000	10000	10000	10000	10000	87
14	10000	10000	10000	10000	10000	10000	10000	10000	10000	10000	86
15	9999	10000	10000	10000	10000	10000	10000	10000	10000	10000	85
16	9998	9999	10000	10000	10000	10000	10000	10000	10000	10000	84
17	9995	9998	9999	10000	10000	10000	10000	10000	10000	10000	83
18	9989	9995	9997	9999	9999	10000	10000	10000	10000	10000	82
19	9976	9988	9994	9997	9999	9999	10000	10000	10000	10000	81
20	9950	9973	9986	9993	9997	9998	9999	10000	10000	10000	80
21	9904	9946	9971	9985	9992	9996	9998	9999	10000	10000	79
22	9825	9898	9942	9968	9983	9991	9996	9998	9999	10000	78
23	9698	9816	9891	9938	9966	9982	9991	9995	9998	9999	77
24	9504	9685	9806	9885	9934	9963	9980	9990	9995	9997	76
25	9224	9487	9672	9797	9879	9930	9961	9979	9989	9994	75
26	8841	9204	9471	9660	9789	9873	9926	9958	9977	9988	74
27	8346	8820	9185	9456	9649	9780	9867	9922	9956	9976	73
28	7736	8325	8800	9168	9442	9638	9773	9862	9919	9954	72
29	7021	7717	8305	8781	9152	9429	9628	9765	9857	9916	71
30	6224	7007	7699	8287	8764	9137	9417	9618	9759	9852	70
31	5376	6216	6994	7684	8270	8748	9123	9405	9610	9752	69
32	4516	5376	6209	6982	7669	8254	8733	9110	9395	9602	68
33	3683	4523	5375	6203	6971	7656	8240	8720	9098	9385	67
34	2912	3696	4530	5375	6197	6961	7643	8227	8708	9087	66
35	2229	2929	3708	4536	5376	6192	6953	7632	8216	8697	65
36	1650	2249	2946	3720	4542	5376	6188	6945	7623	8205	64
37	1181	1671	2268	2961	3731	4547	5377	6184	6938	7614	63
38	0816	1200	1690	2285	2976	3741	4553	5377	6181	6932	62
39	0545	0833	1218	1708	2301	2989	3750	4558	5378	6178	61
40	0351	0558	0849	1235	1724	2316	3001	3759	4562	5379	60
41	0218	0361	0571	0863	1250	1739	2330	3012	3767	4567	59
42	0131	0226	0371	0583	0877	1265	1753	2343	3023	3775	58
43	0075	0136	0233	0380	0594	0889	1278	1766	2355	3033	57
44	0042	0079	0141	0240	0389	0605	0901	1290	1778	2365	56
45	0023	0044	0082	0146	0246	0397	0614	0911	1301	1789	55

Cumulative binomial probabilities (Continued)

r	n = 100 (*Continued*)										r
	$p = 31$	32	33	34	35	36	37	38	39	40 = $(1 - p)$	
46	0012	0024	0046	0085	0150	0252	0405	0623	0921	1311	54
47	0006	0012	0025	0048	0088	0154	0257	0411	0631	0930	53
48	0003	0006	0013	0026	0050	0091	0158	0262	0417	0638	52
49	0001	0003	0007	0014	0027	0052	0094	0162	0267	0423	51
50	0001	0001	0003	0007	0015	0029	0054	0096	0165	0271	50
51		0001	0002	0003	0007	0015	0030	0055	0098	0168	49
52			0001	0002	0004	0008	0016	0030	0056	0100	48
53				0001	0002	0004	0008	0016	0031	0058	47
54					0001	0002	0004	0008	0017	0032	46
55						0001	0002	0004	0009	0017	45
56							0001	0002	0004	0009	44
57								0001	0002	0004	43
58									0001	0002	42
59										0001	41
	$p = 41$	42	43	44	45	46	47	48	49	50 = $(1 - p)$	
1	10000	10000	10000	10000	10000	10000	10000	10000	10000	10000	99
2	10000	10000	10000	10000	10000	10000	10000	10000	10000	10000	98
3	10000	10000	10000	10000	10000	10000	10000	10000	10000	10000	97
4	10000	10000	10000	10000	10000	10000	10000	10000	10000	10000	96
5	10000	10000	10000	10000	10000	10000	10000	10000	10000	10000	95
6	10000	10000	10000	10000	10000	10000	10000	10000	10000	10000	94
7	10000	10000	10000	10000	10000	10000	10000	10000	10000	10000	93
8	10000	10000	10000	10000	10000	10000	10000	10000	10000	10000	92
9	10000	10000	10000	10000	10000	10000	10000	10000	10000	10000	91
10	10000	10000	10000	10000	10000	10000	10000	10000	10000	10000	90
11	10000	10000	10000	10000	10000	10000	10000	10000	10000	10000	89
12	10000	10000	10000	10000	10000	10000	10000	10000	10000	10000	88
13	10000	10000	10000	10000	10000	10000	10000	10000	10000	10000	87
14	10000	10000	10000	10000	10000	10000	10000	10000	10000	10000	86
15	10000	10000	10000	10000	10000	10000	10000	10000	10000	10000	85
16	10000	10000	10000	10000	10000	10000	10000	10000	10000	10000	84
17	10000	10000	10000	10000	10000	10000	10000	10000	10000	10000	83
18	10000	10000	10000	10000	10000	10000	10000	10000	10000	10000	82
19	10000	10000	10000	10000	10000	10000	10000	10000	10000	10000	81
20	10000	10000	10000	10000	10000	10000	10000	10000	10000	10000	80
21	10000	10000	10000	10000	10000	10000	10000	10000	10000	10000	79
22	10000	10000	10000	10000	10000	10000	10000	10000	10000	10000	78
23	10000	10000	10000	10000	10000	10000	10000	10000	10000	10000	77
24	9999	9999	10000	10000	10000	10000	10000	10000	10000	10000	76
25	9997	9999	9999	10000	10000	10000	10000	10000	10000	10000	75

Cumulative binomial probabilities (Continued)

r	$n = 100$ (*Continued*)										r
	$p = 41$	42	43	44	45	46	47	48	49	$50 = (1 - p)$	
26	9994	9997	9999	9999	10000	10000	10000	10000	10000	10000	74
27	9987	9994	9997	9998	9999	10000	10000	10000	10000	10000	73
28	9975	9987	9993	9997	9998	9999	10000	10000	10000	10000	72
29	9952	9974	9986	9993	9996	9998	9999	10000	10000	10000	71
30	9913	9950	9972	9985	9992	9996	9998	9999	10000	10000	70
31	9848	9910	9848	9971	9985	9992	9996	9998	9999	10000	69
32	9746	9844	9907	9947	9970	9984	9992	9996	9998	9999	68
33	9594	9741	9840	9905	9945	9969	9984	9991	9996	9998	67
34	9376	9587	9736	9837	9902	9944	9969	9983	9991	9996	66
35	9078	9368	9581	9732	9834	9900	9942	9968	9983	9991	65
36	8687	9069	9361	9576	9728	9831	9899	9941	9967	9982	64
37	8196	8678	9061	9355	9571	9724	9829	9897	9941	9967	63
38	7606	8188	8670	9054	9349	9567	9721	9827	9896	9940	62
39	6927	7599	8181	8663	9049	9345	9563	9719	9825	9895	61
40	6176	6922	7594	8174	8657	9044	9341	9561	9717	9824	60
41	5380	6174	6919	7589	8169	8653	9040	9338	9558	9716	59
42	4571	5382	6173	6916	7585	8165	8649	9037	9335	9557	58
43	3782	4576	5383	6173	6913	7582	8162	8646	9035	9334	57
44	3041	3788	4580	5385	6172	6912	7580	8160	8645	9033	56
45	2375	3049	3794	4583	5387	6173	6911	7579	8159	8644	55
46	1799	2384	3057	3799	4587	5389	6173	6911	7579	8159	54
47	1320	1807	2391	3063	3804	4590	5391	6174	6912	7579	53
48	0938	1328	1815	2398	3069	3809	4593	5393	6176	6914	52
49	0644	0944	1335	1822	2404	3074	3813	4596	5395	6178	51
50	0428	0650	0950	1341	1827	2409	3078	3816	4599	5398	50
51	0275	0432	0655	0955	1346	1832	2413	3082	3819	4602	49
52	0170	0278	0436	0659	0960	1350	1836	2417	3084	3822	48
53	0102	0172	0280	0439	0662	0963	1353	1838	2419	3086	47
54	0059	0103	0174	0282	0441	0664	0965	1355	1840	2421	46
55	0033	0059	0104	0175	0284	0443	0666	0967	1356	1841	45
56	0017	0033	0060	0105	0176	0285	0444	0667	0967	1356	44
57	0009	0018	0034	0061	0106	0177	0286	0444	0667	0967	43
58	0004	0009	0018	0034	0061	0106	0177	0286	0444	0666	42
59	0002	0005	0009	0018	0034	0061	0106	0177	0285	0443	41
60	0001	0002	0005	0009	0018	0034	0061	0106	0177	0284	40
61		0001	0002	0005	0009	0018	0034	0061	0106	0176	39
62			0001	0002	0005	0009	0018	0034	0061	0105	38
63				0001	0002	0005	0009	0018	0034	0060	37
64					0001	0002	0005	0009	0018	0033	36
65						0001	0002	0005	0009	0018	35
66							0001	0002	0004	0009	34
67								0001	0002	0004	33
68									0001	0002	32
69										0001	31

appendix B

Table of Areas for Standardized Normal Probability Distribution

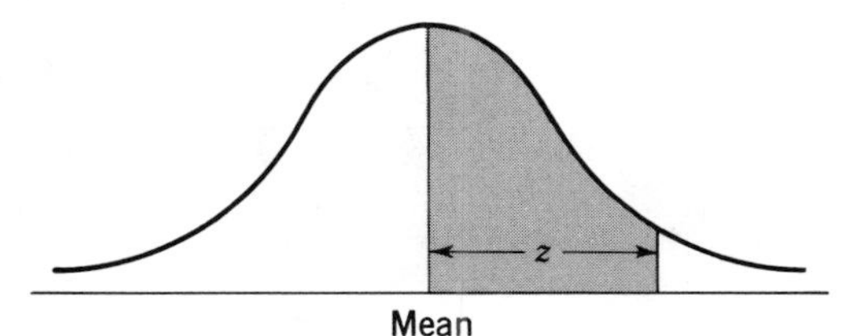

Example: For $z = 1.64$, the shaded area is .4495 out of a total area under the curve of 1.

z	.00	.01	.02	.03	.04	.05	.06	.07	.08	.09
0.0	.0000	.0040	.0080	.0120	.0160	.0199	.0239	.0279	.0319	.0359
0.1	.0398	.0438	.0478	.0517	.0557	.0596	.0636	.0675	.0714	.0753
0.2	.0793	.0832	.0871	.0910	.0948	.0987	.1026	.1064	.1103	.1141
0.3	.1179	.1217	.1255	.1293	.1331	.1368	.1406	.1443	.1480	.1517
0.4	.1554	.1591	.1628	.1664	.1700	.1736	.1772	.1808	.1844	.1879
0.5	.1915	.1950	.1985	.2019	.2054	.2088	.2123	.2157	.2190	.2224
0.6	.2257	.2291	.2324	.2357	.2389	.2422	.2454	.2486	.2518	.2549
0.7	.2580	.2612	.2642	.2673	.2704	.2734	.2764	.2794	.2823	.2852
0.8	.2881	.2910	.2939	.2967	.2995	.3023	.3051	.3078	.3106	.3133
0.9	.3159	.3186	.3212	.3238	.3264	.3289	.3315	.3340	.3365	.3389
1.0	.3413	.3438	.3461	.3485	.3508	.3531	.3554	.3577	.3599	.3621
1.1	.3643	.3665	.3686	.3708	.3729	.3749	.3770	.3790	.3810	.3830
1.2	.3849	.3869	.3888	.3907	.3925	.3944	.3962	.3980	.3997	.4015
1.3	.4032	.4049	.4066	.4082	.4099	.4115	.4131	.4147	.4162	.4177
1.4	.4192	.4207	.4222	.4236	.4251	.4265	.4279	.4292	.4306	.4319
1.5	.4332	.4345	.4357	.4370	.4382	.4394	.4406	.4418	.4429	.4441
1.6	.4452	.4463	.4474	.4484	.4495	.4505	.4515	.4525	.4535	.4545
1.7	.4554	.4564	.4573	.4582	.4591	.4599	.4608	.4616	.4625	.4633
1.8	.4641	.4649	.4656	.4664	.4671	.4678	.4686	.4693	.4699	.4706
1.9	.4713	.4719	.4726	.4732	.4738	.4744	.4750	.4756	.4761	.4767
2.0	.4772	.4778	.4783	.4788	.4793	.4798	.4803	.4808	.4812	.4817
2.1	.4821	.4826	.4830	.4834	.4838	.4842	.4846	.4850	.4854	.4857
2.2	.4861	.4864	.4868	.4871	.4875	.4878	.4881	.4884	.4887	.4890
2.3	.4893	.4896	.4898	.4901	.4904	.4906	.4909	.4911	.4913	.4916
2.4	.4918	.4920	.4922	.4925	.4927	.4929	.4931	.4932	.4934	.4936
2.5	.4938	.4940	.4941	.4943	.4945	.4946	.4948	.4949	.4951	.4952
2.6	.4953	.4955	.4956	.4957	.4959	.4960	.4961	.4962	.4963	.4964
2.7	.4965	.4966	.4967	.4968	.4969	.4970	.4971	.4972	.4973	.4974
2.8	.4974	.4975	.4976	.4977	.4977	.4978	.4979	.4979	.4980	.4981
2.9	.4981	.4982	.4982	.4983	.4984	.4984	.4985	.4985	.4986	.4986
3.0	.49865	.4987	.4987	.4988	.4988	.4989	.4989	.4989	.4990	.4990
4.0	.4999683									

appendix C

Percentage Points for the Sampling Distribution of t

Values in the heading refer to two-tail probabilities corresponding to t values found in the body. (For one-tail probabilities, divide by 2).

Example 1: For 9 degrees of freedom, and $t = 1.833$, the two-tail probability is .10.

Example 2: For 9 degrees of freedom and $t = 3.05$, the two-tail probability is between .01 and .02.

Degrees of freedom	Probability P .20	.10	.05	.02	.01
1	3.078	6.314	12.706	31.821	63.657
2	1.886	2.920	4.303	6.965	9.925
3	1.638	2.353	3.182	4.541	5.841
4	1.533	2.132	2.776	3.747	4.604
5	1.476	2.015	2.571	3.365	4.032
6	1.440	1.943	2.447	3.143	3.707
7	1.415	1.895	2.365	2.998	3.499
8	1.397	1.860	2.306	2.896	3.355
9	1.383	1.833	2.262	2.821	3.250
10	1.372	1.812	2.228	2.764	3.169
11	1.363	1.796	2.201	2.178	3.106
12	1.356	1.782	2.179	2.681	3.055
13	1.350	1.771	2.160	2.650	3.012
14	1.345	1.761	2.145	2.624	2.977
15	1.341	1.753	2.131	2.602	2.947
16	1.337	1.746	2.120	2.583	2.921
17	1.333	1.740	2.110	2.567	2.898
18	1.330	1.734	2.101	2.552	2.878
19	1.328	1.729	2.093	2.539	2.861
20	1.325	1.725	2.086	2.528	2.845
21	1.323	1.721	2.080	2.518	2.831
22	1.321	1.717	2.074	2.508	2.819
23	1.319	1.714	2.069	2.500	2.807
24	1.318	1.711	2.064	2.492	2.797
25	1.316	1.708	2.060	2.485	2.787
26	1.315	1.706	2.056	2.479	2.779
27	1.314	1.703	2.052	2.473	2.771
28	1.313	1.701	2.048	2.467	2.763
29	1.311	1.699	2.045	2.462	2.756
30	1.310	1.697	2.042	2.457	2.750
∞	1.28155	1.64485	1.95996	2.32634	2.57582

This table is taken from Table IV of Fisher: "Statistical Methods for Research Workers," published by Oliver & Boyd Ltd., Edinburgh, and by permission of the author and publishers.

appendix **D**

Unit Normal Loss Integral

The values in the body of the table $N(D)$ are expected opportunity losses for linear loss functions and a normal distribution with a mean of 0 and a standard deviation of 1. The value D represents the standardized deviation of the break-even value from μ.

Example: Given $\mu_o = 250$, $\mu_b = 200$ and $\sigma = 150$, $D = \left| \frac{\mu_o - \mu_b}{\sigma} \right| = .33$ and $N(D) = .2555$

D	.00	.01	.02	.03	.04	.05	.06	.07	.08	.09
.0	.3989	.3940	.3890	.3841	.3793	.3744	.3697	.3649	.3602	.3556
.1	.3509	.3464	.3418	.3373	.3328	.3284	.3240	.3197	.3154	.3111
.2	.3069	.3027	.2986	.2944	.2904	.2863	.2824	.2784	.2745	.2706
.3	.2668	.2630	.2592	.2555	.2518	.2481	.2445	.2409	.2374	.2339
.4	.2304	.2270	.2236	.2203	.2169	.2137	.2104	.2072	.2040	.2009

Unit Normal Loss Integral (Continued)

D	.00	.01	.02	.03	.04	.05	.06	.07	.08	.09
.5	.1978	.1947	.1917	.1887	.1857	.1828	.1799	.1771	.1742	.1714
.6	.1687	.1659	.1633	.1606	.1580	.1554	.1528	.1503	.1478	.1453
.7	.1429	.1405	.1381	.1358	.1334	.1312	.1289	.1267	.1245	.1223
.8	.1202	.1181	.1160	.1140	.1120	.1100	.1080	.1061	.1042	.1023
.9	.1004	.09860	.09680	.09503	.09328	.09156	.08986	.08819	.08654	.08491
1.0	.08332	.08174	.08019	.07866	.07716	.07568	.07422	.07279	.07138	.06999
1.1	.06862	.06727	.06595	.06465	.06336	.06210	.06086	.05964	.05844	.05726
1.2	.05610	.05496	.05384	.05274	.05165	.05059	.04954	.04851	.04750	.04650
1.3	.04553	.04457	.04363	.04270	.04179	.04090	.04002	.03916	.03831	.03748
1.4	.03667	.03587	.03508	.03431	.03356	.03281	.03208	.03137	.03067	.02998
1.5	.02931	.02865	.02800	.02736	.02674	.02612	.02552	.02494	.02436	.02380
1.6	.02324	.02270	.02217	.02165	.02114	.02064	.02015	.01967	.01920	.01874
1.7	.01829	.01785	.01742	.01699	.01658	.01617	.01578	.01539	.01501	.01464
1.8	.01428	.01392	.01357	.01323	.01290	.01257	.01226	.01195	.01164	.01134
1.9	.01105	.01077	.01049	.01022	$.0^{2}9957$	$.0^{2}9698$	$.0^{2}9445$	$.0^{2}9198$	$.0^{2}8957$	$.0^{2}8721$
2.0	$.0^{2}8491$	$.0^{2}8266$	$.0^{2}8046$	$.0^{2}7832$	$.0^{2}7623$	$.0^{2}7418$	$.0^{2}7219$	$.0^{2}7024$	$.0^{2}6835$	$.0^{2}6649$
2.1	$.0^{2}6468$	$.0^{2}6292$	$.0^{2}6120$	$.0^{2}5952$	$.0^{2}5788$	$.0^{2}5628$	$.0^{2}5472$	$.0^{2}5320$	$.0^{2}5172$	$.0^{2}5028$
2.2	$.0^{2}4887$	$.0^{2}4750$	$.0^{2}4616$	$.0^{2}4486$	$.0^{2}4358$	$.0^{2}4235$	$.0^{2}4114$	$.0^{2}3996$	$.0^{2}3882$	$.0^{2}3770$
2.3	$.0^{2}3662$	$.0^{2}3556$	$.0^{2}3453$	$.0^{2}3352$	$.0^{2}3255$	$.0^{2}3159$	$.0^{2}3067$	$.0^{2}2977$	$.0^{2}2889$	$.0^{2}2804$
2.4	$.0^{2}2720$	$.0^{2}2640$	$.0^{2}2561$	$.0^{2}2484$	$.0^{2}2410$	$.0^{2}2337$	$.0^{2}2267$	$.0^{2}2199$	$.0^{2}2132$	$.0^{2}2067$
2.5	$.0^{2}2004$	$.0^{2}1943$	$.0^{2}1883$	$.0^{2}1826$	$.0^{2}1769$	$.0^{2}1715$	$.0^{2}1662$	$.0^{2}1610$	$.0^{2}1560$	$.0^{2}1511$
3.0	$.0^{3}3822$	$.0^{3}3689$	$.0^{3}3560$	$.0^{3}3436$	$.0^{3}3316$	$.0^{3}3199$	$.0^{3}3087$	$.0^{3}2978$	$.0^{3}2873$	$.0^{3}2771$
3.5	$.0^{4}5848$	$.0^{4}5620$	$.0^{4}5400$	$.0^{4}5188$	$.0^{4}4984$	$.0^{4}4788$	$.0^{4}4599$	$.0^{4}4417$	$.0^{4}4242$	$.0^{4}4073$
4.0	$.0^{5}7145$	$.0^{5}6835$	$.0^{5}6538$	$.0^{5}6253$	$.0^{5}5980$	$.0^{5}5718$	$.0^{5}5468$	$.0^{5}5227$	$.0^{5}4997$	$.0^{5}4777$

appendix **E**

Glossary of Symbols

Symbol	Meaning
$<$	Less than
$\leq$	Less than or equal to
$>$	Greater than
$\geq$	Greater than or equal to
$!$	Factorial
$\lvert\ \rvert$	Absolute value of
$\cong$	Approximately equals
$\mid$	Given
α	(Lowercase alpha) level of significance—maximum risk of a type I error
AL	Action limit
β	(Lowercase beta) risk of a type II error
c	Criterion number; action limit for a hypothesis concerning a proportion
$C(n,r)$	Combination of n things r at a time
COL	Conditional opportunity loss
CP	Conditional profit
d	Coded midvalue; deviation from an assumed mean in class interval units
D	Standardized deviation used in determining unit normal loss integral
e	The constant 2.71828 · · ·
E	Expectation; expected value
EM	Estimated mean
EMV	Expected monetary value
EMV^*	Expected monetary value of the optimal act

EOL	Expected opportunity loss
EOL^*	Expected opportunity loss of the optimal act
EPC	Expected profit under certainty
$EVPI$	Expected value of perfect information
$EVSI$	Expected value of sample information
f	Frequency; number of items in a class
i	Class interval
IC	Information content
L	Absolute slope of conditional opportunity loss function
μ	(Lowercase mu) arithmetic mean of a population
MV	Midvalue
n	Number of trials; size of a sample
N	Size of a population
$N(D)$	Unit normal loss integral
OC	Operating characteristic
p	Population proportion; probability of a success in a Bernoulli process
P	Probability
P_b	Binomial probability
P_H	Hypergeometric probability
P_N	Normal probability
$\bar{p}$	Sample proportion, r/n
$P(A)$	Marginal probability of A
$P(A \text{ and } B)$	Joint probability of A and B
$P(A\|B)$	Conditional probability of A given B
π	(Lowercase pi) the constant 3.14159 · · ·
r	Number of successes in a sample
s	Sample estimate of a population standard deviation
σ	(Lowercase sigma) standard deviation of a population
Σ	(Capital sigma) summation
s^2	Sample estimate of a population variance
σ^2	Population variance

$s_{\bar{p}}$	Sample estimate of the standard deviation of the sampling distribution of a proportion
$\sigma_{\bar{p}}$	Standard deviation of the sampling distribution of a proportion
$s_{\bar{p}_1-\bar{p}_2}$	Sample estimate of the standard deviation of the sampling distribution of the difference between two population proportions
$\sigma_{\bar{p}_1-\bar{p}_2}$	Standard deviation of the sampling distribution of the difference between two population proportions
$s_{\bar{x}}$	Sample estimate of the standard deviation of the sampling distribution of the mean
$\sigma_{\bar{x}}$	Standard deviation of the sampling distribution of the mean
$s_{\bar{X}_1-\bar{X}_2}$	Sample estimate of the standard deviation of the sampling distribution of the difference between two population means
$\sigma_{\bar{X}_1-\bar{X}_2}$	Standard deviation of the sampling distribution of the difference between two population means
t	Standardized deviate for student's (t) distribution
U	Universal set
$\bar{X}$	Arithmetic mean of a sample
z	Standardized normal deviate

Index